Charles Birkeland

D1360821

The Systematics of Sympatric Species in West Indian Spatangoids

STUDIES IN TROPICAL OCEANOGRAPHY No. 7
INSTITUTE OF MARINE SCIENCES, UNIVERSITY OF MIAMI

The Systematics of Sympatric Species in West Indian Spatangoids:

A Revision of the Genera *Brissopsis*, *Plethotaenia*, *Paleopneustes*, and *Saviniaster*

By RICHARD H. CHESHER

UNIVERSITY OF MIAMI PRESS
Coral Gables, Florida

This volume may be referred to as
Stud. trop. Oceanogr. Miami 7:
viii + 168 pp., 35 pls., November 1968

PREFACE

A series of publications entitled *Studies in Tropical Oceanography* was established in 1963 by the Institute of Marine Sciences of the University of Miami to accommodate research reports too large for inclusion in regular periodicals. The first volume of this series was Dr. Donald P. deSylva's "Systematics and Life History of the Great Barracuda, *Sphyraena barracuda* (Walbaum)," followed by five additional numbers covering a diversity of marine topics. As the seventh volume of *Studies in Tropical Oceanography,* the editors now present the results of Dr. Richard Chesher's investigations of the systematics and biology of sympatric species in West Indian spatangoid sea urchins.

This study represents a major advance in placing the systematics and ecology of a poorly known group of echinoderms, the spatangoid sea urchins, on a firm scientific basis. Spatangoids have long excited the interest of zoologists and paleontologists and have been the subjects of many research papers. They burrow in sand or mud and occur from just below the low tide mark to great depths. Marine fossil deposits often contain large numbers of spatangoids, but the burrowing habits that ensure their entombment after death also effectively protect them from the eyes and dredges of marine biologists. Sand or mud swallowers, they are highly specialized members of bottom communities, and are responsible for the recycling of nutrients trapped in the sediment. Adult urchins may be eaten by other marine animals such as crustaceans, molluscs, and fishes, and their planktonic larvae must form an important source of food for a great variety of pelagic and benthic plankton feeders.

Dr. Chesher, in examining the systematics of these interesting animals, has produced a study of unusual depth. Here methods of measuring and analyzing taxonomic characters have been developed to standardize the systematic treatment of spatangoids, and to minimize the subjective aspect of distinguishing species that previously was prevalent. In addition to a thorough systematic treatment of each species, burrowing, feeding, and other aspects of the animals' activities — topics seldom discussed in systematic papers — are described in detail for several species.

The material for this study has come largely from the rich collections obtained through the University of Miami-National Geographic Society Deep-Sea Biology Program which conducts trawling from the research vessels JOHN ELLIOTT PILLSBURY and GERDA. Additional studies were completed at the Museum of Comparative Zoology at Harvard University, and at the United States National Museum.

This work deals with ten species and subspecies belonging to four genera; three of the species are new to science. The characters of each species are discussed in detail, measured, and mathematically analyzed. Photographs and diagrams show the general appearance of the urchins and their important systematic details, and illustrate the burrowing activities of some of the species. Taxonomic characters have been meticulously examined and evaluated for their reliability for defining and recognizing the species concerned. In addition to providing thorough discussions of each species, the author carefully explains his methods and the rationale behind them. Seldom has any invertebrate group received such a thorough scrutiny and never before has a group of sea urchins been subjected to such a penetrating investigation.

This work will be a necessity to marine biologists, ecologists, and paleontologists, to those interested in the biology and evolution of echinoderms, and to museum workers involved in making accurate determinations of species.

THE EDITORS

TABLE OF CONTENTS

Preface v

Abstract 1

Statement of the Problem 3

Materials and Methods 4

Genus *Brissopsis* L. Agassiz 11

   Brissopsis alta Mortensen 15

   Brissopsis atlantica Mortensen 43

   Brissopsis elongata Mortensen 63

   Brissopsis mediterranea Mortensen 77

   Brissopsis lyrifera capensis Mortensen 90

Genus *Plethotaenia* H. L. Clark 97

   Plethotaenia spatangoides (A. Agassiz) 99

   Plethotaenia angularis, n. sp. 111

Genus *Paleopneustes* A. Agassiz 121

   Paleopneustes tholoformis, n. sp. 125

   Paleopneustes cristatus A. Agassiz 134

Genus *Saviniaster* Lambert 142

   Saviniaster enodatus, n. sp. 143

Taxonomic Conclusions 149

The Variability of Characters 154

The Fascioles 154

The Higher Classification of Spatangoids 158

Biological and Ecological Conclusions 159

Summary 161

Literature Cited 163

Plates 169

THE SYSTEMATICS OF SYMPATRIC SPECIES IN WEST INDIAN SPATANGOIDS: A REVISION OF THE GENERA *BRISSOPSIS*, *PLETHOTAENIA*, *PALEOPNEUSTES* AND *SAVINIASTER*[1]

RICHARD H. CHESHER[2]

Institute of Marine Sciences, University of Miami
and
Museum of Comparative Zoology, Harvard University

ABSTRACT

Analysis of the echinoid genera *Brissopsis*, *Plethotaenia* and *Paleopneustes* indicates that each genus has two species which live sympatrically in the West Indian area. Each species is described and illustrated. The following species and sub-species of the genus *Brissopsis* are recognized in the Atlantic Ocean: *B. alta*, *B. atlantica*, *B. elongata*, *B. elongata jarlii*, *B. mediterranea*, *B. lyrifera*, *B. lyrifera capensis*, and *B. evanescens*. There are two species of the genus *Plethotaenia*: *P. angularis* n.sp. and *P. spatangoides* (A. Agassiz, 1883). These species are described and the genus placed in the family Spatangidae on the basis of numerous characters. Two species of *Paleopneustes* are described: *P. cristatus* A. Agassiz, 1873 and *P. tholoformis* n. sp. *Paleopneustes* is shown to be closely related to *Plesiozonus*, *Pericosmus*, and *Faorina*. These four genera are united as a revised family, the Paleopneustidae. The genera remaining in Mortensen's (1950) concept of the Paleopneustidae are placed in the Asterostomatidae as suggested by Fischer (1966). A new species of *Saviniaster*, *S. enodatus* n. sp., is described from deep water south of Grand Bahama, B.W.I. The genus was previously known by one species from the Eocene deposits of France.

Where possible, allometric, individual, and geographic variation are compared for each of the species. The characters of the test are shown to be relatively stable and do not vary greatly with changes in habitat or geographic distance. Inhibitor genes which prevent the expression of fascioles and pedicellariae are discussed. The value of the fascioles as a taxonomic character is discussed, and the path of fascioles over the plates is shown to be a useful taxonomic feature.

Sympatric species-pairs are common in spatangoids of other parts of the world and from the fossil record. The differences between the members of each species-pair are surprisingly constant in the various genera. The possibility that the paired forms are a non-sex-linked polymorphism is rejected in favor of their representing distinct species.

A system of measurements is developed which statistically represents the external morphology of a spatangoid. This system is intended to promote standardization of measuring spatangoids for investigation of their taxonomy, zoogeography and speciation.

[1] This paper forms No. 41 of the series entitled Biological Investigations of the Deep Sea. Scientific Contribution No. 946 from the Institute of Marine Sciences, University of Miami.

[2] Present address: College of Guam, Agana, Guam.

1

Echinoids offer the student of evolution an excellent subject for analysis. The literature and all the described species, fossil and recent, have been catalogued by Mortensen 1928-1951. The paleontological record is excellent, and most of the known genera have living representatives. Most of the genera which have ever existed have probably been described. Even so, in the order Spatangoida, Mortensen (1950-1951b) lists only 237 genera. The oldest spatangoids are the toxasterids from the lower Cretaceous. One of the best known examples of continuous evolution is found in a group of spatangoids from the Chalk of England (Nichols, 1959).

Echinoids are perfectly suited for a biometric analysis. Their features are quite stable, there are numerous characters which are easily counted or measured, and the animals are usually available in large numbers. The features of the habitat are easily determined, particularly in the spatangoids which burrow in mud or sand. Echinoids are easily studied in the field and they will live for long periods of time in aquaria. Finally, they normally breed well in captivity, providing an opportunity to study their genetics. Among echinoids, spatangoids are unfortunately the most difficult to breed.

Zoogeographic and evolutionary studies in the spatangoids are made difficult or impossible by the lack of consistent or thorough descriptions of the vast majority of the species. The works of Döderlein and Koehler provide an occasional exception to this general lack of definitive descriptions. It is axiomatic that workers in any group of animals must develop a standardized system of measuring the characters with which they are dealing. In many animal groups it is difficult to find characters to measure, but in echinoids it is possible to define the entire animal statistically.

In this study, 30 measurements and 11 counts were taken on each specimen. This might seem excessively time consuming, but only fifteen to twenty minutes were required to measure each specimen. The combination of measurements produces a numerical representation of gross external anatomy. Thus, when samples are obtained from different ecological or geographic areas, one can assess morphological changes. The data were collected in anticipation of a more comprehensive study on the genetics and speciation of spatangoids.

Before such a program can be carried out, it is necessary to delineate the species and subspecies that are being studied. The measurement of numerous characters analyzed by simple and well known statistical procedures, can satisfactorily show the number of principal genetic taxa involved.

The present report is designed to describe the various species and subspecies of some problematic spatangoid genera and to show the type and direction of variability in the taxonomic characters of these taxa. It is hoped that the system of measurements which is used here will serve as a step toward the adoption of a standardized system of measurements for spatangoids.

Nichols (1959, 1962) and Kongiel (1962) have produced the only studies on the variability of recent spatangoids. Others (Kermack, 1954; Rowe, 1899; Hayward, 1943; Nichols, 1959) have provided an excellent biometric analysis of the spatangoid fossils from the English Chalk. No study has been made, however, on the variability of the majority of characters actually used by echinoid systematists. Nothing is known of the geographic variation of spatangoids.

To interpret the results of any biometric analysis, it is necessary to learn as much as possible about the ecology of the animals. In this study, based on relatively deep-water specimens, little ecological information could be obtained. The nature of the substrate was determined (in most cases) from the gut contents of the specimens. As spatangoids are non-selective detritus feeders, their intestine provides a miniature core of the substrate. Specimens of two species of *Brissopsis* were kept alive in the laboratory for nine months. Biological observations are described under those species (*B. alta* and *B. atlantica*).

The author expresses his sincere thanks to Dr. F. M. Bayer whose cooperation and supervision have been of invaluable aid in the preparation of this manuscript and in the progress of the research. Thanks are also due to Drs. W. A. Starck, L. A. Greenfield, W. Drost-Hansen, E. J. F. Wood, E. S. Iversen, and H. B. Moore for their advice and encouragement. Drs. H. B. Fell, D. L. Pawson and A. M. Clark, and Miss Maureen Downey were extremely helpful and cooperative in supplying specimens for this research, for which I am deeply grateful. I am also grateful to my wife, Judy, without whose support and encouragement this study would not have been possible.

This research was supported in part by the National Science Foundation under Grant GB 2037; this paper constitutes a report to that agency. The specimens collected by R/V GERDA and R/V JOHN ELLIOTT PILLSBURY were obtained during operations supported by the National Science Foundation under Grants G 20355 and GB 1204 for biological ship time, and partly by the National Geographic Society—University of Miami Deep-Sea Biology Program. This paper forms No. 41 in the series Biological Investigations of the Deep Sea.

STATEMENT OF THE PROBLEM

Recent expeditions of the Institute of Marine Sciences, University of Miami, Florida, have resulted in the collection of many spatangoids of the genera *Paleopneustes, Plethotaenia,* and *Brissopsis*. The examination of these specimens indicated a need for the revision of the existing systematics of these three genera. The interspecific relations of the West Indian sympatric species of *Paleopneustes, Plethotaenia,* and *Brissopsis* are paralleled by other spatangoid genera in the fossil record and in other parts of the world. The lack of information on variability of the taxonomic characters of spatangoids makes it necessary to describe the species of these genera as completely as possible in order to separate the animals into their proper taxa.

All three genera are represented by sympatric species which have been found sharing the same ecological niche. This situation is not common in the animal world and is discussed in the descriptions of the various species and in the taxonomic conclusions.

A fourth genus, *Saviniaster,* is also considered in this study. The genus *Saviniaster* was previously known from species found in the Eocene deposits of France. The R/V GERDA captured a single specimen of a closely related species south of Grand Bahama Island, B.W.I., in 366 meters of water. *Saviniaster* is closely related to *Prenaster,* a large and problematic fossil group. It is hoped that the description of this new species of *Saviniaster* will be of value in determining the relations of *Prenaster.*

MATERIALS AND METHODS

Specimens were obtained by dredging operations of the R/V GERDA and R/V PILLSBURY conducted by the Institute of Marine Sciences, University of Miami, Florida. Specimens in the collections of various museums were also examined and are listed under "Material Examined" in the description of each species. Since some of the material was fragmentary, not all specimens were used for biometric analysis. In the tables containing the statistical summary of each species, the number of specimens measured is given for each character.

The characters were selected for measurement on the basis of a preliminary examination of the specimens of each species and on the basis of characters employed in the taxonomic literature of this group. Initially, each measurement was made several different ways. The best correlation between the various characters and the reproducibility of the measurements determined the way each character was to be measured. Figure 1 indicates the various measurements. The index to that figure explains the measurements fully. The most satisfactory method of measuring these animals is to determine a fixed geometric plane and to take measurements in relation to that plane. The plastron of spatangoids offers the best "reference plane." Since the animals have a hard, inflexible test, projected measurements can be taken accurately. The total length of the test, measured on the plastronal plane, was a more indicative and constant representation of size than the length taken from the floor of the anterior notch to the posterior end of the test. The use of the total length makes comparisons between species more reliable since some species have a deep frontal notch and others have no notch at all. It is desirable to establish relations between the length, volume, respiratory surfaces, and fasciolar

4

systems. The use of the "notch length" may indicate a significant difference in these relations between two specimens whereas the total length will be more indicative of the volume and show no difference.

Meristic characters were found to be numerous and of great taxonomic interest. The number of plates from the peristome to the petaloid portion of the ambulacra does not vary with growth. This number was found to be of specific importance in the groups studied. The number of inter-ambulacral plates from the peristome to the fasciolar systems is amazingly constant and, in some groups, is of familial importance. In other taxa, however, this character was only of specific importance. The stability of the subanal fasciole in relation to the interambulacral plates is such that it is of superfamilial importance.

The plates were counted using Lovén's (1874) system. Since the animals are bilaterally symmetrical, only the counts for the left side were recorded (unless the other side was significantly different). By counting the plates in interambulacrum 4 (the left, lateral interambulacrum) confusion is avoided concerning the "heteronomy" described by Lovén (1874, 1883). Gordon (1926) indicates that Lovén was in error in assuming that two plates were fused into one (i.e., plates 2a + 2b) in interambulacrum 1. I agree with Lovén, but to avoid a lengthy discussion, only the counts in interambulacrum 4 were recorded. The counts are the same for interambulacrum 1, if Lovén's work is correct.

Apparently, both Lovén and Gordon were mistaken in assuming that the unpaired interambulacral plates nearest the peristome are single. There are two unpaired plates here. The plate nearest the peristome is small and the suture between it and the following plate is obscure. In some genera (i.e., *Paleopneustes*) this plate is easier to see than in others but when the plates are sectioned, the smaller one becomes evident in all of the genera I have examined. It is this small plate which expands into the coelom to form the perignathic apophysis. Frequently, this plate is densely covered with tubercles whereas the following plate is naked (Plate 12*f*). The labrum is also a compound plate, derived from two interambulacral and (on the underside of the lip) two peristomal plates. These facts are significant for understanding the phylogenetic history of the spatangoids as a whole, but make little difference in how the plates are counted. For convenience, Lovén's system is adopted and the first plate (really two plates) is counted as number one for both the anterior and posterior plate series. In the "b" series of the frontal ambulacrum (III) and in the "a" series of the left, anterior ambulacrum (IV), there are two pore-pairs adjacent to the peristome. These two are on a single plate which is counted as plate number 1, not as two plates.

The number of respiratory tube-feet increases exponentially with growth. There is no point in counting all of the pore-pairs in the petals. The anterior series is almost always equal to the posterior pore-series in each petal and the bilateral symmetry is constant (if not equal) in the various

5

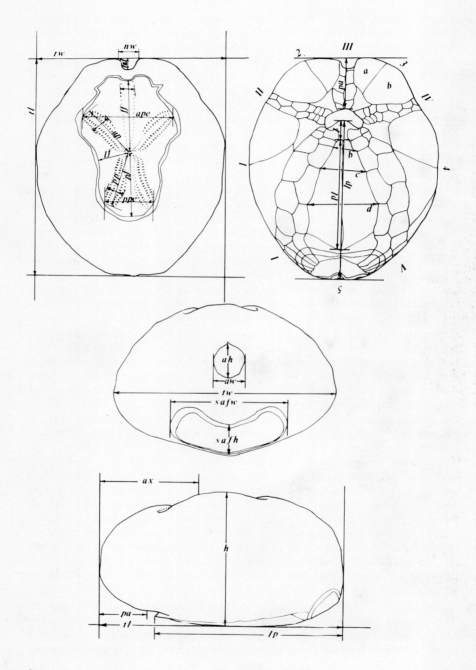

6

species. Therefore, only the posterior pore-series of the left, anterior petal and the anterior pore-series of the left, posterior petal were counted. These were the easiest to count. To obtain the total number of pore-pairs (both developed and rudimentary) it is necessary to multiply my counts by 4.

In the frontal ambulacrum, the tunneling tube-feet were all counted. The change in the size and shape of the pore-pairs is such that the number of functional and non-functional tunneling tube-feet can be determined on naked tests. The data in the text and graphs represent functional tunneling tube-feet.

The fascioles were measured with dividers and vernier calipers. The dividers were set at 1 to 5 mm, depending on the size of the specimen, and the length of the fasciole was measured by "walking" the dividers along the fasciole. The fasciolar area was measured by determining the area of short lengths of uniform width and summing them up. The width of any particular segment was measured to 0.01 mm in three different places and these figures averaged. This average was multiplied by the length of that particular segment of the fasciole. In some species the fasciole is so uniform in width that only three measurements of its width and one of its length were necessary to determine the fasciolar area. This method is accurate (cf. Figs. 5, 16) and rapid. The method of Nichols

←

FIGURE 1. Abbreviations used in designating measurements of spatangoids: *ah*, height of the periproct; *ap*, length of anterior petal (from ocular to most distant pore-pair) ambulacrum IV only; *ape*, span of distal ends of anterior petals; *apw*, width of anterior petal; *aw*, width of periproct; *ax*, apical system to anterior end of test (see text); *b, c, d,* the width of plastron measured at the expansions between the junctions of ambulacral plates (the first expansion is always "a"); *ff*, apical system to peripetalous fasciole along center of ambulacrum III (center of genital pores to anterior edge of fasciole); *h,* height; *l,* length of labrum; *lf*, apical system to peripetalous fasciole along center of interambulacrum 4; *lp,* anterior edge of labrum to posterior end of test (see text); *nd,* depth of the notch in anterior ambitus, taken from anteriormost portion of test (holding vernier calipers parallel with plane of plastron, place jaws for inside measurements into notch from below; open calipers until edge of jaw is level with anteriormost portions of adjoining interambulacra); *nw,* width of notch in anterior ambitus, taken from anteriormost portion of the test between the raised nodes of the adjoining interambulacral plates (this is about the center of these plates); *pa,* anterior edge of peristome to anterior end of test (see text); *pf,* apical system to peripetalous fasciole along center of interambulacrum 5; *pl,* length of plastron; *pp,* length of posterior petal (from ocular pore to most distant pore-pair within peripetalous fasciole) ambulacrum V only; *ppe,* span of distal ends of posterior petals; *ppfl,* length of peripetalous fasciole measured by "walking" dividers along its length; *ppw,* width of posterior petal (outer edge of the pore series); *safh,* height of area enclosed by subanal fasciole; *safl,* length of subanal fasciole; *safw,* width of area enclosed by subanal fasciole; *tl,* total length, *tw,* total width; *wIII,* width of ambulacrum III (outer edges of pore series, nearest the peripetalous fasciole); I, II, III, IV, V, Lovén's designations for the ambulacra; 1, 2, 3, 4, 5, the interambulacra.

(1959) was found to agree with the results of this method but, since his process is more time consuming, it was not adopted. Further descriptive remarks on the fascioles are found in the descriptions of the individual species and in the conclusions, under the section on the variability of the taxonomic characters.

The projected measurements used in this study are: the distance from the apical system to the anterior end of the test; the distance of the leading edge of the peristome to the anterior end of the test; and the distance of the anterior end of the labrum from the posterior end of the test. The projected measurements were made as follows: A rectangular block of plastic was placed on a sheet of graph paper. The block provided a vertical axis from the table (90.09°). The cleaned test was placed on the graph paper so the long axis of the test (anterior notch through the periproct) was perpendicular to the vertical surface. The anterior end of the test was held against the vertical surface and adjusted so the plane of the plastron was parallel with the plane of the table. The latter was accomplished by examining the test from the side and adjusting it so the anterior and posterior ends of the plastron were equally distant from the table. In many spatangoids, this is not difficult as the plastron is flat and the animal naturally rests on the table in the proper orientation. The distance from the apical system (the center of the genital pores) to the vertical surface was measured to 0.1 mm with vernier calipers, using the sharply pointed jaws designed for measuring inside diameters. The calipers were held parallel to the table during the measurement and, with one point on the apical system, the calipers were moved slightly up and down. The shortest distance is, of course, the correct one. The measurements on the oral side of the test were made with the test placed on its dorsal surface and the plane of the plastron was aligned by eye. In small specimens (less than 20 mm test length), where meaurements are the most critical, the process was done under a dissecting microscope and the alignment of the test on the oral side was determined optically. When the entire plastron was in focus along its long axis (using only one ocular of the microscope) the test was considered in proper alignment and the measurement made to 0.01 mm with the vernier calipers. Tests of error (Kermack, 1954) showed that the measurements were sufficiently accurate and representative of the true variation of the animals (i.e., total contribution of the errors to the estimation of population variance not greater than 1 per cent). The accuracy of these measurements is evident from the low variability of these characters in the animals studied. For the purpose of this study, the measurements were converted to percentages of the test lengths and rounded off to the nearest 1 per cent.

There are three statistical techniques used in this study, none of which is complex. Most of the measurements are given as the mean percentage of the test length plus or minus the standard error of the mean. The standard deviation (S.D.) and the coefficient of variability (C.V. $=$ S.D. $\times$ 100/

8

mean) are also given. The area of the fascioles and some meristic characters vary allometrically to such an extent that it is necessary to give their interrelationships in terms of the regression equations of the characters. In some cases the relationship is logarithmic and in others it is semilogarithmic. The standard error and correlation coefficient of the regression equations are given also. The well known diagram of Hubbs & Perlmutter (1942) is used where visual representation of the data is helpful (i.e., Figs. 11, 21).

To compare population means, the probability of significance was determined using F tables. For practical reasons, it is desirable to know how many misclassifications would occur when using any given character. Following the method of Lubischew (1962), the coefficient of discrimination (K) was determined for those characters which were highly significant. Thus, it is possible to state that, using character X alone, there will probably be one misclassification for every Y specimens examined. As can be seen from Fig. 21, the probability of misclassification may be relatively great even when the population ranges do not overlap in the specimens examined.

In some closely related species, the variation of all characters overlaps so that no one character is satisfactory for identification. In these species, combinations of characters are used and plotted on an identification diagram. One to several characters are used on each axis to clearly delineate two closely related species (Fig. 3). Rather than calculate the multiple discriminant function of the characters of each axis (Lubischew, 1962) the various characters, given as percentages of the test lengths, were simply added up and their sum used as the X or Y coordinate. While this technique is not as useful statistically as Lubischew's methods, it is much easier and, for purposes of identification, it is adequate. In determining which characters to use for each axis, the characters of species *A* which have a higher mean than species *B* were used for the Y axis and those characters which have a lower mean were used for the X axis. In each case, as few characters as possible were used to achieve a clear separation of the two groups. This technique is illustrated in Figs. 2 and 3.

In species which can only be distinguished by a single character (a difference in tuberculation or pedicellariae or a single meristic character) the use of an identification diagram often permits identification of specimens which do not have the "key" character (i.e., small specimens, or partially broken, worn, naked or fossilized specimens). In addition, if all the specimens which were identified using the "key" character fall into the correct group on the chart, the key character can be used with more confidence. If the use of such a graph does not distinguish two groups or show a distinct bimodality, the validity of the key character is highly questionable.

Considering the numerous arguments in recent literature (Maze, 1966; Mayr, 1965; Sokal *et al.*, 1965; Heywood & McNeill, 1964) concerning

9

"numerical" versus "classical" taxonomy, it is necessary to comment on my emphasis on measurements. There is no doubt that the human mind, particularly that of a trained and experienced taxonomist, can outperform any computer in deciding if two unknown forms are one or two species. It would be a waste of time to perform a complex statistical analysis on something which already is obvious to the systematist. Two problems exist, however, which require more than the ability to differentiate between various forms and pass judgment on their taxonomic status. The first is in communicating the results to those who might use them and the second is in determining how the various features of the animals vary with time and with geographic and ecologic changes.

Without measurements, it is extremely difficult for others to utilize the systematist's results. Often, the illustrations provided with the descriptions save the taxonomist's work from the trash heap. If the illustrations are poor, the work may simply be ignored (i.e., the work of Roig). Some workers have gone so far as to describe species from illustrations drawn by an artist (A. Agassiz). This has resulted in some unfortunate misunderstandings which are invariably expensive in terms of the time and effort necessary to correct them. In the majority of cases, descriptions of echinoids do not differentiate the species from closely related forms. The authors rely on such vague terms as "the peristome is more anterior in species *A* than in species *B*." Such statements are, of course, worthless to someone who does not have both forms before him, and frequently they are not valid anyway. When a few of these characters are measured it becomes clear that the character either is invalid (at least by itself) or can be expressed in terms of a definite value in a meaningful way. Even if the species being considered is found to be misidentified the description remains valuable in that the measurements may offer important information on geographic variation. It is not necessary to measure a large series of animals and it is not necessary to treat the data statistically (although this is to be preferred). Measurements on a single animal are far better than no measurements at all. It may be argued that it is not necessary to include measurements on so many characters, particularly the ones that do not vary within a genus or family, but it is as important to record the stability of characters as it is to record their variability.

To return to the second point in favor of a statistical approach to taxonomic problems, a systematist may be able to perform an instantaneous, multivariate analysis on the material on his desk, but he will find it a less objective operation if he is dealing with variation in a large population. The task will become more difficult if he is expected to intuitively determine the geographic or geologic changes in the species. Obviously, he will have to use something to assist and confirm his intuitive judgment, particularly if he does not study all the specimens at the same time. Of course, he could photograph and describe each specimen, but this is not nearly as objective, and is considerably more laborious

10

than measuring the animals, placing the measurements on computer cards, and programming a computer to provide accurate and reproducible solutions to questions of variation. If the systematist is to study what he purports to be studying (evolution), he can hardly object to having such a valuable aid as a pair of calipers. Neither can he object to a method for storing his data and providing him with answers to various statistical questions as, "Does the length of the anterior petal change significantly between Florida and Brazil?" or "Does the diameter of the anal system increase significantly in deeper water?" Most systematists today agree that statistical methods are a helpful and necessary tool in systematics. The results of any biometrical analysis, whether calculated by hand or by computer, are only as valid as the data incorporated in the study, the method of analysis, and the interpretation of the results.

Genus *Brissopsis* L. Agassiz

Brissopsis L. Agassiz, 1840. p. 3, 16.
Brissopsis, L. Agassiz, *in* Agassiz & Desor, 1847, p. 14.
Brissopsis, Mortensen, 1951b, p. 371 (complete synonymy).
Brissopsis, Fischer, 1966, p. U584

Diagnosis.—Test of elongate, oval outline, subanal snout not present; petaloid ambulacra confluent or diverging to a varying degree, the unpaired ambulacrum forming a shallow notch in the anterior ambitus; well developed tunneling tube-feet within the petaloid portion of III. Subanal fasciole bilobed (except for *B. persica* in which it is heart-shaped and *B. evanescens* which lacks it in the adult) with more-or-less developed anal branches of the fasciole. No large primary tubercles on the aboral surface. Four genital pores, the apical system ethmolytic.

Description.—It would be premature to expand on the description of this genus given by Mortensen (1951b, p. 372).

Type-species.—*Brissus lyrifer* Forbes, 1841, = *Brissopsis lyrifera* (Forbes) Agassiz & Desor, 1847, by subsequent designation: Desor, 1858.

Comments.—Mortensen (1951b) discusses the affinities of and differences between related genera and *Brissopsis.* It is beyond the range of this study on inter- and intra-specific variation to expand on his discussion.

    Brissopsis, in addition to being the most wide-spread and largest spatangoid genus, has been subjected to more hours of study by more taxonomists with less satisfactory results than any other spatangoid genus. There are two main reasons for this. The first is that a single worker seldom has had sufficient material of several forms of *Brissopsis* for examination and the second is that even the most thorough workers (Mortensen, Clark, Agassiz) did not submit the animals to actual measurement. Although some workers examined "more than 400 specimens" (Clark, 1917 p. 200) it was impossible for them, without measuring the characters, to reach any definite conclusions on the specific status of many of the species or the amount of variability to expect in each species. It is of course, impossible for other workers to utilize their efforts fully. Thus, the researcher faced with a new species or sub-species, or with a problem of zoogeography or identification, is at a loss to determine just how widely any given species is distributed or how, and in what direction, variation occurs in the genus to which it belongs.

Brissopsis is one of the commonest echinoids between 40 and 300 meters depth in most of the world's oceans and it has been collected in large numbers by almost all of the major biological deep-sea cruises. Seventy-five fossil species have been assigned to this genus (Mortensen, 1951b). The necessity of distinguishing between the different forms of *Brissopsis,* considered to be the most perplexing spatangoid genus (Clark, 1917), is self evident. It can be expected that valuable information as to zoogeography, variation, and speciation of spatangoids can be gained from an analysis of this genus.

To begin such a project, it is necessary to analyze each species carefully and to describe it (verbally, statistically, and pictorially) with sufficient clarity that populations from various localities can be compared. The main features of the *Brissopsis* species can be defined by a few measurements which, treated statistically, will give taxonomists a clear picture of what types of variation occur in the various features of the test. In addition, meristic characters are abundant and easily determined. In most cases, the meristic characters are so constant that statistical treatment is not necessary.

Interpretation of the data, once compiled, will be (and should be) subjective to a certain extent. Measurements and statistical analyses are only aids to help determine the genetic make-up of the animals involved. It is left to the systematist to interpret these data in correlation with the biological and paleontological data at his disposal.

Key to the Atlantic Species and Subspecies of the Genus *Brissopsis*

1. Labrum extending to the second adjoining ambulacral plates 2
1. Labrum not extending past the first adjoining ambulacral plates 3

2. Thorns of the globiferous pedicellariae on the mid-line of the back (Caribbean) .... *B. elongata* s.s.
2. Thorns of the globiferous pedicellariae not on the mid-line of the back (Gulf of Guinea) .... *B. elongata jarlii.*

3. Posterior petals confluent proximally, plates entering the subanal fasciole 4 or 5 4
3. Posterior petals divergent from the apical system, plates entering the subanal fasciole 4 5

12

4. Plates entering the subanal fasciole normally 4, peripetalous fasciole never crosses plate 4b (interambulacrum 3) (Gulf of Guinea, Mediterranean, eastern United States) .... *B. mediterranea*.
4. Plates entering the subanal fasciole normally 5, peripetalous fasciole frequently dips down to plate 4b (interambulacrum 3) (E. Florida, Bahamas, Gulf of Mexico to N. coast of S. America) .. *B. atlantica*.
5. Two end teeth on globiferous pedicellariae, first plate crossed by peripetalous fasciole in III is 5b. 6

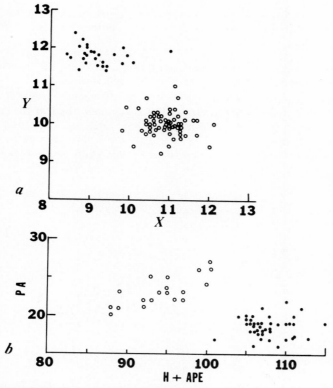

FIGURE 2. Identification diagrams for *Brissopsis alta, B. atlantica,* and *B. mediterranea.* A, *Brissopsis alta* (solid dots), *B. atlantica* (circles): X = peristome to anterior end of test (per cent test length) + length of posterior petal (V) as percentage of the length of anterior petal (IV); Y = sum of height of test, width of plastron (point D) and distance from apical system to lateral portion of peripetalous fasciole (all as percentages of test length).—B, *Brissopsis alta* (solid dots), *B. mediterranea* (circles): H + APE = sum of height of test and span of distal ends of the anterior petals (both as percentages of test length); PA = distance from peristome to anterior end of test (percentage of test length).

13

5. Many small teeth surrounding the terminal opening, first plate crossed by peripetalous fasciole in III is 6b (Florida and Gulf of Mexico) .... *B. alta.*

6. Test low (less than 60 per cent test length), posterior petals short (less than 25 per cent test length) (Norway, Iceland, to African coast *ca.* 8°N) .... *B. lyrifera* s.s.

6. Test high (greater than 60 per cent test length), posterior petals long (greater than 25 per cent test length) (S. Africa from Agulhas Bank to Gulf of Guinea *ca.* 3°45′N) .... *B. lyrifera capensis.*

6. Test low, subanal fasciole vanishing in adults, paired petals cover almost entire aboral surface (S.W. Africa, off Walfisch Bay). *B. evanescens.*

For additional differences and similarities between the species, refer to Figures 2 and 3 and to the discussions of each species.

Brissopsis caparti Cherbonnier, 1959, is discussed under *B. lyrifera capensis. B. evanescens* Mortensen 1950 is not described in this study, no material being at my disposal. For further reference, see Mortensen 1951b. p. 429, Pl. 22, Figs. 1-5, Pl. 59, Fig. 11. Text figs. 205, 206, 207. *B. lyrifera* (Forbes 1841) is not described in this study since I have only a

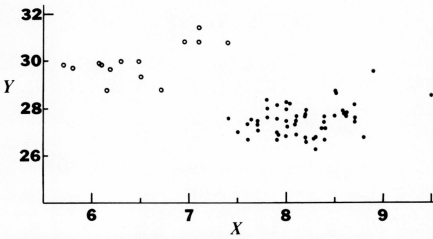

FIGURE 3. Identification diagram for *Brissopsis atlantica* (solid dots) and *B. mediterranea* (circles): X = sum of span of distal ends of anterior petals (percentage of test length) and one-half of the anus width (percentage of anus height) all divided by 10; Y = sum of width of test, height of test, twice the distance from apical system to anterior portion of peripetalous fasciole, and twice the width of plastron)point D) all as percentage of test length, and all divided by 10.

14

few specimens for examination. Measurements and descriptions by Nichols (1959), Kongeil (1962), Lovén (1883), Mortensen (1951b), Döderlein (1906), and Brattström (1946) are utilized where possible.

TABLE 1

ANALYSIS OF THE TAXONOMIC CHARACTERS OF SPECIFIC VALUE IN THE GENUS *Brissopsis*

A. CHARACTERS TOO STABLE FOR INTERSPECIFIC USE:
Apical system to anterior portion of peripetalous fasciole;
Width of periproct;
Peripetalous fasciole crossing plates 4a (6, 7, or 8), 4b (6 or 6 and 7), 5a (10 or 11).

B. CHARACTERS TOO VARIABLE OR SHOWING EXCESSIVE OVERLAP BETWEEN SPECIES:
Width of test;
Width of petals;
Height/width of area enclosed by subanal fasciole;
Width/height of periproct.

C. CHARACTERS SHOWING ALLOMETRIC VARIATION (A) OR GEOGRAPHIC OR ECOLOGICAL VARIATION (G), BUT STILL INFORMATIVE:
Length of the petals (A);
Number of plates from peristome to petals (G?);
Distance from apical system to lateral portion of peripetalous fasciole (A) (G);
Length of peripetalous fasciole (A);
Length of subanal fasciole (A);
Length and width of plastron (A);
Apical system to anterior end of test (G).

D. CHARACTERS WHICH ARE NORMALLY STABLE BUT SEPARATE THE SPECIES INTO AT LEAST TWO GROUPS:
Height of test (G?);
Position of peristome;
Length of anterior petal;
Posterior extension of labrum;
First plate entering subanal fasciole;
Distance from apical system to posterior portion of peripetalous fasciole;
Number of tube-feet (A) (G).

E. CHARACTERS WHICH SHOW LITTLE VARIATION AND SEPARATE OUT SEVERAL SPECIES:
Number of plates entering the subanal fasciole;
Path of fasciole on IIIb and 3a, b;
Width of area enclosed by subanal fasciole;
Span of ends of anterior petals;
Degree of divergence of posterior petals;
Characters of globiferous pedicellariae.

Brissopsis alta Mortensen, 1907
Figures 2, 4-10; Plates 1-5, 11g; Tables 1, 2, 3, 12

Brissopsis lyrifera, A. Agassiz, 1883, pl. 26, figs. 13-15. Not *Brissopsis lyrifera* (Forbes 1841).
Brissopsis alta Mortensen, 1907, p. 159, pl. 3, figs. 5, 8, 9, 13, 16; pl. 18,

15

figs. 7, 24, 26, 27.
Brissopsis alta, H. L. Clark, 1917, p. 202.
Brissopsis alta, H. L. Clark, 1925, p. 212.
Brissopsis altum, Lambert and Thiery, 1925, p. 489.
Brissopsis alta, Mortensen, 1951b, p. 390; pl. 57, fig. 21; text figs. 184b, 185b, 187b, 188b, 190a.

Material examined.—9 specimens, 14 to 23.4 mm test length, sta. RHCT1, off Government Cut, Miami, Florida, 25°45′N., 80°02′W., 90 to 146 m, 7 Jan. 1966.—3 specimens, 41.7 to 54.3 mm test length, GERDA sta. G-110, off Dry Tortugas, Florida, 24°21′N., 82°55′W., 183 m, 17 June 1963.—3 specimens, 25.2 to 34.3 mm test length, sta. G-172, off Ft. Pierce, Florida, 27°25′N., 79°56′W., 183 m, 29 June 1963.—3 specimens, 40 to 62.5 mm test length, sta. G-462, off Dry Tortugas, Florida, 24°20′N., 80°06′W., 183 m, 25 Jan. 1965.—37 specimens, 11 to 21 mm test length, sta. G-623, off Government Cut, Miami, Florida, 25°46′N., 80°06′W., 110 m, 16 April 1965.—1 specimen, 16.8 mm test length, sta. G-657, off St. Lucie River, Florida, 27°14′N., 79°49′W., 210 m, 16 July 1965.—3 specimens, 21.5 to 41 mm test length, ALBATROSS sta. 2378, Gulf of Mexico, 29°14′N., 88°09′W., 124 m, 11 February 1885; U.S.N.M. 10637. —3 specimens, 26.4 to 36.5 mm test length, ALBATROSS sta. 2401, Gulf of Mexico, 28°38.5′N., 85°52.5′W., 260 m, 14 March 1885; U.S.N.M. 10640.—7 specimens, 52 to 76 mm test length, BLAKE sta. 49, Gulf of Mexico, 28°51.3′N., 89°01.5′W., 216 m; U.S.N.M. 6813 and 6827.

Diagnosis.—Plates III6b, I.A.3, 4 a and 3 b crossed by the peripetalous fasciole; plates 6, 7, 8, 9 of the posterior series of ambulacra I and V crossed by the subanal fasciole; anal branches absent. Posterior petals divergent, not confluent proximally; test high, subglobular (height normally greater than 65 per cent of the test length); globiferous pedicellariae with 6 to 9 small teeth surrounding the terminal opening.

Description.—The test has a rounded, subglobular appearance (Plate 1). Its mean width is 86.66 ± 0.39 per cent of the test length (S.D. 2.79, C.V. 3.2) and its mean height is 66.77 ± 0.26 per cent of the test length (S.D. 1.87, C.V. 2.8). The width tends to increase proportionally with growth, smaller specimens (test length 10 to 20 mm) having a width 81 to 88 per cent of the test length and larger (test length 50 to 63 mm) specimens having a width 89 to 98 per cent of the test length. The height does not change significantly with growth or geographic location, resulting in the low coefficient of variation.

The shape of the test, viewed laterally, varies with age. In smaller specimens (test length 15 mm or less) the posterior end of the test slopes obliquely so that the periproct is visible from above (Plate 2 *a, c, e*) and the anterior portion of the test is low, giving the urchin a wedge-shaped appearance. As the animal grows, the anterior end becomes higher and more rounded and the posterior end becomes vertically truncated (Plate 2 *a-f*).

16

The dorsal interambulacral plates, outside the peripetalous fasciole, develop a raised node from which tubercles radiate in fairly regular series. In larger specimens, the nodes of successive plates form a low, irregular elevation from the peripetalous fasciole to the ambitus in both plate series of interambulacra 4 and 5.

The Anterior Ambulacrum

The anterior ambulacrum is slightly sunken from the apex to the peristome, creating a shallow notch in the anterior ambitus. The proportional depth of this notch does not change markedly with age. The peripetalous fasciole crosses ambulacrum III at a mean distance from the apical system of 40.45 ± 0.31 per cent of the test length (S.D. 2.19, C.V. 5.4). This percentage decreases with growth. In smaller specimens (test length 11 to 15 mm) the fasciole crosses III at a distance from the apical system of 37 to 43 per cent of the test length. In larger specimens, the ambulacrum is crossed at a distance of 35 to 37 per cent of the test length.

Within the peripetalous fasciole, the frontal ambulacrum is divided into two areas, one nearest the apex containing developing tube-feet and the other containing functional, tunnel-building tube-feet. The number of functional tube-feet varies with age from 10 to 11 for specimens 11 mm in test length to 38 in a specimen 76 mm in test length. When plotted against the natural log of the length, this increase in the number of tunneling tube-feet becomes linear and has the regression equation shown on Figure 4 and 7 of:

$$Y = 10.9 \ Ln \ X - 16.2 \qquad Y = \text{Tunneling tube-feet}$$
$$S_{Y.LnX} = \pm \ 0.645 \ \text{tube-feet} \qquad X = \text{Test length (mm)}.$$
$$r = 0.989.$$

The tunneling tube-feet will be discussed again in the section on the peripetalous fasciole and on the borrowing habits.

New plates are split off from the ocular plate as the urchin grows. These plates bear undeveloped, globular tube-feet situated over a slit-like pore. The tube-feet progressively mature into functional, tunneling tube-feet with a terminal disc having 9 to 20 fringing digits, each supported by a calcite spicule (Plate 11*g*). This disc with its spicules is larger in *B. alta* (*ca.* 1 mm in diameter) than in *B. atlantica* (*ca.* 0.8 mm in diameter) but is otherwise not different. There seem to be more C-shaped spicules in the stalk of the tube-feet in *B. atlantica* (Plate 11*c*) than in *B. alta* (Plate 11*g*). The function of these tube-feet is described below in the section on burrowing.

The tunneling tube-feet issue from circular depressions near the dorsolateral edge of the ambulacral plates. The central portion of the peripodium is elevated to form a projection which is more pronounced in the larger specimens and which functions as a muscle support for the tube-feet. At the ventro-lateral base of this projection is the single, slit-like pore (Plate 4*d).*

TABLE 2

SPECIES GROUPS OF *Brissopsis*, BASED ON SELECTED CHARACTER STATES
(Method adopted from Throckmorton, 1965)

Character states	B. alta	B. lyrifera capensis	B. lyrifera	B. atlantica	B. mediterranea	B. elongata	B. elongata jarlii
Fasciole on Plate (I.A. 3a) A=4, B=4 and 5.	A	A	A	B	B	B	B
Fasciole on Plate (I.A. 3b) A=4, B=4 and 5 (angles up), C= 5 or 4 and 5 (angles down), D=5, 5 and 6, or 5-7.	A	B	A	C	D	D	D
Posterior petals A= divergent, B= confluent.	A	A	A	B	B	B	B
Amb. plate 6 in subanal fasciole A=yes, B=no.	A	A	A	A	A	B	B
Labrum extends to ambulacral plate A=1, B=2.	A	A	A	A	A	B	B
Ambulacral plates in subanal fasciole, A=4, B=5.	A	A	A	B	A	B	B

Globiferous pedicellariae, A= 2 teeth, B= 2 teeth with thorns on back, B'= thorns on side, C= many small teeth.

C	A	A	A(C)	A(C)	B	B'

Fasciole on IIIb, A=5, B=6, C=7.

B	A	A	B	B	BC	C

Mean test height A=50-60, B=65-70 per cent of test length.

B	B	A	A	A	A	A

Mean *sa/w*, A=35-40, B=40-45, C=45-50 per cent of test length.

A	C	A	B	B	B	B

Mean *ax*, A=10-15, B=15-20 per cent of test length.

B	B	A	A	B	B

Eleven characters appearing in one of four states (A,B,C, or D) distinguish three species-groups within the seven species tabulated. The degree of genetic divergence is indicated by the length of the line separating the letters. This line is lengthened by successive increments each time adjacent character states differ from each other.

TABLE 3

Summary of Statistical Data: *Brissopsis alta*

Character	Mean	S.E.M	S.D.	Range	N	C.V.
tl‡	20.10	1.56	11.27	11-62.5	53	
tw	86.66	0.39	2.79	81-98	53	3.2
h	66.77	0.26	1.87	63-70	53	2.8
ax	40.54	0.31	2.19	35-47	50	5.4
pa	18.68	0.19	1.30	16-22	50	7.0
lp	69.80	0.39	2.73	66-77	50	3.9
ap	24.42	0.28	2.05	21-30	52	8.4
apw*	43.53	0.77	5.36	27-55	52	12.3
pp	17.81	0.26	1.85	15-23	52	10.4
ppw*	52.24	0.97	6.74	36-64	52	12.9
ff	39.12	0.22	1.59	35-43	52	4.1
lf	16.87	0.17	1.19	13-20	52	7.1
pf	21.79	0.27	1.94	19-28	52	8.9
pf/af†	56.06	0.75	5.39	49-74	52	9.6
ppfl	167.37	1.52	10.85	152-197	52	6.5
ape	41.54	0.33	2.19	38-49	50	5.3
safw	36.54	0.23	1.59	32-40	48	4.4
safh/w†	63.54	1.18	8.06	42-77	48	12.7
safl	93.56	0.69	4.89	83-110	52	5.2
pl	46.27	0.28	2.01	41-53	52	4.4
b	16.97	0.29	1.79	12-20	40	10.5
c	27.25	0.32	2.02	23-32	41	7.4
d	35.09	0.25	1.72	32-39	49	4.9
aw	13.15	0.26	1.83	8-16	52	13.9
aw/ah†	76.79	0.98	6.98	63-95	52	9.1

The data given as percentages of the test length unless otherwise indicated.
Character symbols as given in index of Figure 1.
*Per cent of the petal length.
†The ratio as a percentage.
‡The test length in mm.

Ambulacrum III is widest near the peripetalous fasciole. Measurements of its width were taken from the outer edge of the pore-series. The width varies with the size of the specimen, being 9 to 10 per cent of the test length in small specimens (test length 11 to 15 mm) and 5 to 7 per cent of the test length in larger specimens (test length 53 to 76 mm).

There are six plates per plate-series from the peripetalous fasciole to the peristome. This number does not change with growth. The mature urchin (test length over 20 mm) usually has the three tube-feet nearest the peristome developed into feeding tube-feet in both plate-series. In smaller urchins, only the tube-foot nearest the peristome in series a, and two tube-feet in series b, are developed into feeding tube-feet; the adjacent tube-feet are sensory and later develop a penicillate disc. The feeding tube-feet are located over large, single pores and the sensory tube-feet over slit-like single pores. The function of these tube-feet will be described in the section on burrowing.

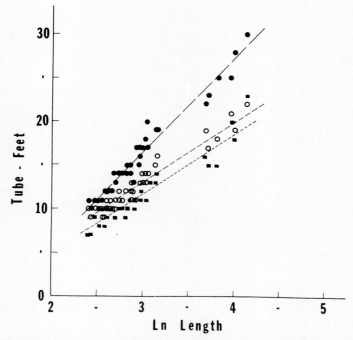

FIGURE 4. Tube-feet versus test length in *Brissopsis alta*. Solid dots = functional tunneling tube-feet, Amb. III; circles = pore-pairs in petal IV, series b; squares = pore-pairs in posterior petal V, series a.

The tuberculation of III can be seen in Plate 2*d*. There is a regular series of fairly large tubercles medially to the pore-series. Each ambulacral plate usually has two to three (occasionally one or four) tubercles medially to the pore. These tubercles support spatulate spines which aid in protecting and cleaning the tunneling tube-feet. Normally, only small tridentate pedicellariae are found in the portion of the anterior ambulacrum enclosed by the peripetalous fasciole. Between this fasciole and the peristome, large tridentate pedicellariae and rostrate pedicellariae are common.

Ambulacra II and IV
(the anterior paired petals)

The peripetalous fasciole crosses ambulacrum IV on plate 9a or 10a. This position does not change with growth and the ratio of 9a to 10a in the specimens examined was about 1:2. The lectotype and paratypes have 10 plates from the peristome to the petal in the anterior series of ambulacrum IV. The plates outside the peripetalous fasciole are heavily tuberculated,

21

with only a narrow median strip left bare. Nearest the peristome, there are feeding tube-feet, the number of which increases with growth to 9 or 10 per phyllode in the larger adults. Each feeding podium is situated over a single, large pore located on the adoral edge of the plate (Plate 3e). Sensory podia are located on the adoral edge of each plate from the phyllode to plates 8a and 7b or 8b of ambulacrum IV.

The petals are slightly sunken within the peripetalous fasciole. The two series of pore-pairs bend medially at their distal ends. The anterior series of pore-pairs have about 30 per cent (50 per cent in the smallest specimen) of the apicalmost pore-pairs underdeveloped. Over these underdeveloped pore-pairs are rudimentary, knob-like tube-feet. The larger pore-pairs bear respiratory tube-free (Plate 4h). In the posterior series, only one or two of the apicalmost pores are underdeveloped. As in ambulacrum III, the number of plates in the petaloid portion of ambulacrum IV increases throughout growth. Figure 4 shows the number of pore-pairs in ambulacrum IV, series b, plotted against the natural log of the test length. The regression equation shown on the graph is:

$$Y = 6.83 \text{ Ln } X - 7{:}35 \qquad Y = \text{Pore-pairs (IVb)}$$
$$S_{Y.LnX} = \pm 1.2 \text{ pore-pairs} \qquad X = \text{Test length (mm)}.$$
$$r = 0.917.$$

During growth, there is an increase in the number of tubercles adjacent to each pore-pair. These tubercles bear small spines which clean the respiratory tube-feet. The anterior, paired petals have a mean length of 24.42 ± 0.28 per cent of the test length (S.D. 2.05, C.V. 8.4) and their width is 43.53 ± 0.77 per cent of the petal length (S.D. 5.36, C.V. 12.3). The proportional length of the petal increases with size (21 per cent for an 11-mm specimen, 27 per cent for a 62.5-mm specimen). This allometry accounts for most of the large coefficient of variation of this character. The petal width decreases proportionally with an increase in size (50 per cent of the petal length for an 11-mm specimen to 27 per cent for a 62.5-mm specimen). The distance between the ends of the anterior petals has a mean of 41.54 ± 0.33 per cent of the test length (S.D. 2.19, C.V. 5.3). There is no significant change in this proportion with growth or with geographic location; individual variation accounts for most of the coefficient of variation. The posterior pore-series forms an almost straight line, the anterior pore-series bends posteriorly creating the illusion that the petal has a posterior bend.

Ambulacra I and V
(the posterior paired petals)

The peripetalous fasciole crosses ambulacrum V on plate 16a (occasionally plate 15a or 17a). This position does not change with growth. The plate outside the peripetalous fasciole are tuberculated from the fasciole to the ambitus, with only a narrow space left naked on the lateral margin of the anterior plate series. The plates of both series are about the same width as the adjoining plates of interambulacrum 5. Orally of plate number 6, the ambulacra are naked except for pedicellariae, sphaeridia, and small tertiary spines. A few larger tubercles are occasionally found on the margins of the plates. Nearest the peristome there are feeding tube-feet. In larger specimens, there are 8 or 9 feeding tube-feet in each phyllode. Only one or two sensory tube-feet are found in each plate series posterior to the phyllode. Within the subanal fasciole, there are two or three subanal tube-feet (Plate 4f) in plate series Ia and Vb. The subanal fasciole consistently crosses ambulacral plates numbers 6, 7, 8, and 9. In one specimen plate 10a of ambulacrum I had a small area of the fasciole on it and in another specimen, plate 9b of ambulacrum V was excluded from the fasciole so that only three plates were crossed by the fasciole.

The petals are slightly sunken within the peripetalous fasciole. The pore-pairs close distally. The posterior series of pore-pairs has 30 to 40 per cent of the apicalmost pore-pairs underdeveloped. The exact number is difficult to determine as there is a gradual decrease, apically, in the size of the pore-pairs. In the anterior series of the posterior petals, only the apicalmost one or two pore-pairs are reduced.

The number of plates in the petaloid region of ambulacrum V increases throughout growth. Figure 4 shows the number of pore-pairs of V, series a, plotted against the natural log of test length. The regression equation shown on the graph is:

$$Y = 6.78 \text{ Ln } X - 8.6. \qquad Y = \text{Pore-pairs Va.}$$
$$S_{Y.LnX} = \pm 1.4 \text{ pore-pairs} \qquad X = \text{Test length (mm)}$$
$$r = 0.784.$$

While the regression equations of the pores in the anterior and posterior petals are not significantly different, it should be noted that in any one specimen, the number of pore-pairs is seldom equal in the two petals. The posterior petal almost always has fewer pore-pairs than the anterior paired petal.

The posterior petals have a mean length of 17.81 $\pm$ 0.26 per cent of the test length (S.D. 1.85, C.V. 10.4) and a mean width of 52.24 $\pm$ 0.97 per cent of the petal length (S.D. 6.74, C.V. 12.9). The proportional length of the petal increases with size (15 per cent for an 11.4-mm specimen to 23 per cent for a 52.8-mm specimen) and the proportional width decreases with size (59 per cent of the petal length for an 11.4-mm T.L. specimen to 38 per cent for a 52.8-mm specimen). The length of the posterior petal is 73.25 $\pm$ 0.76 per cent of the anterior petal length (S.D. 5.47, C.V. 7.5).

The paired, posterior petals are divergent along their entire length. The angle of divergence varies with growth. In all specimens, large tubercles were found on the separating interambulacrum within one or two plates of the madreporite. The anterior pore-series is nearly straight, bending

23

posteriorly at its distal end. The posterior pore series bends laterally. The interporiferous zone is straight (Plate 1a).

The Interambulacra

The number of interambulacral plates from the peristome to the fascioles is a constant and important character which is discussed in the following section on the fascioles and summarized on Table 12.

The tuberculation is uniform in the interambulacra. The size of the tubercles increases on the plastron, near the apex, and adjoining ambulacrum III. There are naked areas on the aboral surface from the ambitus to the peripetalous fasciole medially in interambulacra 1, 4, and 5. With the exception of the labrum, interambulacral plates number 1 generally have a few large tubercles on them. Near the peristome, these plates have small, numerous, closely packed tubercles which bear spines that clean and protect the oral tube-feet and probably remove large particles from the oral area. They do not seem to be used to assist ingestion.

The plastron is shield-shaped, with a mean length of 46.27 ± 0.28 per cent of the test length (S.D. 2.01, C.V. 4.4). The plastron becomes slightly longer, proportionally, in larger specimens. Its width, measured at points B, C, and D are as follows:

Point	Mean	S.E.	S.D.	C.V.
B	16.97	0.29	1.79	10.5
C	27.25	0.32	2.02	7.4
D	35.09	0.25	1.72	4.9

The large tubercles of the plastron bear spatulate spines which aid in the forward movement of the urchin. These spines radiate anteriorly from a node on the medial, posterior edge of the plastron. The labrum is short, not reaching back past the first adjoining ambulacral plates (Plate 3e). Its proportional length varies greatly with size and is 13 per cent of the test length in an 11-mm specimen and only 6.9 per cent of the test length in a 62.5 mm test length specimen. No large tubercles are present on the labrum. Along the anterior edge is a line of tertiary tubercles which bear small, curved spines.

The Apical System

The apical system is ethmolytic, situated anteriorly on the dorsal surface at a mean distance from the anterior end of the test of 41.54 ± 0.54 per cent of the test length (S.D. 2.19, C.V. 5.4). During growth, the apical system shifts to a more posterior position. In small specimens (test length 11 to 15 mm) the apical system is 35 to 42 per cent of the test length from the anterior end of the test. In larger specimens (test length 40 to 54 mm) the apical system is situated 43 to 44 per cent of the test length from the anterior end. There are 4 genital pores, the posterior two appearing first during growth at a test length of 15 to 19 mm. All four are normally present at about 20 mm, but there is considerable variation; genital pores are absent in some specimens 22 mm test length and present in some 18 mm test length. One specimen, only 12 mm test length, had two genital pores. The madreporic plate crowds backwards separating the posterior genital plates. The posterior growth increases with age and eventually separates the apicalmost interambulacral plates. In a specimen 62.5 mm in test length, the lateral expansion of the madreporite has separated the apicalmost interambulacral plate (5 series b) from its ocular plate. As indicated by Kier (1956), separation of the plate series from the ocular marks the end of production of new plates in that series.

The oculars are not separated from any of the other plate series throughout the animal's life-span. Genital papillae are present. No obvious differences are apparent between male and female urchins.

The Periproct

The periproct is situated high on the posterior end of the test (Plate 1d), enclosed by interambulacral plates 6, 7, and sometimes 8. It is finely tuberculated and surrounded by the larger spines which form the anal tuft. Rostrate and tridentate pedicellariae are common. The periproct is oval-shaped, with the longer diameter vertical. The mean width of the periproct is 76.79 ± 0.98 per cent of its height (S.D. 6.98, C.V. 9.1) and 13.15 ± 0.26 per cent of the test length (S.D. 1.83, C.V. 13.9). The proportional width decreases with increasing size (15 per cent of the test length for an 11-mm specimen to 8 per cent of the test length for a 62.5-mm specimen). The number and shape of plates forming the periproct varies considerably and is not considered taxonomically valuable.

The Peristome

The peristome is situated anteriorly; its leading edge has a mean distance from the anterior end of the test of 18.68 ± 0.19 per cent of the test length (S.D. 1.30, C.V. 7.0) and the anterior edge of the labrum has a mean distance from the posterior end of the test of 69.90 ± 0.39 per cent of the test length (S.D. 2.73, C.V. 3.9). Rostrate, globiferous, and tridentate pedicellariae are found on the peristome, along with small spines which assist in cleaning the oral tube-feet of mud during feeding. The general outline of the peristome varies with size, from hemispherical, to crescent-shaped, to rectangular as the urchin grows (Plates 1c; 2c,d).

The Peripetalous Fasciole

The peripetalous fasciole in small specimens (test length 11 mm) is fairly constant in width and curves gently around the ends of the petals. In large specimens, the width becomes more irregular; it is greatest at the

25

ends of the petals and medially in interambulacra 1, 4, and 5. The path of the fasciole becomes more sinuous and several angles are formed as the urchin grows. Despite these changes, the proportional length of the peripetalous fasciole remains relatively constant with a mean of 167 ± 1.52 per cent of the test length (S.D. 10.85, C.V. 6.5). The path of the fasciole across interambulacrum 3 is constant. There are no re-entrant angles and the fasciole crosses plates 4a and 4b. The path of the fasciole over the other plates of the test is summarized in Table 12.

The total area of the peripetalous fasciole increases exponentially with an increasing test length as is illustrated in Figure 7. Figure 5 shows the natural log of the area of the peripetalous fasciole plotted against the natural log of the test length. The regression equation shown on the graph is:

$$\text{LnY} = 1.694 \text{ LnX} - 2.354 \qquad \text{Y} = \text{PP.F. area (mm}^2)$$
$$S_{\text{LnY.LnX}} = \pm 0.139 \qquad\qquad \text{X} = \text{Test length (mm)}.$$
$$r = 0.985$$

Thus, the area of the peripetalous fasciole maintains a constant relationship with the volume of the urchin. The relationship between the tube-

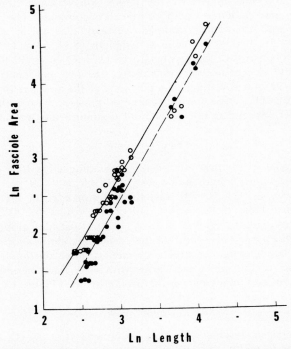

FIGURE 5. Fasciolar area (mm²) versus test length (mm) in *Brissopsis alta*. Solid dots = area of subanal fasciole; circles = area of peripetalous fasciole.

26

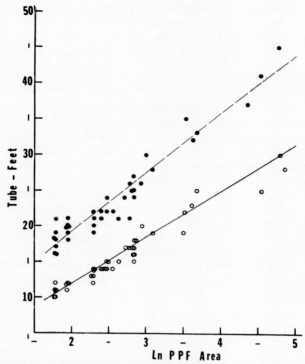

FIGURE 6. Tube-feet versus the fasciolar area in *Brissopsis alta*. Solid dots = pore-pairs in paired petals (IV, series b, and V, series a); circles = functional tunneling tube-feet of III.

feet and the peripetalous fasciole differs in being a semi-logarithmic function; the number of tube-feet decreases per unit of fasciole or unit of volume. When plotted against the natural logarithm of the peripetalous fasciole area, the regression equation of the tunneling tube-feet is (Fig. 6):

$Y = 6.54 \, LnX - 1.35$ $Y =$ Tunneling tube-feet
$S_{Y.LnX} = \pm \, 0.560$ $X =$ PP.F. area (mm²)
$r = 0.992$

The number of respiratory tube-feet (IVb+Va), when plotted against the natural logarithm of the peripetalous fasciole area, has a regression equation of (Fig. 6):

$Y = 835 LnX + 2.2$ $Y =$ Pore-pairs (IVb, Va)
$S_{Y.LnX} = \pm \, 0.785$ $X =$ PP.F. area (mm²)
$r = 0.992.$

Thus, the tube-foot production decreases with growth and the number of tube-feet per unit of fasciole decreases steadily as shown in Figure 8. The regression equation for this line is:

$$LnY = 3.34 - 1.105\ LnX \qquad Y = \text{Tunneling tube-feet per unit}$$
$$S_{LnY.LnX} = \pm\ 0.065 \qquad\qquad \text{of PP.F. area.}$$
$$r = 0.806 \qquad\qquad X = \text{Test length (mm)}$$

Figure 7 shows the regression lines, and their standard errors, of the tunneling tube-feet and the peripetalous fasciole plotted against the test length. The peripetalous fasciole increases rapidly in the larger specimens while the production of tunneling tube-feet slows in the larger specimens. These parameters are explained fully under the description of *B. atlantica*. Briefly, the number of tube-feet needed to construct and maintain the respiratory tunnel is not much greater in an urchin 100 mm in test length than in an urchin 30 mm in test length. As the urchin grows, it burrows deeper. The increase in size of the urchin reduces the proportion of surface area to volume within the urchin and within the burrow. The reduced surface area per unit volume of the urchin requires a proportional increase in the water flow over the respiratory surfaces. The reduced surface area per unit of volume of the burrow makes water loss through the

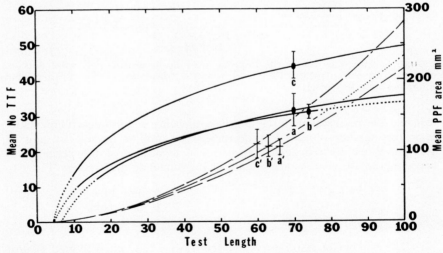

FIGURE 7. Tube-foot and fasciole production in *Brissopsis atlantica*, *B. alta*, and *B. elongata*. The production of tunneling tube-feet and peripetalous fasciole (mm²) with increasing test length (mm). Data from calculated regression lines of Figs. 4, 5, 12, 13, 16. The vertical lines represent twice the standard error on either side of the line. The solid lines represent the tunneling tube-feet and the dashed lines represent the peripetalous fasciole. *a, Brissopsis atlantica;* *b, B. alta; c, B. elongata*.

28

burrow wall more difficult. The rapidly inceasing peripetalous fasciole area of older specimens is ascribed to the decreasing permeability of the burrow wall as the urchin burrows deeper and to the deceasing proportional surface area of the burrow wall, and the inceasing water flow over the respiratory surfaces as the urchins grow. The production of tube-feet and fascioles must be under fairly rigid genetic control as it does not vary greatly, even though the populations are from substrates with considerably different characteristics.

The peripetalous fasciole is indented between the paired petals (interambulacrum 1 and 4) to a mean distance from the apical system of 16.87 $\pm$ 0.17 per cent of the test length (S.D. 1.19, C.V. 7.1). Between the posterior paired petals (interambulacrum 5) the peripetalous fasciole is located at a mean distance of 21.79 $\pm$ 0.27 per cent of the test length from the apical system (S.D. 1.94, C.V. 8.9). Whereas the lateral distance from the apical system to the peripetalous fasciole does not change with size, the proportional distance from the apical system to the posterior portion of the peripetalous fasciole increases with size from 20 per cent of the test length in smaller specimens (test length 11 mm) to 26 per cent of the test length in larger specimens.

The distance from the apical system to the posterior portion of the peripetalous fasciole is 56.06 $\pm$ 0.75 per cent of the distance from the apical system to the anterior portion of the peripetalous fasciole (S.D. 5.39, C.V. 9.6).

The Subanal Fasciole

The subanal fasciole varies greatly in shape with an increase in size. In small specimens (test length 11 mm) the height of the area enclosed by the subanal fasciole is 77 per cent of its width. The fasciole is oval, with no angles. In large specimens (test length 54.3 mm) the height of the enclosure is only 42 per cent of its width. The fasciole is more angular, with dorsal re-entrant angles which divide the fasciole into two lobes. The mean height of the area enclosed by the subanal fasciole, expressed as a percentage of its width, is 63.54 $\pm$ 1.19 (S.D. 8.06, C.V. 12.7). The proportional width of the area enclosed by the subanal fasciole increases with increasing test length from 35 per cent of the test length (11-mm specimen) to 39 per cent of the test length (54.3-mm specimen). The mean width of the area enclosed by the subanal fasciole is 36.54 $\pm$ 0.23 (S.D. 1.59, C.V. 4.4) per cent of the test length. The proportional length of the subanal fasciole has a mean of 93.56 $\pm$ 0.69 per cent of the test length (S.D. 4.89, C.V. 5.2).

The area of the subanal fasciole increases exponentially with increasing test length, keeping pace with the volume of the urchin as does the peripetalous fasciole. Figure 5 shows the natural log of the area of the subanal fasciole plotted against the natural log of the length. The regression equation shown on the graph is:

$$LnY = 1.76 \, LnX - 2.84 \qquad Y = \text{Area of subanal fasciole (mm}^2)$$
$$S_{LnY.LnX} = \pm \, 0.156. \qquad X = \text{Test length (mm)}$$
$$r = 0.975.$$

The subanal fasciole is red on living specimens. Its function will be described in the section on ciliary currents. The plates crossed by the subanal fasciole are summarized in Table 12, and discussed in the section on ambulacra I and V.

The Spines

Plate 3 gives the relative size, shape and distribution of the spines. They are of the normal spatangoid type: no differences were found between the spines of the *Brissopsis* species examined. The sphaeridia were also examined but are of no taxonomic value.

The Pedicellariae

The pedicellariae are accurately described by Mortensen (1907). Like Mortensen, I do not agree with Clark (1917) that the pedicellariae are of "little use in identifications of *Brissopsis* species, for they are very variable and not particularly distinctive. . . ." I have found the globiferous pedicellariae remarkably constant and reliable taxonomic characters. In *B. alta,* they are located in the ventral portions of the ambulacra and are yellow to yellow-orange in color. The stalk has a heavily calcified limb and the valves have 7 to 9 small teeth arranged around the terminal opening (Plate 4e). These pedicellariae are not very similar to the short-valved form described by Mortensen (1907) from *B. atlantica.* For a comparison, see under *B. atlantica.* The tridentate, rostrate, and triphyllous pedicellariae have been described and figured by Mortensen (1907, 1951b).

Internal Anatomy

No characters of specific value were found in the internal anatomy of this species and it is beyond the scope of the present work to describe the anatomy and histology in detail. It might be mentioned, however, that there are two siphons and one caecum. The right, anterior gonad is reduced and the left anterior gonad is bilobed.

Lectotype.—Mortensen (1907) did not designate a holotype nor did he give museum numbers of specimens he examined. He did mention various stations where the specimens he examined were caught; those from Albatross stas. 2400 and 2401, and Blake sta. 49 are deposited in the U.S. National Museum, the Museum of Yale College, and the British Museum of Natural History. The specimen illustrated by Mortensen (1907, pl. 3, fig. 17) is in the Copenhagen Museum (Madsen, personal communication) but it is broken. It would be convenient to have the lectotypes of both *B. alta* and *B. atlantica* in the same museum. A lectotype was, therefore, selected from the specimens from Blake sta. 49 in

30

the U.S. National Museum. The container had a label with Mortensen's signature designating the specimens as *Brissopsis alta* (1906). The lectotype closely resembles the specimen figured by Mortensen (1907, pl. 3, figs. 5, 8). The lectotype is 76 mm in test length. Its various dimensions, given as percentages of the test length, are: height, 68; width, 89; apical system to anterior end of test, 38; peristome to anterior end of test, 15; labrum

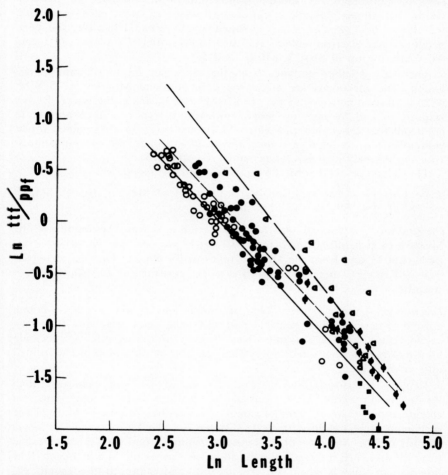

FIGURE 8. The number of tunneling tube-feet per unit area of peripetalous fasciole versus the test length: ttf = tunneling tube-feet; ppf = peripetalous fasciole (mm²); length = test length (mm); Ln = the natural logarithm; circles with solid regression line = *Brissopsis alta;* solid dots, fine dashed line = *B. atlantica,* Florida; solid dots with vertical bar = *B. atlantica,* Colombia; reversed D = *B. mediterranea,* Gulf of Guinea and Florida, heavy dashed regression line, squares = *B. lyrifera capensis.*

to posterior end of test, 69; length of the anterior left paired petal, 27; width of that petal, 33 of the petal length; length of posterior petal, 22; width of the posterior petal, 38 of the posterior petal length; width of ambulacrum III, 6.6; apical system to the peripetalous fasciole, anterior portion 37, posterior portion 26, lateral portion 15; peripetalous fasciole, 171; subanal fasciole, 99; span of the anterior petal ends, 39, of the posterior petal ends, 25; labrum length, 6.6; plastron length, 42; plastron width, 30; subanal fasciole enclosure, 41 wide, 15 high; periproct width, 9.3. Plates 6, 7, 8, and 9 are included in the subanal fasciole, the peripetalous fasciole crosses plates III (6b), *3* (4a, 4b), IV (10a), *4* (6 and 7a, 7 and the tip of 8b), V (16a), and *5* (10a).

There are 4 other syntypes from the same jar, 52 to 65 mm in test length. The specimens are all in the U.S. National Museum (U.S.N.M. 6827). Two other specimens (U.S.N.M. 6813) from the same BLAKE station, 54 and 59 mm test length, are also syntypes. It is important to point out that other material which Mortensen may have examined might contain mixed lots of *B. atlantica* and *B. alta,* and should be re-examined (see the discussion of Lectotype under *B. atlantica).*

The lectotype, U.S.N.M. 6813, is a dried, denuded test.

Type Locality.—The type locality is the Gulf of Mexico, BLAKE Station 49, 28°51.3'N., 89°01.5'W., 216 m.

Distribution.—*Brissopsis alta* has been collected from the mouth of the Mississippi at depths from 216 to 310 m (BLAKE sta. 49, ALBATROSS sta. 2400, 2401) and from the Dry Tortugas to Ft. Pierce, Florida, in depths from 90 to 210 meters. It appears to be endemic to the southwestern Atlantic.

Discussion.—Abnormalities: One specimen was found which, although normal in every other respect, had traces of anal branches from the subanal fasciole. The specimen was 20 mm in test length. A specimen 54.3 mm in test length had the petaloid portion of ambulacrum I deformed into an S-shape.

Ecology: *Brissopsis alta* has not been found in depths shallower than 90 meters. Probably, the urchins are not subject to much environmental change other than a slight seasonal temperature variation. Many large specimens were obtained from 183 meters off the Dry Tortugas, Florida (G-462). The majority of specimens examined biologically were taken from an area 120 meters in depth, about two miles off Miami Beach. The muddy substrate is grey, loosely packed, and slimy to the touch. No macroalgae were observed in the dredge hauls which contained the urchins. The median particle size of the calcite sediment from the Tortugas station is 0.054 mm, with a sorting coefficient of 1.96. The silt and clay fraction of the sediment is 76.42 per cent, by weight, of the total. Off Miami, the substrate is markedly different, with a median particle size of

0.190 mm and a sorting coefficient of 6.70. The silt and clay fraction of the sediment is 24.20 per cent, by weight, of the total sample. Apparently, *B. alta* can survive in a wide variety of muds. The larger specimens come from the finer, more sorted substrate. It was not possible to determine other physical parameters for sediments of the Dry Tortugas station. Sediments from off Miami Beach have a total porosity of 58.1 per cent and a permeability of 0.019. H_2S was not detected in any of the samples. Organic carbon is low for a mud environment, averaging 2.05 per cent by weight of the total substrate. The dominant macro-infauna is composed of amphiurid brittle-starfish, spatangoid echinoids (*Brissopsis atlantica, B. alta, Schizaster orbignyanus*), brachyuran crabs, small pelecypods and gastropods. Congrid eels are also abundant in some areas. Foraminifera are less numerous than in shallow-water mud samples. The genera *Triloculina, Peneropolis, Rosalina* and *Bolivina* are well represented. *Globigerina* are also present. Larval and micro-molluscs are abundant.

Few diatoms or encrusting algae were observed. Nematodes, flagellates, and protozoans are common.

Predators and parasites: Congrid eels and crabs probably make up the main predators although the inaccessibility of the habitat made direct observations impossible.

Several specimens were found with gregarine cysts (Protozoa) in the coelom. The cysts are from a species of *Lithocystis* which is probably closely related to similar forms found in *Moira atropos*.

About 60 per cent of the specimens of *B. alta* had a specimen of an erycinacean bivalve, *Montacuta* sp., attached by its byssus to the anal tuft spines or to the naked areas adjacent to the plastron. Such a specimen is visible in Plate 5. Gage (1966) found a closely related species, *Montacuta substriata* (Montagu), to be non-specific in its host selection, attaching to *Spatangus purpureus, Echinocardium cordatum, E. pennatifidum*, and *E. flavacens*. It is surprising, therefore, to note that *Montacuta* sp. of *B. alta* is specific in its host selection, and although *Schizaster orbignyanus* and *B. atlantica* are present in the same habitat, the mollusk was found only on *B. alta*.

Burrowing: Since *Brissopsis alta* was not encountered in depths less than 90 meters, it was not investigated in its natural habitat. However, specimens collected by Brattström dredge were kept alive and observed in the laboratory. Only urchins which were undamaged were studied. The Brattström dredge digs into the substrate, and urchins trapped by the dredge are protected by several inches of soft mud. The specimens were gently removed from the mud and, without cleaning, were placed directly in refrigerated sea water. It was found that only a momentary exposure to air or warm water seriously altered their subsequent behavior. Therefore, the cool mud was not removed when the urchins were taken from the dredge and placed in water of approximately the same temperature as the coolest mud (about 15°C). The animals were examined immedi-

33

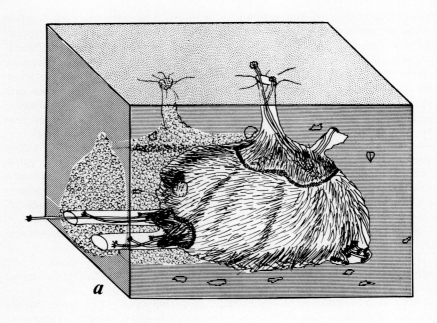

a

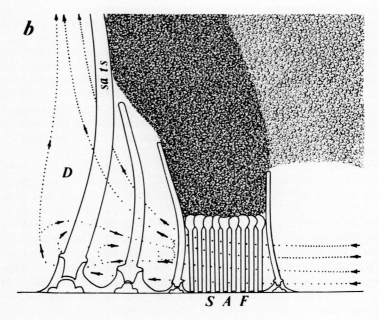

b

sa ts

D

S A F

34

ately upon return to the laboratory, 4 to 6 hours after capture.

The urchins were kept in small, transparent, plastic containers, 10 × 17 × 13 cm in dimension. These containers each received a 3-cm layer of mud, 2 echinoids, and 6 cm of water. When not being examined, the containers were covered and stored in a refrigerator at about 15°C. Several specimens survived 9 months of storage and were still apparently normal and active.

Burrowing activities of the urchins were examined in these containers, and ciliary activity was studied under a dissecting microscope in finger bowls containing 15°C sea water. Food dyes and fluorescent particles were used to follow the ciliary currents.

Digging in: When placed on the surface of the mud, *B. alta* begins excavating its burrow with a slow left to right rocking movement caused by the synchronous movement of plastronal spines. Ventro-lateral spines actively move mud to either side, passing the substrate along before a "wave" of spines. This wave progresses, by metachronal movement of the spines, from the naked areas adjacent to the plastron outward, around the edge of the test, then medially towards the petaloid areas. The substrate is thus pushed from beneath the urchin by the spines of the plastron and ventro-lateral region and carried onto the aboral side by the dorso-lateral spines. The anterior spines also move mud onto the dorsal surface, causing *B. alta* to angle downwards as it moves slowly from left to right, spiraling downward into the substrate. In the most rapid of 5 specimens examined, the process required 18 minutes to complete (Plate 5*a-f*). Very little forward movement accompanied the excavation.

Movement within the burrow was sporadic and showed no definite periodicity. The most rapid movement observed for *B. alta* (test length 19 mm) was 2 cm per hour while burrowed and 15 cm per minute on

←

FIGURE 9. *Brissopsis alta. a,* Schematic drawing of the animal in its burrow. At the upper right portion of the burrow, the tunneling tube-feet are excavating a new respiratory tunnel and maintaining the respiratory tunnel which is open to the surface. The remains of an old respiratory tunnel are to the left of the tunnel in use. At the lower left portion of burrow, the subanal tube-feet are maintaining twin drainage tubes. These drainage tubes facilitate loss of water entering burrow through respiratory tunnel. Feeding tube-feet are shown at lower right of the urchin. The position of *Montacuta* on anal tuft spines is indicated. "Waves" of spines can be seen along the flanks of the urchin moving the substrate toward the posterior portion of the animal where, mixed with mucus, it fills in the burrow as the urchin moves on (indicated by the disturbed sediment).—*b,* Hydromechanics of the subanal fasciole shown in diagrammatic cross section through fasciole. The area enclosed by the fasciole (*D*) is on the left, and the area to the right is ambulacrum V. Water is entering from the right and its currents are indicated by dotted lines. The closer the dots, the slower the current; widely spaced dots indicate a rapid current. The dark area abive clavulae of the subanal fasciole (*SAF*) is sediment heavily laden with mucus. Additional sediment is adjacent to the mucus laden sediment. The subanal tuft spines (*sa t s*) are forming the base of the drainage tube (*D*).

35

the surface of the sediment. Rapid movement along the surface was maintained for 30 to 40 seconds after which time the urchins stopped and began to burrow.

The burrow communicates with the surface of the mud via a mucus-lined tunnel constructed and maintained by the tube-feet of the frontal ambulacrum. These tunnel-building podia have specialized penicillate discs, each digit of which contains a supporting calcite spicule (Plate 11g). The epithelium of these podia has mucous glands which eject mucus onto the wall of the tunnel exactly as described by Nichols (1959) for *Echinocardium*. Mucus is also obtained from the apical tuft spines through which the tube-feet pass before entering the lower end of the tunnel. New tunnels are constructed every centimeter or so as the animal progresses through the substrate (Plate 11a shows this for *B. atlantica*). Construction of the tunnel is very similar to the method described by Chesher (1963) for *Moira atropos* and by Buchanan (1965) for *Echinocardium*. The tube-feet nearest the peripetalous fasciole begin the excavation (in *Moira,* tube-feet nearest to the apex begin the new tunnel). The podia push against the substrate and the discs oscillate due to a swaying motion of the stalk. The foot is retracted, leaving a cylindrical indentation. Difficulties of observation made it uncertain whether sediment was compressed within the tunnel or excavated and removed by the spines. Figure 9a illustrates the animal in its burrow.

The completed tunnel apparently is used mainly for respiration. Feeding from the surface of the sediment, such as described in *Moira atropos* (Chesher, 1963), does not seem to occur. The tube-feet do not regularly rake the surface materials into the tunnel and no mucus string was observed in ambulacrum III. Particles of fluorescent plastic introduced into the respiratory tunnel were found in the burrow wall adjacent to the apical spines and on the floor of the burrow.

The greatest depth to which this species burrows in the substrate was determined by placing the urchins in a 3-gallon aquarium with 5 cm of mud on the bottom. None of the three specimens placed in the aquarium appeared on the plastic bottom when viewed from below. The deepest burrower had its apex about 28 mm from the surface of the mud. It is likely that the urchins burrow deeper in the natural environment. *Moira,* for example, never burrows as deeply in the laboratory as it does in nature. The dorsal tube-feet of a specimen of *B. alta* 30 mm in test length are capable of an extension of at least 5 cm.

As *B. alta* progresses through the mud, the spines are kept free of mud by hydraulic pressure and mucus production. Under normal conditions, only the ends of the spines are in contact with the mud, the areas between the spines are bathed in respiratory currents pumped into the burrow by ciliary action of the epithelium and fascioles.

Water and mucus help liquefy the mud, facilitating burrowing and transport of sediment. As indicated in Fig. 10, ciliary currents leave the

36

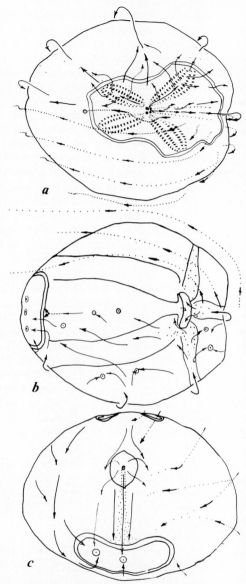

FIGURE 10. Water currents (solid arrows) and movement of sediment (dotted arrows) over the test in *Brissopsis alta*. Dotted circles represent movement off the test toward the viewer. *a*, Dorsal view; *b*, Ventral view; *c*, Posterior view.

37

test at the anterior ambitus. These currents aid in loosening the mud as the urchin moves forward. The mud is cleared away by the long anterior spines, and passed over and around the test by the dorsal and the ventro-lateral spines (Fig. 10). Contrary to Nichols' (1959) observations, I found the naked areas adjacent to the plastron always free of sediment. These areas are, in the urchins studied, pathways for ciliary currents in transit from the trivium to the subanal drainage tubes. Figure 10 shows particle movements over the test (the dotted lines on the right side of the test). Metachronal waves of spines move posteriorly and slightly dorsally. Ridges of mud, excavated from the anterior portion of the burrow, are carried along before the advancing wave of spine-tips. In addition to being transported posteriorly as the urchin moves forward, the mud is compressed along the burrow walls, reducing the amount of material moved posteriorly. The buccal area, like the naked areas adjacent to the plastron, is kept free of sediment at all times. Thus, specimens observed through glass-bottomed aquaria and specimens which were frozen in their burrow (Chesher, 1963) had no sediment in the buccal area or in the naked areas adjacent to the plastron. Sediment movement on the ventral side is in a posterio-lateral direction.

The fascioles: The fascioles are composed of a dense band of small spines, called clavulae, which have two bands of cilia along their shanks. The fleshy, globular distal ends of the clavulae continuously produce mucus. The composite system serves to facilitate water flow through the burrow. The fascioles maintain a layer of mud and mucus along their distal surfaces. The sediment adhering to the fleshy ends of the clavulae flows in a posterior direction. This phenomenon, described by Von Uexküll (1907) for *E. cordatum,* by Tornquist (1911) for *Brissus unicolor,* and by Nichols (1959) for *Brissopsis lyrifera,* does not contribute greatly to the posterior transport of sediment within the burrow, as pointed out by Nichols (1959). The layer of mucus-laden sediment covering the fasciole increases the efficiency of the fasciole by compartmentalizing the burrow into separate chambers. Thus, once water has passed through the heavily ciliated peripetalous fasciole, it can not return to the petaloid area by eddy currents and a better flow of water can be maintained. This fasciolar "valve" assures a unidirectional current movement within the burrow, making it possible to draw water down through the respiratory funnel and to force it out through the burrow walls and subanal drainage areas. In *Brissopsis,* three separate areas can be defined within the burrow: an area for movement, one for respiration, and one for drainage. The respiratory chamber is located within the peripetalous fasciole. Here the gill-like respiratory tube-feet (Plate 4*h*) are bathed in oxygenated sea water pulled down the respiratory tunnel by the peripetalous fasciolar pump and valve. The water is drawn through the ciliated fence of spines into the second chamber, which is primarily concerned with sediment transport and feeding. As discussed below, the fasciole directs water away from the test. The water is thus utilized to liquefy the sediment being transported posteriorly, a function which also permits a certain amount of water loss from the burrow. The currents can not re-enter the respiratory chamber because of the mucus-laden sheath produced by the peripetalous fasciole. As the animal moves forward, the mucous sheath is extended backwards over the entire petaloid area. The major opening in this protective mucous cover leads to the surface of the mud and is kept open by the tunneling tube-feet and apical tuft spines.

A similar situation occurs in the posterior, ventral portion of the animal where the subanal fasciole produces a mucous sheath and acts as a valve and pump to remove the water drawn down from the surface. The mucous sheath begins on the distal ends of the clavulae (Fig. 9b) and lines the first few centimeters of the subanal drainage system. The long spines of the subanal tuft form two conical projections on either side of the bilobate subanal fasciole. These spines describe a circle with their collective ends, facilitating the construction and maintenance of two drainage tubes which are left behind as the animal burrows through the mud (Fig. 9a; Plate 4a, b). These drainage tubes are maintained by the subanal tube-feet. These tube-feet have discs with numerous digits resembling those of the oral tube-feet but limited to the edge of the disc and supplied with sturdier calcite spicules (Plate 4f). The subanal tube-feet are able to extend several centimeters posterior of the tuft spines and can, in addition to keeping the original drainage tubes open, excavate branches from the main tube (Plate 4a) or excavate an entirely new drainage tube. They are extended into the drainage tube until the disc is pressed against the blind end of the tube. Its digits packed with mud, the tube-foot retracts and wipes its load of mud onto the subanal tuft spines. This process, predicted by Nichols (1959), was observed clearly many times. The tube-foot merely brings its disc into contact with the tuft spines and the load of mud drops to the floor of the excavation to be incorporated into the wall of the drainage tube by the tuft spines. It is the action of the subanal tube-feet which disrupts the mucus sheath produced by the subanal fasciole permitting the drainage of water flowing into the tubes.

Ciliary currents: The currents flowing over the test are illustrated in Fig. 10. As in all spatangoids, the currents diverge from the apical system. The reverse current noted by Nichols (1959) for B. lyrifera was not detected at the apical system. Sea water enters the burrow via the respiratory tunnel and is diverted into all five ambulacra. The anterior three ambulacra receive the major portion of the flow and the anterior paired petals have the most rapid circulation (indicated by the time necessary to clear the ambulacral areas of food dye). As the currents pass along the axis of the petals, small diverging currents are given off which flow between the respiratory surfaces of the gill-like tube-feet. Currents within the hydrovascular system of these gill-shaped tube-feet flow in an opposing direction causing a counter-current system, enhancing the respiratory abilities of these structures (cf. Prosser & Brown, 1965). After bathing the respiratory tube-feet, the external ciliary currents pass into the inter-ambulacral areas and accelerate toward the peripetalous fasciole. After passing through the fasciole the currents divide; some pass close to the test, over the ambitus to the ventral side and some angle away from the test to facilitate sediment movement and increase water loss from the burrow wall. As the only connection with the surface of the mud is via the respiratory tunnel, disposal of expended respiratory water becomes a major problem, particularly to mud dwellers where the substrate may be relatively impermeable (permeability 0.019). The peripetalous fasciole, by directing water away from the test, facilitates water loss through the dorso-lateral and anterior portions of the burrow wall. Spine movements produced as the animal burrows ahead also facilitate water loss through the burrow wall.

Water that reaches the ventral side of the urchin moves obliquely toward the median area of the plastron and posteriorly toward the subanal fasciole. The plastronal spines, moving the urchin forward through the substrate, create an area of water loss along the ventral portion of the burrow. Currents enter the subanal fasciole from the ventral ambulacral areas, the plastron, and from three ciliary tracts leading from the periproct to the subanal fasciole. The fasciole creates a flow of water into the enclosed area. As with the peripetalous fasciole, there are two main currents, one close to the test, the other at an angle away from the test (Fig. 9b). The cilia on the test create currents which flow centrally, away from the subanal fasciole. These currents are diverted away from the test where they converge at the central portion of the fasciolar enclosure. The cilia of the spines within the subanal fasciole create a flow of water toward the fasciole. This flow forces the current from the upper portion of the subanal fasciole away from the test and out the drainage tunnels (Fig. 9b).

A thin-walled plastic tube, 1.5 cm long and 1.8 mm bore, was mounted on a plastic cap from a specimen jar. The tube was then marked one centimeter from its distal end and the assembly carefully placed over the respiratory tunnel of a burrowed B. alta. A drop of dark green food dye was placed at the opening of the tube with a syringe. The dye was swept into the tube, past the one-cm mark, and into the burrow. The rate of flow into the burrow was thus calculated and found to average 0.53 ml/min for an urchin 19.8 mm in test length having a volume of 3.0 ml. The spines were experimentally clogged with gelatin and the volume of the urchin increased to 4.2 ml, indicating that the specimen had about 1.2 ml of water surrounding it while in its burrow. At the indicated rate of influx, the water was exchanged every two to three minutes. Two drainage tunnels were present during the experiment. The tunnels were 1.7 mm in diameter at the proximal end tapering slightly to about 1.5 mm in diameter at the abrupt termination 31 mm and 23 mm from the urchin.

The rate of flow into the tunnels was observed (again with concentrations of food dyes) to be only about 0.09 cm/second or, with the two tubes each 1.7 mm in diameter, at a rate of (0.12 ml/min $\times$ 2) 0.24 ml/min. Thus, only about half of the inflow passes into the drainage tunnels. The current within the drainage tunnels slows gradually and is almost negligible 20 mm from the urchin. Most of the drainage, therefore, occurs at the proximal end of the tunnel. If 20 mm from each tube (40 mm total) is required to drain off 0.24 ml/min, then a surface area of only 214 mm^2 is required to drain off the subanal flow. Since the burrow of the echinoid has a surface area of about (πD^2 with D = 20) 1250 mm^2, it is evident that not all areas of the test are suitable for drainage areas and that the subanal fasciole must be remarkably efficient; disposing of a large quantity of water with a very small area of burrow wall. The plastron, the area just outside the peripetalous fasciole, and a few areas along the posterior-lateral ambitus seem to be the major areas of drainage within the second chamber of the burrow. This hypothesis is supported not only by direct observations of currents which leave the surface of the test at these points, but also by the location of food dye concentrations found in the burrow walls of quick frozen specimens.

Feeding: *Brissopsis alta,* like probably all other species of *Brissopsis,* is a non-selective detritus feeder. The feeding tube-feet (Plate 4*g*), which surround the peristome, push their discs into the substrate, filling the digits with mud. The disc, as the podium is extended, is convex (Plate 11*d* illustrates this for *B. atlantica*). It flattens when contact is made with the mud and is concave, compressing the clump of mud, as the podia is retracted and slipped into the oral opening. When the tube-foot enters the buccal opening, it everts again to a convex condition and its load of detritus is deposited in the muscular oesophagus. There are no "oral rakers" as are present in *Moira atropos,* and only occasionally are the spines of the peristome used to wipe the tube-feet clean. At times, the podia are extended an apparently considerable distance down the oesophagus, possibly to aid in packing down the accumulated detritus.

Sediment samples taken from the intestines of *B. alta* do not differ significantly in particle size from the samples taken from the middle of the dredge. Since very few large particles exist in their habitats, the urchins can ingest the substrate non-selectively. Probably, the main source of nutrition is derived from micro-molluscs and Foraminifera, but it is interesting to speculate on the possible survival of an urchin on a bacterial diet alone. Several specimens of *B. alta* were kept alive in plastic containers for 9 months. The containers were in total darkness within a refrigerator most of the time. The substrate showed, at the end of a four month period, no live Forminifera, diatoms, molluscs, or algae. Only echinoids and a thriving bacterial population were present. Perhaps the urchins are able to withstand long periods of starvation. No growth was noted during the experiment, although regeneration of spines did occur.

The organic content of the mud from off Miami Beach was low for a mud environment, about 2 per cent by weight, determined by ignition (Krumbein & Pettijohn, 1938).

Respiration: Studies of respiration, other than current movements over and within the respiratory structures, were not conducted for this species. As mentioned in the section on ciliary currents, water from the respiratory tunnel is directed down the ambulacra, particularly the anterior paired petals, where smaller currents diverge between each leaf-shaped respiratory tube-foot. The respiratory tube-feet (Plate 4*h*) have a thin, convoluted epithelium with an internal network of small canals which transport the hydrovascular fluid from the outer pore to the inner pore, thus creating a current opposing that on its outer surface. Such counter-current systems are a frequent respiratory phenomenon in the animal kingdom (Prosser & Brown, 1965).

Growth: The various allometric changes which occur in *B. alta* are described above. Nothing is known of the rate of growth, but growth rings on the plastron of a specimen 54.3 mm in test length, compared with specimens of other lengths, indicate a growth pattern similar to that of *Moira atropos*. A test length of about 24 mm is reached the first year, 33 mm the second, 40 mm the third, and so on. The 54.3-mm specimen shows seven rings. When plotted on the growth curve for *Moira atropos* (Chesher, in preparation) it is of a length which could be expected in animals seven or eight years old.

Fossil history: *B. alta* is not known as a fossil.

Comments: Mortensen states that "the high, almost globular test, the position of the peristome near the anterior end of the test, and the rounded posterior end, mark this species pronouncedly against all the other species of the genus *Brissopsis*." The test of *B. alta* is higher than most of the other species except *B. lyrifera capensis* but there is considerable overlap, particularly in the younger specimens. The peristome is statistically nearer the anterior end in this species than in any of the others, but again, there is considerable over-lap, particularly in the younger specimens. The same may be said of the rounded posterior end, which is a convenient character if several species are available for comparison. Figure 2 indicates one method which successfully distinguishes the specimens of *B. alta* from the specimens of *B. atlantica*. In addition, the number of plates entering the subanal fasciole is a useful character to separate *B. alta* from *B. atlantica* and *B. elongata;* there are four plates on each side in the former species and five in the latter two species. The lack of a re-entrant angle in the peripetalous fasciole in interambulacrum 3, series a, provides an easily recognized character even in living specimens. In all the other species of *Brissopsis* except, perhaps, *B. lyrifera,* there is a sharp angle in the peripetalous fasciole in interambulacrum 3 so that the fasciole crosses plates 4a and 5a, then angles over to plates 4 or 5b.

The pedicellariae offer a unique character not duplicated in any other

Atlantic *Brissopsis* species. The terminal opening of the valves are surrounded by many small teeth.

Other differences are given in the discussions of the other species and in the section on general conclusions.

Brissopsis atlantica Mortensen, 1907
Figures 2, 3, 7, 8, 11-15; Plates 6-14;
Tables 1, 2, 4, 12

Brissopsis lyrifera, A. Agassiz, 1883, pl. 26, figs. 7-8, not *B. lyrifera* (Forbes 1841).
Brissopsis atlantica Mortensen, 1907, p. 160, pl. 3, figs. 6, 10; pl. 18, figs. 5, 9, 10, 13, 19, 20, 24; pl. 19, figs. 1, 4, 5, 11, 25, 28, 32, 33.
Not *Brissopsis atlantica*, Koehler, 1909, p. 238.
Brissopsis atlantica, Lambert, 1915, p. 8.
Brissopsis atlantica, H. L. Clark, 1917, p. 203 (part).
Not *Brissopsis atlantica*, Grieg, 1921, p. 44.
Brissopsis atlantica, Jackson, 1922, p. 81.
Brissopsis atlantica, H. L. Clark, 1925, p. 213 (part).
Kleinia atlantica, Lambert & Thiery, 1925, p. 490 (part).
Brissopsis atlantica, Mortensen, 1927a, p. 338 (part).
Not *Brissopsis atlantica*, Mortensen, 1927b, p. 32.
Not *Brissopsis atlantica*, Kolosvary, 1937, p. 461.
Brissopsis atlantica, H. L. Clark, 1941, p. 126 (part).
Brissopsis atlantica, Wythe Cooke, 1942, p. 49 (part).
Not *Brissopsis atlantica*, Mortensen, 1951a, p. 301.
Brissopsis atlantica, Mortensen, 1951b, p. 415, pl. 31, fig. 11; pl. 59, fig. 7.

Material examined.—12 specimens, 25 to 54.5 mm test length, ALBATROSS sta. 2378, Gulf of Mexico, 29°14′30″N., 88°09′30″W., 124m, Feb. 1885; U.S.N.M. 10637.—2 specimens, 46.5 mm and 57.4 mm test length, ALBATROSS sta. 2401, Gulf of Mexico, 28°38.5′N., 85°52.5′W., 260 m, March 1885; U.S.N.M. 10640.—25 specimens, 16.5 to 34.4 mm test length, GERDA sta. G-263, off Government Cut, Miami, Florida, 25°46′N, 80°06′W., 110 m, April 1965.—26 specimens, 16.5 to 44.6 mm test length, off Government Cut, Miami, Florida, 25°45′N., 80°02′W., 90 to 146 m, Jan. 1966.—1 specimen, 25.7 mm test length, sta. G-657, off St. Lucie River, Florida, 27°14′N., 79°49′W., 210 m, July 1965.—7 specimens, 25 to 64.2 mm test length, sta. G-110, off Dry Tortugas, Florida, 24°21′N., 82°55′W., 183 m, June 1963.—8 specimens, 56.3 to 67.2 mm test length, sta. G-462, off Dry Tortugas, Florida, 24°20′N., 82°46′W., 183 m, Jan. 1965.—2 specimens, 24.3 and 44.6 mm test length, sta. G-239, off Browns Cay, eastern Florida Straits, 25°20′N., 79°15′W., 348 to 256 mm, Jan. 1964.—1 specimen, 46.5 mm test length, sta. G-540 (caught accidentally in plankton net which hit bottom), Northwest Channel, B.W.I., 25°28′N. 78°07′W., 183 m, April 1965.—2 specimens, 45.6 to 57.2 mm test length, Jim Moore, coll., off Panama City, Florida, 100 m, 1963.—1 specimen (broken), sta. G-589, off Long Key, Florida, 24°39.5′N., 80°48′W., 148 m, April 1965.—2 specimens, 44.1 to 57.2

mm test length, PILLSBURY sta. P-324, off north coast of Panama, 9°44′N., 79°31′W., 63 to 34 m, July 1966.—1 specimen, 89 mm test length, sta. P-340, off N.E. Panama, 9°13.5′N., 77°46′W., 305 m, July 1966.—2 specimens, 93 to 111 mm test length, sta. P-445, off N.W. Panama, 9°02.3′N., 81°23.8′W., 338 to 342 m, July 1966.—7 specimens, 46.6 to 100.5 mm test length, sta. P-446, off N.W. Panama, 8°58′N., 81°26.3′W., 295 to 109 m, July 1966.—1 specimen, fragment, sta. P-362, off N.W. Colombia, 8°57.5′N., 76°33.6′W., 64 to 54 m, July 1966.—1 specimen, 27.5 mm test length, sta. P-367, off N.W. Colombia, 9°31.1′N., 75°49.6′W., 34 to 36 m, July 1966.—2 specimens, 29 to 36.5 mm test length, sta. P-371, off N.W. Colombia, 9°40′N., 76°01.5′W., 45 to 54 m, July 1966.—1 specimen, 84 mm test length, sta. P-386, off N.W. Colombia, 10°30′N., 75°41′W., 272 to 373 m, July 1966.—1 specimen, 69.3 mm test length, sta. P-399, off N.W. Colombia, 9°01.3′N., 76°40.2′W., 118 to 177 m, July 1966.

Diagnosis.—Subanal fasciole distinct, crossing five ambulacral plates on either side (rarely four); the first is plate 6. The peripetalous fasciole traverses plates 4 and 5 in series a of interambulacrum 3 and plate 5 (or 4 and 5 if the fasciole dips downward) in series b. Anal branches from the subanal fasciole present, rudimentary, often reaching to the peripetalous fasciole. Posterior petals confluent proximally, diverging from about one-half their length. Test low, posterior end oblique to a varying degree, the periproct visible from above. Globiferous pedicellariae with two teeth surrounding the terminal opening (rarely with many teeth). Anterior petals with only a slight curve, not confluent proximally. Labrum not reaching past the first adjoining ambulacral plates. See Figures 2 and 3.

Description.—The test has a low, angular appearance (Plate 6). Its mean width is 82.93 ± 0.36 per cent of the test length (S.D. 3.38, C.V. 4.08) and its mean height, 56.37 ± 0.37 per cent of the test length (S.D. 3.44, C.V. 6.12). The width tends to increase in proportion very slightly with an increase in size. The proportional width varies geographically and the specimens from Colombia are narrower than those from Florida (Fig. 11). The proportional height decreases slightly with growth, more so in the Colombian specimens than in those from Florida, and shows a fairly wide range of individual variation. Despite this variation, the mean height of *B. atlantica* remains fairly constant throughout its range. The shape of the test does not significantly change from specimens 16 mm in length to the largest specimens. The oblique posterior end of the younger specimens (Plate 7d) is frequently retained in the adults (Plate 6c). Some specimens are more vertically truncate than others but the posterior truncation seldom, if ever, reaches an angle of 90° with the plastron and more commonly is between 70° and 80°.

The dorsal interambulacral plates outside the peripetalous fasciole develop a raised node from which the tubercles radiate in a fairly regular

44

TABLE 4
SUMMARY OF STATISTICAL DATA: *Brissopsis atlantica*

Character	Mean	S.E.	S.D.	Range	N	C.V.
tl*	39.99	2.36	21.98	16.5-111	87	
tw	82.93	0.36	3.38	74-91	87	4.08
h	56.37	0.37	3.44	49-65	87	6.12
ax	41.93	0.23	2.09	36-47	85	5.00
pa	21.51	0.19	1.77	18-29	85	8.24
lp	70.27	0.26	2.38	65-77	85	3.39
ap	24.39	0.22	2.04	21-30	87	8.39
apw†	36.81	0.60	5.14	27-49	75	13.9
pp	21.83	0.24	2.26	18-30	87	10.3
ppw†	32.68	0.61	5.22	20-45	75	15.95
pp/ap‡	89.50	0.62	5.83	78-109	87	6.51
wIII	7.07	0.16	1.43	4.3-11	85	20.2
ff	37.53	0.17	1.55	33-42	84	4.14
pf	25.51	0.24	2.22	21-33	84	8.70
lf	13.11	0.15	1.39	10-16	84	10.6
pf/af‡	68.07	0.64	5.90	58-85	84	8.69
ppfl	172.66	1.18	10.97	148-207	87	6.35
ape	38.94	0.29	2.66	32-49	83	6.83
safh/w‡	58.63	0.92	8.42	39-77	82	14.3
safw	37.23	0.20	1.84	34-43	83	4.94
safl	95.91	0.58	5.40	73-107	86	5.65
l	9.39	0.17	1.58	5.7-13	83	16.85
pl	45.57	0.40	3.62	36-56	83	7.93
b	12.84	0.18	1.41	10-15	63	11.0
c	21.51	0.22	1.86	19-27	74	8.65
d	29.69	0.22	1.97	26-36	80	6.64
aw	12.19	0.16	1.50	9-16	87	12.3
aw/ah‡	84.99	0.91	8.52	48-105	87	10.0

*Test length (mm).
†Percentage of petal length.
‡Ratio given as a percentage.
Data are given as percentage of test length unless otherwise indicated.

series. In large specimens, the nodes of successive plates form an irregular elevation from the peripetalous fasciole to the ambitus in both plate series of interambulacra 1, 4, and 5, giving the large urchins a more angular appearance than the smaller specimens.

The Anterior Ambulacrum

The anterior ambulacrum is slightly sunken from the apical system to the peristome and creates a shallow notch in the anterior ambitus. The proportional depth of this notch does not change markedly with growth or with geographic location. The peripetalous fasciole crosses III at a mean distance from the apical system of 41.93 ± 0.23 per cent of the test length (S.D. 2.09, C.V. 4.99). This proportion shows very little variation.

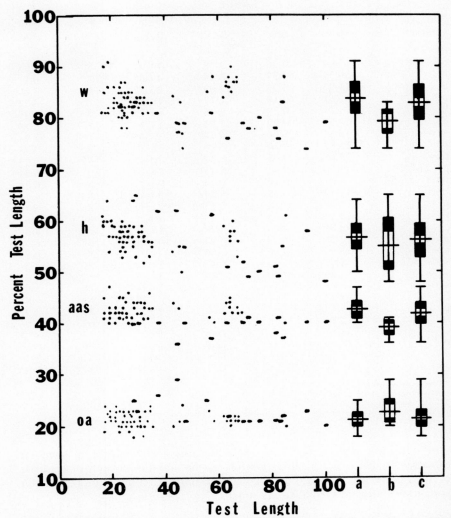

FIGURE 11. Geographic variation in *Brissopis atlantica*. Small dots = Florida specimens; large dots = Colombian specimens. a = Population range diagram (after Hubbs & Perlmutter 1942), *B. atlantica*, Florida specimens. Vertical line represents total variation; horizontal line represents the mean. Dark rectangle represents one standard deviation on either side of the mean, and hollow rectangle equals two standard errors on either side of the mean.—b = Same, Colombian specimens.—c = Same, total specimens.—w = Test width.— h = Test height.—aas = Apical system to anterior portion of test.—oa = Distance from leading edge of peristome to anterior portion of test.

Within the peripetalous fasciole, the frontal ambulacrum is divided into two areas, one nearest the apical system, containing developing tube-feet and the other containing the functional, tunneling tube-feet. The number of tunneling tube-feet varies with growth from 12 (16.5 mm test length) to 34 (100 mm test length). When plotted against the natural log of the length, the increase in the number of functional tube-feet with growth becomes linear (Fig. 12) and has a regression equation of:

$Y = 12.96 \, LnX - 24$ $Y =$ Tunneling tube-feet
$S_{LnY.LnX} = \pm 2.09$ tube-feet
$r = 0.949$ $X =$ Length of test (mm).

The specimens from Colombia were not used in deriving this equation. It is evident from Figure 12 that the production rate does not vary greatly in the specimens examined.

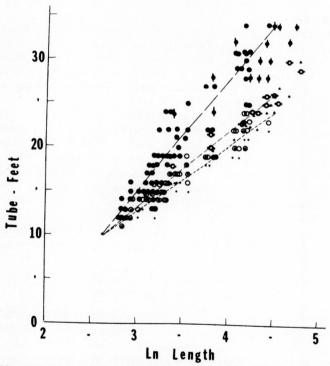

FIGURE 12. Tube-feet versus test length (mm) in *Brissopsis atlantica*. Solid dots = total number of tunneling tube-feet (functional); circles = pore-pairs in the anterior petal (IV, series b); squares = pore-pairs in the posterior petal (V, series a), specimens from Florida; triangles = pore-pairs (V, series a), specimens from Colombia. Symbols with bar (dots or circles) = Colombian specimens; others are from Florida.

New plates are split off from the ocular plate as the urchin grows. These plates bear undeveloped, globular tube-feet situated over a slit-like pore. The tube-feet progressively mature into functional, tunneling tube-feet with a terminal disc having 10 to 20 fringing digits each supported with a calcite spicule (Plate 11c). The discs are about 0.8 mm in diameter. Their size remains fairly constant throughout the life span of the urchin. The stalk is lined with C-shaped calcite spicules (Plate 11c). The function of these tube-feet is, as far as could be determined, the same as that described for the tube-feet of *B. alta*.

The tunneling tube-feet issue from circular depressions near the dorso-lateral edge of the ambulacral plates. The central portion of the peripodium is elevated to form a projection which is more pronounced in the larger specimens and functions as a support for the basal end of the tube-feet. The pore-slit is located on the ventro-medial portion of this projection (Plate 6f). The pores are in a single series, and occluded and demi-plates do not normally occur.

Ambulacrum III is widest near the peripetalous fasciole. Measurements of its width were taken from the outer edge of the pore series. The width varies with the size of the specimen, and is about 10 per cent of the test length in specimens 16 mm test length and about 4 per cent of the test length in specimens 100 mm test length. There is considerable individual variation in this character (C.V. 18.5).

There are six plates per plate-series from the peripetalous fasciole to the peristome. This number is constant and does not change with growth or geographic location. The mature urchin (test length greater than 20 mm) has those three tube-feet of each series nearest the peristome developed into feeding tube-feet (Plate 11d,e). In smaller urchins, only one tube-foot in series a and two tube-feet in series b are feeding tube-feet; the adjacent feet are sensory tube-feet (Plate 11b) which later develop penicillate discs.

The tuberculation of III can be seen in Plate 8 f. The tubercles are small and irregularly distributed, only a small area is left clear near each peripodium.

Ambulacra II and IV
(the anterior paired petals)

In the Florida specimens, the peripetalous fasciole crosses ambulacrum IV on plates 10a or 11a. This number does not change with growth and the ratio of 10a to 11a in the specimens examined is 1:3.8. In many Colombian specimens, plate 10a is crossed by the fasciole but only one specimens had the fasciole on plate 11a. Instead, the plates crossed most commonly (in a 50:50 ratio) were 12a and 13a. The ratio between 10a and 12a + 13a is 1:3.6.

Tuberculation outside the peripetalous fasciole varies considerably with growth and among individuals. In younger specimens, the ambulacra may

48

be bare or may have one or two larger tubercles per plate (Plate 7a). In the larger specimens, tuberculation is fairly dense except along the medial, naked area which is found between the peripetalous fasciole and the peristome (Plate 6a). Nearest the peristome, there are penicillate, feeding tube-feet arranged in a distinct phyllode. In the large specimens, there are 9 or 10 feeding tube-feet in each phyllode. Each podium is situated over a single large pore located on the adoral edge of the plate. Sensory tube-feet are found from the phyllode to plates 8a and 7 or 8b in ambulacrum IV.

The petals are slightly sunken within the peripetalous fasciole. The two series of pore-pairs bend mesially at their distal end. The anterior pore-series has 29 to 47 (mean: 41) per cent of the apicalmost pore-pairs underdeveloped. In the specimens from Colombia, this number is reduced to 26 to 37 (mean 35) per cent. Rudimentary, knob-like tube-feet are located over these reduced pore-pairs. The larger pore-pairs bear respiratory tube-feet (Plate 12d). In the posterior pore-series, only one or two of the apical pore-pairs are underdeveloped. The total number of tube-feet (pore-pairs, plates) increases logarithmically throughout growth. Figure 12 shows the number of pore-pairs of ambulacrum IV, series b, plotted against the natural log of the test length. The regression equation shown on the graph is:

$$Y = 8.54 \, \mathrm{Ln}X - 12.2 \qquad\qquad Y = \text{Pore-pairs, IVb.}$$
$$S_{Y.\mathrm{Ln}X} = \pm \, 1.855 \text{ tube-feet} \qquad X = \text{Test length (mm).}$$
$$r = 0.841$$

The specimens from Colombia were not used in calculating this equation but are plotted on Figure 12. They do not differ significantly from the Florida specimens with respect to their respiratory tube-feet. During growth, there is an increase in the number of tubercles adjacent to each pore-pair. These tubercles bear small spines which clean and protect the respiratory tube-feet.

The anterior petals have a mean length of 24.39 ± 0.22 per cent of the test length (S.D. 2.04, C.V. 8.4). This proportion increases with growth from about 22 per cent of the test length (16.5-mm specimens) to 30 per cent of the test length (111-mm specimens) thus accounting for much of the large coefficient of variation. The mean width of the anterior paired petals is 36.81 per cent of the petal length (S.D. 5.14, C.V. 13.9). Again, allometric growth accounts for much of this high coefficient of variation but individual variation also is great. The distance between the ends of the anterior petals has a mean of 38.94 ± 0.29 per cent of the test length (S.D. 2.66, V.C. 6.84). This proportion increases slightly with age but individual variation is sufficient to mask any definite trend. In one population (Miami, Florida) the C.V. is quite low (ca. 3.3). In the Colombian population, the specimens are much more variable (C.V. 8.24) and have a greater mean distance between the petal ends

49

(42.19 ± 0.89 per cent of the test length, S.D. 3.43). This difference in the two populations is not the result of size difference as the smaller Colombian specimens are higher in this proportion than the larger specimens. The variation in this character is apparently correlated with the presence or absence of *B. elongata* in the same population. With the exception of the stations where both *B. altantica* and *B. elongata* were collected, the proportional distance between the anterior petal ends does not vary significantly over the geographic range of *B. atlantica*.

The posterior pore-series of ambulacra II and IV form an almost straight line. The anterior pore-series bends posteriorly, however, creating the illusion that the petals have a posterior bend.

Ambulacra I and V
(the posterior paired petals)

The peripetalous fasciole crosses ambulacrum V on plate 16, 17, or 18 of series a. Plate 17a is the plate most commonly crossed, but I do not have exact proportions for the Florida specimens. This number does not change with growth. The plates between the peripetalous fasciole and the ambitus are heavily tuberculated. Only a narrow strip is left bare on the lateral margin of the anterior plate series (Plate 6a). The plates of ambulacra I and V, between the peripetalous fasciole and the ambitus, are distinctly wider than the adjacent plates of interambulacrum 5. Orally of plate 6 of the posterior plate series the ambulacra are naked except for pedicellariae, sphaeridia, and small tertiary spines. A few large tubercles may be found on the extreme margin of the plates. Nearest the peristome, there are penicillate, feeding tube-feet. In large urchins, there are 8 to 9 feeding tube-feet in each phyllode. One or two sensory tube-feet are found in each plate series posterior to the phyllode (Plate 11b). There are three to four subanal tube-feet within the subanal fasciole. There are no tube-feet in ambulacrum I or V from the ambitus to the peripetalous fasciole.

The petals are slightly sunken within the peripetalous fasciole. The pore-pairs close distally. The posterior series of pore-pairs have 40 to 60 per cent of their apicalmost pore-pairs underdeveloped. The exact number is difficult to determine as there is a very gradual decrease in the size of the pore-pair apically.

The number of plates in the petaloid area of ambulacrum V increases throughout growth. Figure 12 shows the number of pore-pairs of ambulacrum Va plotted against the natural log of the test length. The equation shown by the solid line is:

$$Y = 7.34 \, LnX - 9.2 \qquad Y = \text{Pore-pairs (Va)}.$$
$$S_{Y.LnX} = \pm 1.4 \text{ pore-pair} \qquad X = \text{Test length (mm)}.$$
$$r = 0.899$$

50

The Colombian specimens were not used in calculating this line. They are plotted on Figure 12 and are not significantly different from the Florida sample. The proportional length of the posterior paired petals is 21.83 ± 0.24 per cent of the test length (S.D. 2.26, C.V. 10.3). The mean width of the posterior petal is 32.68 ± 0.61 per cent of the petal length (S.D. 5.22, C.V. 16.0). The large variation is due primarily to allometric changes. The petals are proportionally shorter and wider in smaller specimens. The proportions are 19 per cent of the test length long by 38 per cent of the petal length wide in a 16-mm test length specimen. In a specimen 100 mm in test length, the proportional length of the posterior petal is 26 per cent of the test length and its width is 27 per cent of the petal length. The length of the posterior petal is 89.50 ± 0.62 per cent of the anterior petal length (S.D. 5.83, C.V. 6.5).

The posterior paired petals are confluent, or slightly divergent, from the apical system to about 50 per cent of their length where they curve laterally. This character does not change markedly with growth, but it is difficult to see any clear difference between *B. alta* and *B. altantica* in very small specimens (Plates 2a, 7a). *B. atlantica* lacks large tubercles on the first few interambulacral plates adjacent to the apical system between the posterior paired petals. In *B. alta,* the tubercles continue to the apical system. The interporiferous zone is curved in *B. atlantica* and straight in *B. alta.*

The Interambulacra

The number of interambulacral plates from the peristome to the fascioles is a constant and important character which is discussed in the following section on the fascioles.

The tuberculation is uniform in the interambulacra. The size of the tubercles increases on the plastron, near the apex, and bordering ambulacrum III. There is a naked area, on the aboral surface, from the ambitus to the peripetalous fasciole, medially, in interambulacra 1, 4, and 5. Interambulacral plates number 1 (including the labrum) are generally naked except for one or two large tubercles and a cluster of small spines near the peristome. These clusters are slightly elevated in interambulacra 2 and 3 (Plate 3e), superficially resembling the bourrelets of some cassiduloids. The spines on these areas are used to protect and clean the oral tube-feet and to remove large particles from the oral area.

The plastron is shield-shaped, with a mean length 45.57 ± 0.40 per cent of the test length (S.D. 3.62, C.V. 7.94). This proportion increases with growth from 40 per cent in 16- to 17-mm specimens to 50 per cent in large specimens. Geographic variation is not evident in this character and most of the large variation is individual or due to growth. The width of the plastron, as per cent of the test length and measured at points B, C, and D, is:

point	mean	S.E.M.	S.D.	C.V.
B	12.84	0.18	1.41	11.0
C	21.51	0.22	1.86	8.65
D	29.69	0.22	1.97	6.65

The width becomes slightly less with an increase in size. The width of the plastron does not vary geographically.

The large tubercles of the plastron bear spatulate spines and radiate anteriorly from the medial, posterior edge of the plastron (Plate 12c).

The labrum is short, not reaching back past the first adjoining ambulacral plates (Plate 3e). The proportional length varies considerably with growth and individually. In smaller specimens, the length of the labrum is 10 or 11 per cent of the test length. This proportion decreases to about 8 per cent of the test length in larger specimens. The mean length of the labrum is 9.93 ± 0.17 per cent of the test length (S.D. 1.58, C.V. 15.9). No large tubercles are present on the labrum. Along the anterior edge is a row of small tubercles.

The Apical System

The apical system is ethmolytic, situated anteriorly on the dorsal surface at a mean distance from the anterior end of the test of 41.93 ± 0.23 per cent of the test length. There is, however, considerable overlap be-is no substantial change in this percentage. Most of the variation is geographical and individual. In a single population (Miami, Florida) the C.V. is 3.92 (mean: 42.64, S.D. 1.67). The Colombian specimens have a similar coefficient of variation (3.96) but the mean distance of the apical system from the anterior end of the test has decreased to 39.19 per cent of the test length. There is, however, considerable overlap between the two populations (Fig. 11). There are 4 genital pores which appear, during growth, at a test length of about 16 mm. They are present in a specimen 16.5 mm in test length but absent in another, 25 mm in test length. In the Colombian population, the genital pores are barely visible in specimens 27 to 29 mm in test length. Frequently, the anterior pair of genital pores is smaller than the posterior pair. Occasionally, the right anterior genital pore is not developed. The gonads conform to the usual *Brissopsis* pattern, i.e., the right anterior gonad is small and the left anterior is bilobed, the left posterior gonad is larger than the right posterior gonad. The madreporite passes between the posterior genital plates and may become quite long in larger specimens, reaching back between the first interambulacral plates.

The oculars are pentagonal with the exception of the triangular ocular of the anterior ambulacrum. Genital papillae are present.

The Periproct

The periproct is situated high on the posterior end of the test, enclosed within interambulacral plates 5, 6, 7, and sometimes 8. It is finely tuberculated and surrounded by larger spines which form the anal tuft (Plate 6d). Rostrate and tridentate pedicellariae are common. The periproct is oval, with the vertical diameter the greatest. The mean width is 12.19 ± 0.16 per cent of the test length (S.D. 1.50, C.V. 12.3) and 84.99 ± 0.91 per cent of the periproct height (S.D. 8.52, C.V. 10.0). The proportional width decreases with increasing test length. In small specimens, it is about 14 or 15 per cent of the test length and in larger specimens the width of the periproct is 9 to 11 per cent of the test length. Allometric and individual variation overshadow any geographic variation.

The Peristome

The peristome is situated anteriorly, its leading edge having a mean distance from the anterior end of the test of 21.51 ± 0.19 per cent of the test length (S.D. 1.77, C.V. 8.22). This character does not change significantly with growth. In a single population (Miami, Florida) the coefficient of variation is 7.3, indicating a large individual variation. The Colombian population is even more unstable (C.V. 10.2), and the peristome is more posterior on the test (22.75 per cent of the test length from the anterior end). The peristome is crescent-shaped in younger specimens and pentagonal in larger specimens.

The Peripetalous Fasciole

The peripetalous fasciole does not vary greatly during growth other than becoming better defined and more angular. The widest portions are located at the ends of the petals and in the median area of interambulacra 1, 4, and 5. There is always a re-entrant angle in interambulacra 2 and 3 so the fasciole crosses plates 4 and 5 of the anterior plate series. In the posterior series, the fasciole is either straight, crossing plate 5, or has a downward, V-shaped portion so the fasciole is found on both plates 4 and 5. The path of the peripetalous fasciole over the various plates of the test is summarized in Table 12 and discussed in the sections on the ambulacra.

The proportional length of the peripetalous fasciole is 172.66 ± 1.18 per cent of the test length (S.D. 10.97, C.V. 6.36). Most of the variation is allometric. In smaller specimens (16 mm test length), the fasciole is 140 per cent of the test length and in larger specimens (111 mm test length) it is 201 per cent of the test length. There is also considerable individual variation particularly in the larger specimens. The total area of the peripetalous fasciole increases logarithmically with increasing size (Fig. 7). Figure 13 shows the natural log of the area of the peripetalous fasciole plotted against the natural log of the test length. The regression equation shown on the graph is:

$$LnY = 1.77LnX - 2.76 \qquad Y = \text{Area PP.F. (mm}^2)$$
$$S_{LnY.LnX} = \pm 0.101 \qquad X = \text{Test length (mm)}$$
$$r = 0.899.$$

The Colombian specimens were not used in calculating this line. Their values are plotted on Fig. 13 and are slightly below the values for the Florida population. This is due to a narrowing of the fasciole in the Colombian specimens, not to a difference in fasciolar length.

As the urchin increases in size, its volume and the area of its peripetalous fasciole increase at an exponential rate. Thus, the peripetalous fasciole maintains a constant relationship with the volume of the animal. The relationship between the tube-feet and the peripetalous fasciole differs in being a semi-logarithmic relation; the number of tube-feet decreases per unit of fasciole or unit of volume. When plotted against the natural

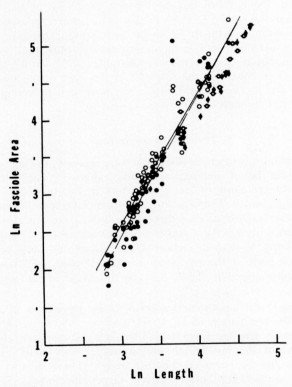

FIGURE 13. Fasciolar area (mm²) versus test length (mm) in *Brissopsis atlantica*. Solid dots = subanal fasciole, Florida specimens; solid dots with a vertical bar = subanal fasciole, Colombian specimens; circles = peripetalous fasciole, Florida specimens; circles with horizontal bar = peripetalous fasciole, Colombian specimens.

logarithm of the peripetalous fasciole area, the regression equation of the numbers of tunneling tube-feet is (Fig. 14):

$$Y = 7.17 LnX - 3.28$$
$$S_{Y.LnX} = \pm 1.84$$
$$r = 0.943.$$

$Y =$ Tunneling tube-feet
$X =$ PP.F. area (mm^2)

The numbers of respiratory tube-feet (IVb + Va), when plotted against the natural logarithm of the peripetalous fasciole area, have a regression equation of:

$$Y = 8.25 LnX + 5.23$$
$$S_{Y.LnX} = \pm 2.02$$
$$r = 0.951.$$

$Y =$ Pore-pairs IVb, Va.
$X =$ PP.F. area (mm^2)

It is evident that the respiratory tube-feet are more closely correlated with the area of the peripetalous fasciole than with the test length. The number of tube-feet (both respiratory and tunneling) does not keep pace with the increase in size of the peripetalous fasciole. Thus, the number of tube-feet per unit of fasciole decreases with growth. This is illustrated in Figue 8 for the tunneling tube-feet. The regression equation indicated on the graph is:

$$LnY = 3.54 - 1.13 LnX$$
$$S_{LnY.LnX} = \pm 0.161$$
$$r = 0.946$$

$Y =$ Tunneling tube-feet per
  unit of PP.F. area.
$X =$ Test length (mm).

The relationship between the tunneling tube-feet, the peripetalous fasciole area, and the test length may be graphically illustrated as in Figure 7, which shows the regression lines (and their standard errors) of the tunneling tube-feet and peripetalous fasciole area plotted against the test length. This graph makes it clear that the tunneling tube-feet develop rapidly in small specimens, then gradually reach a level where production of further tube-feet is unnecessary. The peripetalous fasciole develops slowly in the small specimens but its area expands more and more rapidly in the older specimens.

When the urchins are small, discharge of water from the burrow is easily accomplished. Since they burrow into the substrate while only 16 mm in test length (probably even smaller) they must have tunneling tube-feet to maintain an opening to their burrows. The closer the young urchin is to the surface, the more danger it faces from predators; the deeper it burrows, the more tube-feet are necessary to construct and maintain the respiratory tunnel. Since small urchins have a very small volume, the proportional surface area of the burrow is large and very little fasciolar area is needed to maintain a water flow through the burrow. When the urchin grows to a larger size, it may burrow deeper into the substrate but the numbers of tube-feet necessary to keep the respiratory tunnel open will be developed while the urchin is still young. Thus, there is

55

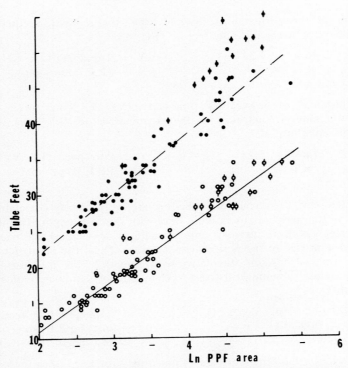

FIGURE 14. Tube-feet versus fasciolar area in *Brissopsis atlantica*. Solid dots = pore-pairs in paired petals (IV, series b + V, series a); circles = functional, tunneling tube-feet. Vertical bar through the symbol indicates Colombian specimens; others are from Florida.

little difference in the requirements of maintaining a respiratory tunnel for an urchin 30 mm in test length and one 100 mm in test length.

The problems of water circulation increase markedly as the urchins grow. The volume of the urchin increases as does the cube of its diameter. Thus, the larger urchins must have a much greater water circulation than the small urchins, particularly since there is no mechanism for the active circulation of the coelomic fluid. In addition, the surface area of the burrow increases as the square of the increasing diameter while the volume is increasing as the cube of the diameter. The proportional area of the burrow per unit of volume thus decreases as the urchins grow. Accordingly, the larger urchins have a smaller burrow wall to remove the water. The porosity and permeability of the substrate decreases with increasing depth of the substrate (Krumbein & Pettijohn, 1938). Therefore, in comparison to the small specimens, the large urchins require a greater water flow over the test and have a proportionally smaller and less permeable burrow wall. The larger urchins require a much larger fasciole to maintain homeostasis than do the smaller specimens. This explains the rapid increase of fasciolar area in the larger specimens of Figure 7.

There is no significant alteration in the relationship shown in Figure 7 even though the populations are from a variety of substrates and cover a large geographic area. This indicates that the control of the production of tube-feet and fasciole is genetic, not environmental, and that there must be an excess of both tube-feet and fasciolar area over those needed for survival in any one substrate.

The peripetalous fasciole is indented between the paired petals (interambulacrum 1 and 4) to a mean distance from the apical system of 13.11 $\pm$ 0.15 per cent of the test length (S.D. 1.39, C.V. 10.6). This proportion does not change significantly with growth or geographic locality. The large coefficient of variation is attributed to individual variation alone. The Colombian specimens are more variable than the Florida specimens (C.V. 15.1 as opposed to C.V. 9.1).

The distance from the apical system to the posterior portion of the peripetalous fasciole is 25.51 $\pm$ 0.24 per cent of the test length (S.D. 2.22, C.V. 8.70) and 68.07 $\pm$ 0.64 per cent of the distance from the apical system to the anterior portion of the peripetalous fasciole (S.D. 5.90, C.V. 8.7). The distance from the apical system to the posterior portion of the peripetalous fasciole increases with growth from 24 per cent in the smaller specimens to 29 per cent in the larger specimens.

The Subanal Fasciole

The shape of this fasciole varies with growth. In small specimens, 16 mm test length, the height of the area enclosed by the fasciole is 74 per cent of its width and in larger specimens, the height is 35 to 50 per cent of its width, becoming more distinctly bilobed. The mean height of the area enclosed by the subanal fasciole is 58.63 $\pm$ 0.92 per cent of its owne width (S.D. 8.42, C.V. 14.3). Some of this variation can be attributed to growth but individual variation is great also. The width of the area enclosed by the subanal fasciole is 37.23 $\pm$ 0.20 per cent of the test length (S.D. 1.84, C.V. 4.95). This proportion does not change with growth, other than becoming less variable. In a population of small specimens the coefficient of variation is 4.5 whereas in a sample of large specimens it is only 2.5. Thus it seems that there is some ecological pressure which eliminates those specimens with unusually narrow or wide subanal fascioles. Nichols (1962) reported a similar mechanism in *Echinocardium*. Large urchins from the Tortugas station have a broader subanal fasciole enclosure (*ca.* 40 per cent of the test length) than those from the Gulf of Mexico and Colombia (*ca.* 37 per cent of the test length). Both populations live in a fine, slimy mud but measurements of the plasticity and permeability will probably show the reason for the broader subanal area in the Tortugas specimens.

The proportional length of the subanal fasciole is 95.91 ± 0.58 per cent of the test length (S.D. 5.40, C.V. 5.64). There is no significant change in this character with size or geographic location. The area of the subanal fasciole increases logarithmically with increasing size, keeping pace with the volume of the urchin as does the peripetalous fasciole. The area of the subanal fasciole is normally almost the same as that of the peripetalous fasciole, particularly in larger specimens. Figure 13 shows the natural log of the subanal fasciole plotted against the natural log of the test length. The regression equation shown on the graph is:

$$S_{LnY} = 1.9 \, LnX - 3.29 \qquad Y = SA.F. \text{ area (mm}^2)$$
$$LnY.LnX = \pm 0.222 \qquad X = \text{Test length (mm)}$$
$$r = 0.964.$$

One specimen (station P-340, 89 mm test length) has no functional subanal fasciole. Only a difference in the tuberculation of the area shows where the fasciole should be. It is interesting that this specimen (also from a mud substrate) was able to grow to such a large size or even to survive at all without the subanal fasciole.

The plates crossed by the subanal fasciole are summarized in Table 12. It should be noted, however, that plates 6, 7, 8, and 9 of the posterior series of ambulacra I and V are always included within the fasciole. Plate 10 is always included in the larger specimens (greater than 30 mm test length) and is normally included within the fasciole in the smaller specimens as well (Plate 6e). It is often difficult to determine if plate 10 is included within the fasciole in smaller specimens. Occasional specimens are found with four plates within the fasciole, but this is an abnormal condition and there are usually five plates included on the other side of the fasciole. As Mortensen (1951b) pointed out, the third or fourth subanal tube-foot may be rudimentary or missing in some specimens but this does not mean that the fifth plate lacks a portion of the subanal fasciole. I have not seen any specimens of *B. atlantica* which have only four ambulacral plates included within both sides of the subanal fasciole. I am, of course, excluding the specimens of *Brissopsis mediterranea*.

Branches from the subanal fasciole are present in most specimens. They are narrow and poorly developed, but extend almost to the peripetalous fasciole along the lateral borders of interambulacrum 5.

The Spines

Plate 12 gives the relative size, shape, and distribution of the spines. There is nothing of taxonomic interest in them. They have a smooth surface, without thorns. The sphaeridia also lack distinctive features.

The Pedicellariae

The pedicellariae have been adequately described by Mortensen (1907, 1951b), but it is necessary to add a few comments, particularly about the

58

two globiferous forms. As pointed out by Mortensen (1907, p. 161), there are both elongate and short forms of globiferous pedicellariae. The short form is described as "like the type found in *alta,* but there are generally only two teeth on either side of the terminal opening." Plate 9*f* shows a photograph of this type. The basal portion of the valve is rounded, the broad lateral auricles are teardrop-shaped. In *B. alta,* the valves have a more angular base and the auricles are shield-shaped. Plate 10*g* shows another valve from the same specimen which has three teeth on either side of the terminal opening and two along the top of the opening. The terminal opening itself is V-shaped in this valve, appearing very similar to the end of a rostrate pedicellaria. Neither of these short forms resembles the globiferous pedicellariae of *B. alta.* The short form was rarely encountered in the specimens examined. The long form (Plates 9*e,* 12*g*) was common in all of the specimens.

Internal Anatomy

Although the anatomy and histology of *B. atlantica* will not be described in this work, these were investigated and will be reported in a subsequent publication. I was unable to find any characters in the internal anatomy or histology which might be of subspecific or specific importance.

Lectotype.—Mortensen (1907) did not designate a holotype and did not give museum numbers of specimens he examined. I was, however, able to locate the specimen figured in Plate 3, figures 6 and 10 *(op. cit.),* and designate it as lectotype. The specimen is from ALBATROSS station 2378 and is 54.5 mm in test length. The following measurements are given as percentages of the test length: width 78; height 51; anterior end of test to apical system 42; peristome — anterior 18; peristome posterior end of the test 72; anterior petal length 23; posterior petal length 22; width of amb. III 5.5; apical system to frontal portion of peripetalous fasciole 36; apical system to posterior portion of peripetalous fasciole 24; apical system to lateral portion of peripetalous fasciole 10; length of peripetalous fasciole 165; length subanal fasciole 92; width of subanal fasciole enclosure 36; height of enclosure 20; span of anterior petal ends 34; posterior petal ends 19; labrum 8.1; plastron length 48; plastron width 28; anus width 12. The path of the fascioles is as described for the species. It crosses IVa on plate 11, Va on plate 17. Anal branches are present from the subanal fasciole to the peripetalous fasciole. The specimen is dried and in the type collection at the U.S.N.M., No. 10637.

Eleven paralectotypes from the same station were examined 25 to 53 mm test length. There were also three specimens of *B. alta* in the same container, which were sorted out to be stored separately. A second lot of syntypes from ALBATROSS station 2401 (U.S.N.M. 10640) were examined. The container had Mortensen's label in it identifying the material as *B. atlantica.* Included were two specimens of *B. atlantica* (57.4 and 46.5

mm test length) and three specimens of *B. alta* (36.5 to 26.4 mm test length). The *B. alta* were removed for separate storage. Several other containers with specimens of the "broad form" (i.e., *B. mediterranea*) were examined, but I did not have the opportunity to sort them out properly.

Type locality.—ALBATROSS station 2378, Gulf of Mexico, 29°14.5′N., 88°9.5′W., 124 m, mud bottom.

Distribution.—*Brissopsis atlantica* is known, with certainty, from northern Florida, parts of the Bahamas, through the Gulf of Mexico to Colombia. Specimens from other localities must be re-examined to determine if they are *B. atlantica* or *B. mediterranea*. Depth: 34 to 373 meters.

Discussion.—Abnormalities: The labrum reached the second adjoining ambulacral plate on the left side of one specimen and on the right side of another. A specimen from GERDA station G-362, broken posteriorly, has an extremely small petaloid area, much as *B. micropetalia*. The posterior petals are only 18 per cent of its test length (estimating its length at about 44 mm). There are far too many functional tube-feet in ambulacrum III (viz. 37) for any of the *Brissopsis* species. Since the posterior end of the test is missing, it is impossible to classify the specimen but it does not closely resemble any of the other species. Although it is not obviously misshapen, I think it is an abnormal specimen, or perhaps a hybrid of *B. atlantica* and *B. mediterranea*. Such a hybrid of these species was found at GERDA station G-110. It is discussed under the latter species.

Definite hybrids occur between *B. atlantica* and *B. elongata* where their ranges overlap in Colombia. Many of the characters of *B. atlantica* show extremely wide variation in the Colombian specimens. In particular, the height and width of the test, the length of the plaston, the position of the peristome and the apical system, the number of tube-feet for a given test length and the span of the anterior petal ends are unusually unstable (see descriptions above). Thus, some urchins are broad and low as in the Florida specimens (Plate 8) and other are high and narrow (Plate 9). Intermediates exist between these two extremes. There are at least five specimens of *B. atlantica* × *B. elongata* which I consider first generation hybrids. Of these, the one illustrated in Plate 13 (36.5 mm test length, PILLSBURY sta. P-371) is the most obvious as it is intermediate in some of the key characters. For example, the labrum of this specimen extends to the second adjoining ambulacral plate as in *B. elongata* but the lip is better deevloped than in that species (but not as well developed as in the typical *B. atlantica*). The first plate entering the subanal fasciole is the sixth in both ambulacra, as is normal for *B. atlantica*. The genital pores are developed, but are not nearly as pronounced as in a *B. elongata* of the same size and more than in a typical *B. atlantica*. The paired petals have characters of both species in regard to configuration. These are illustrated on Plate 13, where *b* and *d* show a normal specimen of *B. elongata* and

60

a and *c,* the hybrid; Plate 10a shows a specimen of *B. atlantica;* all are of comparable size. The number of tunneling tube-feet in the hybrid is closer to that of *B. elongata* than to that of *B. atlantica.* The specimen is higher than most *B. elongata* or *B. atlantica* (62 per cent of the test length). The specimen also has a greater span of its anterior petal ends than would a *B. atlantica* of the same size. A 36-mm *B. atlantica* has a span of 37 per cent of the test length; a 36-mm *B. elongata* has a span of 51 per cent of the test length. The hybrid is intermediate, having a span between the anterior petal ends of 44 per cent of the test length. Thus, it is evident that first generation hybrids of these two species occur and, judging from the shift in population means between the two populations of *B. atlantica* studied, that these hybrids are sometimes fertile, leading to a mixing of the gene pools in this area. It could be argued that the "hybrids" are merely a shallow water ecotype since the hybrids were from the shallower stations. The large specimen in Plate 9, which is probably a hybrid, is from deeper water. Normal *B. atlantica* and *B. elongata* occur at the same stations with the hybrids. Neither *B. elongata* nor *B. atlantica* show pronounced changes in the above characters with depth or changes in the substrate.

Habitat: *Brissopsis atlantica* was not examined in the field due to the lack of shallow water populations accessible to the author. Experiments were carried out as with *B. alta.* The habitats were identical; specimens of both species were commonly taken in the same haul. The only ecological difference between *B. atlantica* and *B. alta* was the presence of *Montacuta* sp. on some specimens of *B. alta.*

Burrowing: The burrowing habits of *B. atlantica* were examined under the conditions outlined for *B. alta.* The burrowing sequence of *B. atlantica* is shown in Plate 14. A comparison between the two species indicates that *B. atlantica* burrows into the substrate more rapidly (only four minutes to cover completely) and with less rotation around its central axis than does *B. alta.* In addition, movement along the surface of the substrate was extremely rapid compared to *B. alta* and reached 25 cm per minute in a specimen 32 mm in test length. Movement within the burrow reached 3.6 cm per hour. These differences may possibly have been the result of superior condition of the specimens of *B. atlantica.* Individuals of both species, seemingly undamaged, moved very little and died after only a week of captivity. In all other respects, the two species examined were alike and the description given under *B. alta* will suffice for both. Plate 11*a* shows the progression of entrances to the burrow as the urchin moves through the substrate.

Ciliary currents: The currents flowing over the test are illustrated in Figure 15. The currents are similar to those described for *B. alta* with one exception. The presence of anal branches of the subanal fasciole tends to cause a flow of water off the test along these areas. This flow coincides with particle movements in this area and the loosened sediment which is

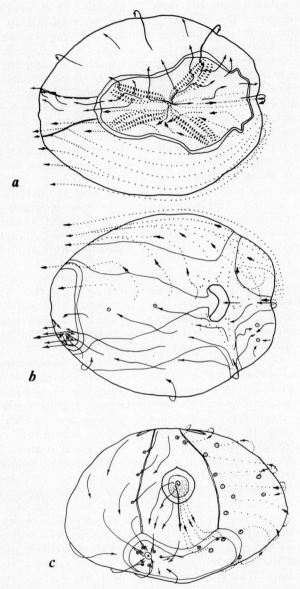

FIGURE 15. Water currents (solid arrows) and movement of sediment (dotted arrows) over the test in *Brissopsis atlantica*. Dotted circles represent movement off the test toward the viewer.

62

left behind facilitates passage of water from the burrow. This is in general agreement with the rapid movement of the animal, the greater total fasciolar and petaloid area, and the greater number of tunneling tube-feet (both dorsal and subanal).

Experiments similar to those performed with *B. alta* were carried out to determine the rate of water flow through the burrow. The current inflow for a specimen 20 mm in test length (volume 2.9 ml) was 0.69 ml/min. Although this is greater than for a comparable *B. alta,* the results are questionable due to the artificial conditions of the experiments. More valuable data will be forthcoming when specimens are collected by hand or measured in the field. The present results are valuable in that they confirm the relative importance and use of the drainage areas within the burrow as determined for *B. alta.* The drainage tunnels of the two species are about the same proportional diameter but those of *B. atlantica* are longer than those of *B. alta.*

Fossil History: *Brissopsis atlantica* is known from the Pliocene of Anguilla (Lambert, 1915).

Comments: Mortensen could not reach a decision on the specific status of the two forms of *B. atlantica* found in the western Atlantic. Two species are apparently involved: *B. mediterranea,* distributed from the Mediterranean and Gulf of Guinea westward through parts of the Bahamas and along the eastern coast of the United States; and *B. atlantica,* known from the Bahamas, Florida, and Gulf of Mexico to Colombia. The ranges of the two species overlap and, although more investigation is needed, it seems that little hybridization occurs. The two species can be identified easily and the young, in particular, are greatly different. Young specimens of *B. mediterranea* have the posterior petals almost parallel throughout their length and the posterior genital pores are well developed before the anterior pair appear. Furthermore, there are only four (sometimes only 3) ambulacral plates enclosed within the subanal fasciole whereas in *B. atlantica,* there are five.

The differences between the various species of *Brissopsis* are summarized in the key to the species of *Brissopsis,* Table 2, and Figures 2 and 3, and discussed in the section on taxonomic conclusions.

The importance of the various characters in the genus *Brissopsis* are summarized in Table 1.

Brissopsis elongata Mortensen, 1907
Figures 7, 16, 17; Plates 13, 15-18; Tables 1, 2, 5, 12

Brissopsis lyrifera, H. L. Clark, 1900, p. 245. Not *B. lyrifera* (Forbes).
Brissopsis elongata Mortensen, 1907, p. 163, pl. 3, figs. 4, 14, 15, 19; pl. 4, figs. 1, 4, 13, 18; pl. 18, figs. 2, 15-17, 21, 28; pl. 19, figs. 12, 17.
Brissopsis elongata, H. L. Clark, 1917, p. 203.
Kleinia elongata, Lambert & Thiery, 1925. p. 490.
Brissopsis elongata, H. L. Clark, 1933. p. 90.
Brissopsis Jarlii, Mortensen, 1951a, p. 302, pl. 1, figs. 1-3.

Brissopsis elongata, Mortensen, 1951b, p. 424, pl. 57, fig. 1.
Brissopsis Jarlii, Mortensen, 1951b, p. 431, pl. 57, figs. 8, 9, 11, 13, 14, 18-20.
Brissopsis jarlii, Cherbonnier, 1959, p. 54, pl. 10, figs. A-L.
Brissopsis jarlii, Chesher, 1966, p. 220.

Material examined.—1 specimen, broken, PILLSBURY sta. P-17, off Ghana, 5°35′N., 00°10′E., 48 m, 26 May, 1964.—1 specimen, broken, sta. P-24, off Ghana, 4°56′N., 0°50′W., 37 m, May 1964.—4 specimens, to 106 mm test length, sta. P-259, off Fernando Póo, 3°53′N., 8°55′E., 59 m, 15 May 1965.—1 specimen, 35.4 mm test length, sta. P-324, N. coast of Panama, 9°44′N., 79°31′W., 63 - 54 m, 7 July 1966.—1 specimen, 18 mm test length, sta. P-331, off N. coast of Panama, 9°31′N., 78°56′W., 33 - 46 m, 8 July 1966.—4 specimens, 17 to 23 mm test length, sta. P-347, Gulf of Uraba, Colombia, 8°43′N., 77°03′W., 54 m, 11 July 1966. —4 specimens, 18 to 35.5 mm test length, sta. P-348, Gulf of Uraba, Colombia, 8°38′N., 77°02.2′W., 58 m, 11 July 1966.—1 specimen, 36 mm test length, sta. P-350, Gulf of Uraba, Colombia, 8°28′N., 77°00.3′ W., 54 m, 11 July 1966.—15 specimens, 32 to 68 mm test length, sta. P-352, Gulf of Uraba, Colombia, 8°20.1′N., 76°53.6′W., 54 to 51 m, 11 July 1966.—46 specimens, 37.2 to 50.5 mm test length, sta. P-353, Gulf of Uraba, Colombia, at the Atrato River mouth, 8°13.2′N., 76°50.1′ W., 29 - 33 m, 11 July 1966.—13 specimens, 12 to 43.5 mm test length, sta. P-362, off N.W. Colombia, 8°57.5′N., 76°33.6′W., 64 to 54 m, 12 July 1966.—12 specimens, 9.8 to 24 mm test length, sta. P-365, off N.W. Colombia, 9°31.3′N., 76°15.4′W., 56 - 58 m, 13 July 1966.—40 specimens, 17.8 to 41.5 mm test length, sta. P-367, off N.W. Colombia, 9°31.1′N., 75°49.6′W., 36 to 34 m, 13 July 1966.—23 specimens, 16 to 35.6 mm test length, sta. P-370, off N.W. Colombia, 9°37.9′N., 75°50.4′W., 36 m, 13 July 1966.—9 specimens, 31 to 43.1 mm test length, sta. P-371, off N.W. Colombia, 9°40′N., 76°01.5′W., 45-54 m, 13 July, 1966.—11 specimens, 19 to 31 mm test length, sta. P-396, off N.W. Colombia, 9°18.2′N., 76°24.8′W., 68 m, 17 July 1966.—17 specimens, 12 to 31 mm test length, sta. P-397, off N.W. Colombia, 9°12.8′N., 76°27.1′W., 62 to 65 m, 17 July 1966.—6 specimens, 23 to 34 mm test length, sta. P-402, off N.W. Colombia, 8°51.2′N., 77°01.6′W., 72 m, 17 July 1966.—8 specimens, 15 to 29 mm test length, sta. P-411, off N.E. Panama, 8°40.7′N., 77°21.8′W., 29 to 42 m, 18 July 1966.—4 specimens, 15 to 29.5 mm test length, sta. P-412, off N.E. Panama, 8°38.9′N., 77°13.2′W., 54 to 60 m, 18 July 1966.—19 specimens, 23 to 46 mm test length, sta. P-425, off N. Panama coast, 9°38.9′N., 79°15.3′W., 65 m, 19 July 1966.—15 specimens, 11.6 to 30.3 mm test length, sta. P-432, off Canal Zone, 9°18.2′N., 80°03.3′W., 24 m, 20 July, 1966.—22 specimens, 11 to 25 mm test length, sta. P-434, off N.W. Panama, 9°14.6′N., 80°21.8′W., 48 m, 20 July 1966.—15 specimens, 14.5 to 42 mm test length, sta. P-437, off N.W. Panama, 9°00.1′N., 80°45.8′W., 54 m, 20 July, 1966.

All specimens were collected by the R/V JOHN ELLIOTT PILLSBURY, of the Institute of Marine Science, University of Miami. All of the specimens were examined carefully for certain characters but only 59 specimens were thoroughly measured. The specimens were grouped and analyzed from each station and then from each depth range (shallower than 36 m, deeper than 36 m).

TABLE 5

STATISTICAL SUMMARY: *Brissopsis elongata* s.s.

Character	Mean	S.E.	S.D.	Range	N	C.V.
tl*	32.87	1.70	13.60	9.8-68	59	
tw	82.31	0.23	1.75	77-86	59	2.12
h	54.49	0.35	2.66	49-59	59	4.89
ax	37.97	0.20	1.51	33-41	59	3.99
pa	25.05	0.18	1.34	23-28	58	5.25
lp	64.76	0.25	1.87	61-68	58	2.99
ap	26.93	0.40	3.02	17-32	59	11.20
apw†	35.56	0.56	4.30	26-47	59	12.10
pp	25.51	0.45	3.40	15-31	59	13.30
ppw†	34.07	0.63	4.77	25-47	59	14.00
pp/ap‡	94.37	0.75	5.74	79-100	59	6.09
wIII	9.19	0.15	1.12	6.4-12	59	12.20
ff	38.95	0.23	1.77	34-43	58	4.55
pf	27.29	0.33	2.49	22-32	58	9.15
lf	17.91	0.19	1.43	14-21	58	7.98
pf/af‡	70.41	0.18	7.42	56-85	58	10.50
ppfl	197.39	1.99	15.17	158-223	59	7.67
ape	48.83	0.46	3.51	39-56	59	7.20
safh/w‡	53.85	0.85	6.47	43-77	59	12.00
safw	42.54	0.26	1.95	39-47	59	4.58
safl	109.92	0.75	5.73	99-123	59	5.23
l	9.95	0.15	1.17	8-12	58	11.75
pl	40.02	0.27	2.00	35-45	58	5.00
b	15.66	0.35	2.66	8-21	58	17.00
c	22.56	0.29	2.18	16-27	57	9.68
d	27.13	0.50	1.93	25-29	16	7.01
aw	14.36	0.19	1.47	11-18	59	10.2
aw/ah‡	83.10	0.85	6.49	72-100	59	7.80

Character symbols are as given in Figure 1. Data are expressed as percentage of test length unless otherwise indicated.
*Test length (mm).
‡Ratio given as a percentage.
†Percentage of petal length.

Diagnosis.—Subanal fasciole distinct, crossing five ambulcral plates on each side, the first being number 7. Posterior petals confluent proximally. Subspecies *B. elongata jarlli* characterized by thorns of globiferous pedicellariae on the side of the valves as opposed to the mid-line of the back of the valve and in having a more oblique posterior truncation than the *B. elongata* s.s.

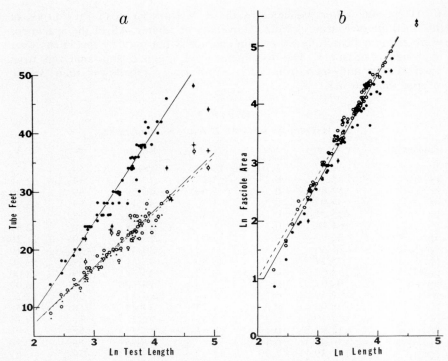

FIGURE 16. Tube-feet and fasciolar area versus the test length in *Brissopsis elongata*. *A,* tube-feet versus the natural logarithm of the test length (mm): solid dots = tunneling tube-feet, *B. elongata* s.s.; solid dots with vertical bar = *B. elongata jarlii;* circles = porepairs in the anterior petal (IV, series b), *B. elongata* s.s.; circles with vertical bar = same, *B. elongata jarlii;* triangles = pore-pairs posterior petal (V, series a), *B. elongata* s.s.; crosses = same, *B. elongata jarlii.—B,* Natural logarithm of peripetalous (circles) and subanal (solid dots) fasciole area (mm²) versus the natural logarithm of the test length (mm); a vertical bar through the dot or circle indicates *B. elongata jarlii.*

Description of B. elongata s.s.—The test has a low, angular appearance. Its mean width is 82.31 ± 0.23 per cent of the test length (S.D. 1.75, C. V. 2.12) and its mean height is 54.49 ± 0.35 per cent of the test length (S.D. 2.66, C.V. 4.89). The width shows no significant change with growth or depth but the proportional height tends to decrease slightly with an increase in size and increases with an increase in depth. Specimens from station P-353 (29 m) were occasionally deformed, the dorsal surface being depressed to a varying degree (Plate 18*c*). The shape of the test varies with growth as illustrated in Plates 15 and 16. The posterior end of the test, viewed from above, becomes more truncated, and viewed laterally, becomes more vertically truncate in larger especimens. It is not known if specimens of equal size from Africa and the Americas develop the same degree of truncation. It appears, however, that the character is quite variable, some large specimens retaining the juvenile configuration and some very small specimens with a vertically truncated posterior end. The subanal plastron, like the plastron, has a straight profile and is set off from the plastron by a distinct node at the median, posterior end of the plastron. The angle is normally 35° but varies about 10° in either direction.

The dorsal interambulacral plates outside the peripetalous fasciole develop a raised node from which the tubercles radiate in a fairly regular series. In the larger specimens, the nodes of successive plates form a low, irregular elevation from the peripetalous fasciole to the ambitus in both plate-series of interambulacra 4 and 5, giving the larger animals a more angular appearance than the smaller ones.

The Anterior Ambulacrum

The anterior ambulacrum is slightly sunken from the apex to just below the ambitus where it becomes very shallow and broad before reaching the peristome. The shallow notch in the anterior ambitus becomes slightly more defined with growth. The peripetalous fasciole crosses ambulacrum III at a mean distance from the apical system of 38.95 ± 0.23 per cent of the test length (S.D. 1.77, C.V. 4.55). This proportion shows little change with size (9.8 to 68 mm test length) and is identical with the same proportion in *B. elongata jarlii*.

Within the peripetalous fasciole, the frontal ambulacrum is divided into two areas, one nearest the apex containing developing tube-feet and the other containing the functional tunnel-building tube-feet. The number of functional tube-feet varies with growth from 18 in a specimen 11.6 mm in test length to 46 in a specimen 68 mm in test length. When plotted against the natural log of the length, the increase in the number of functional tube-feet with growth becomes linear (Fig. 16a), and has the regression equation:

$$Y = 15.5 \mathrm{Ln}X - 22.047 \qquad Y = \text{Tunneling tube-feet.}$$
$$S_{Y.\mathrm{Ln}X} = \pm 1.87 \qquad X = \text{Test length (mm).}$$
$$r = 0.967$$

New plates are split off from the ocular plate as the urchin grows. These plates bear undeveloped, globular, tube-feet which are situated over a single pore. The functional tube-feet issue from circular depressions near the dorsolateral edge of the ambulacral plates. The center portion of these depressions is built up to form a projection for muscle attachment and the slit-like pore is located on the ventro-mesial portion of this projection (Plate 18e). The pores are in a single series and plate crushing does not seem to occur.

Ambulacrum III is widest nearest the peripetalous fasciole. Measurements of its width were taken from the outer edge of the pore series. The proportional width varies with the size of the specimen, being about 11 percent of the test length in specimens 11 mm in test length and about 7 per cent in a specimen 68 mm in test length. The mean width of the anterior ambulacrum is 9.19 ± 0.15 per cent of the test length (S.D. 1.12, C.V. 12.2).

The mature tunnel building tube-foot bears a disc which is about 0.8 mm in diameter and is non-lobate, its periphery being almost perfectly smooth even when the disc is just developing. The supporting calcite laminae of the discs are broad and, as pointed out by Mortensen (1951b), often bi- or tri-lobate.

There are six or seven plates per plate-series from the peripetalous fasciole to the peristome. This number is constant and does not change with growth or depth. The mature urchin (greater than *ca*. 20 mm test length) has the three tube-feet of each series nearest the peristome developed into feeding the tube-feet. The anterior phyllode, like the others, is not strongly developed. The tube-feet between the phyllode and the peripetalous fasciole are sensory tube-feet and are located over single pores.

The tuberculation of the anterior ambulacrum can be seen in Plate 16. There is a series of prominent tubercles arranged in a single series medially of the pore-series. Each plate usually has two tubercles medially of the tube-foot.

Ambulacra II and IV
(the anterior paired petals)

The peripetalous fasciole crosses ambulacrum IV on plates 9, 10, 11, or 12 of series a. This position does not change with growth and is not correlated with depth. The frequencies of the plates crossed in the specimens examined are, 9 (8.5 per cent), 10 (57.5 per cent), 11 (32 per cent), 12 (2 per cent).

The tuberculation outside the peripetalous fasciole is evenly distributed, with no pronounced clear area at the mid-line. Tuberculation ends just below the ambitus leaving the ventral portion of the ambulacra naked. Nearest the peristome, there are feeding tube-feet arranged in a poorly developed phyllode. In the larger specimens, there are 8 to 10 feeding tube-feet per phyllode, each situated over a single, large pore located on the adoral edge of the plate. Sensory tube-feet are found in ambulacrum IV from the phyllode to plates 8 or 9a and 6 to 9b.

Within the peripetalous fasciole, the petals are slightly sunken. The two series of pore-pairs bend mesially at their distal end, but some specimens have open petals, the pore-pairs not converging (cf. Plate 15). The anterior pore-series have only the apicalmost four or five pore-pairs undeveloped. The percentage of reduced pores, therefore, varies from about 30 per cent in the smaller specimens to about 18 per cent in the larger specimens. In the posterior series, only two or three undeveloped pore-pairs occur. The total number of tube-feet (pre-pairs, or plates) increases throughout growth. Figure 16a shows the numbers of pore-pairs of ambulacrum IV, series b, plotted against the natural log of the test length. The regression equation shown on the graph is:

$$Y = 9.71 \, LnX - 12.23 \qquad Y = \text{Pore-pairs.}$$
$$S_{Y.LnX} = \pm 1.34 \qquad X = \text{Test length (mm).}$$
$$r = 0.957$$

During growth, there is an increase in the number of tubercles adjacent to each pore-pair. These tubercles support small spines which clean and protect the respiratory tube-feet.

The anterior petals have a mean length of 26.93 ± 0.40 per cent of the test length (S.D. 3.02, C.V. 11.20). Allometry accounts for much of this large variation, the anterior petal becomes proportionally longer in larger specimens. In addition, specimens from deeper habitats tend to have proportionally shorter petals. The petals have a mean width of 35.56 ± 0.56 per cent of the petal length (S.D. 4.30, C.V. 12.1). This proportion decreases rapidly with an increase in test length from 47 per cent to 26 per cent. The distance between the ends of the petals has a mean of 48.83 ± 0.46 per cent of the test length (S.D. 3.51, C.V. 7.2). This proportion increases with growth and decreases with depth.

The peals are straight, only the anterior pore-series showing a slight posterior curve.

Ambulacra I and V
(the posterior paired petals)

The peripetalous fasciole crosses ambulacrum V on plate 17, 18, or 19 of series a. Plate number 18 is the most commonly crossed; the frequency of each plate crossed in the specimens examined is: 17 (12 per cent), 18 (67 per cent), 19 (21 per cent). The plates outside the peripetalous fasciole are heavily tuberculated from the fasciole to the ambitus, with no naked areas. The plates of these ambulacra are about the same width as (or a little less than) the adjacent plates of interambulacrum 5. Orally of plate 7 of the posterior plate series and plate 10 or 11 of the anterior plate series, the ambulacra are naked except for small tertiary spines, pedicellariae, and sphaeridia. Nearest the peristome, there are feeding tube-feet. In the larger specimens there are 6 to 8 feeding tube-feet per phyllode. Within the subanal fasciole there are normally four subanal tube-feet per ambulacrum which are situated over a slight depression with the pore-pair divided by the raised central muscle attachment (Plate 16f). Plates 7, 8, 9, 10, and 11 are normally inserted into the subanal fasciole (Plate 15f). Plate number 11, however, has only a thin extension reaching down into the subanal fasciole. This extension is not always developed and in about 40 per cent of the specimens examined there are only four plates inserted into the subanal fasciole on one side or the other. About 20 per cent of the specimens examined had only four plates on both sides of the subanal fasciole. In three of the specimens examined, the first plate entering the subanal fasciole in ambulacrum V was number 6 but number 7 was, as usual, the first plate included in the subanal fasciole in ambulacrum I. In four specimens, the first plate of ambulacrum I to enter the subanal fasciole is number 8; number 7 is first on the other side except for one specimen in which number 8 is first on both sides. Obviously, this character, and the number of plates included within the subanal fasciole, are subject to more variation in this species than in any of the other species of *Brissopsis*.

There are no tube-feet from the ambitus to peripetalous fasciole in either posterior ambulacra.

Within the peripetalous fasciole, the petals are slightly sunken. The pore-pairs close distally to a greater degree than in the anterior petals. The posterior series of pore-pairs have, in the larger specimens, about 50 per cent of the apicalmost pore-pairs underdeveloped. The exact number is difficult to determine as there is a very gradual decrease apically in the size of the pore-pairs, particularly in the smaller specimens. The number of plates in the petaloid region of ambulacrum V increases throughout growth. Figure 16a shows the numbers of pore-pairs of series a plotted against the natural log of the test length. The regression equation shown on the graph is:

$$Y = 9.55 \text{ LnX} - 12.12 \qquad Y = \text{Pore-pairs (Va)}.$$
$$S_{Y.LnX} = \pm 1.36 \qquad X = \text{Test length (mm)}.$$
$$r = 0.955$$

In a single specimen (Plate 16d) the pore-pairs continue outside the peripetalous fasciole in both posterior ambulacra.

The mean length of the posterior petals is 25.51 ± 0.45 per cent of the test length (S.D. 3.40, C.V. 13.3) and their mean width is 34.07 ± 0.63 per cent of the petal length (S.D. 4.77, C.V. 14.0). Both of these proportions show considerable allometric and individual variation.

The Interambulacra

The posterior paired petals are confluent from the apical system to about one-half their length where they curve sharply outwards. In very small specimens (Plate 16a) the petals diverge from the apical system.

The number of interambulacral plates from the peristome to the fascioles is a constant and important character which is discussed in the following section on the fascioles of *B. elongata*.

The tuberculation is uniform in the interambulacra. The size of the tubercles increases on the oral side and near the apex and along the lateral edges of ambulacra I, III, and V; particularly along ambulacrum III. There is a narrow, naked zone medially in interambulacrum 5 from the apical system to the periproct. On the oral surface, the first interambulacral plates (including the labrum) are naked except for one or two tubercles on the middle of the labrum and a small cluster of spines adpacent to the peristome.

70

The plastron is shield-shaped, with a mean length of 40.02 ± 0.27 per cent of the test length (S.D. 2.00, C.V. 5.00). This proportion shows no significant change with growth or depth. The width of the plastron, measured at points B, C, and D, is:

point	Mean	S.E.	S.D.	C.V.
B	15.66	0.35	2.66	17.0
C	22.56	0.29	2.18	9.68
D	27.13	0.50	1.93	7.07

These proportions all show a slight decrease with growth.

As mentioned in the description of the shape of the test, the plastron is elevated to form a keel (Plate 15d).

The labrum reaches to the middle of the second adjoining ambulacral plates. The lip is poorly formed except in the largest specimens and even in these it is not prominent. At the juncture of the first ambulacral plates, the labrum is broad, about as wide as the portion of the labrum bordering the peristome (Plate 15e). The mean length of the labrum is 9.95 ± 0.15 per cent of the test length (S.D. 1.17, C.V. 11.75). This proportion tends to decrease with growth. Two or three tubercles are usually found in the center of the labrum in addition to the row of smaller spines along the edge of the peristome.

The Apical System

The apical system is ethmolytic, situated anteriorly on the dorsal surface at a mean distance from the anterior end of 37.97 ± 0.20 per cent of the test length (S.D. 1.51, C.V. 3.99). There is no significant allometric change in this proportion. There are four genital pores, first appearing at a test length of about 16 mm. The time of appearance varies considerably; the pores are present in one specimen 16 mm in test length but are barely visible in a specimen 23 mm in test length. The anterior and posterior genital pores are about the same size but, as usual, the right anterior gonad is underdeveloped, the left anterior gonad is bilobed and the left posterior gonad is larger than the right. The madreporite passes between the posterior genital plates and is long and narrow (Plate 18d). The oculars are triangular. Genital papillae are present.

The Periproct

The periproct is situated high on the posterior end of the test (Plate 15d), enclosed within interambulacral plates 5, 6, 7, 8. It is finely tuberculated and surrounded by the large spines of the anal tuft. Rostrate and tridentate pedicellariae are common. It is oval, its vertical diameter the largest. The mean width of the periproct is 14.36 ± 0.19 per cent of the test length (S.D. 1.47, C.V. 10.2) and 83.10 ± 0.85 per cent of the periproct height (S.D. 6.49, C.V. 7.8). The proportional width decreases slightly with an increasing test length. Individual variation overshadows allometry.

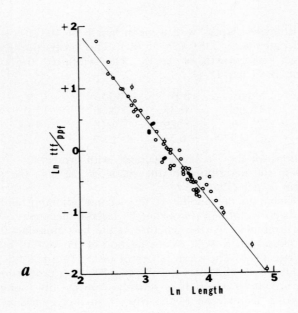

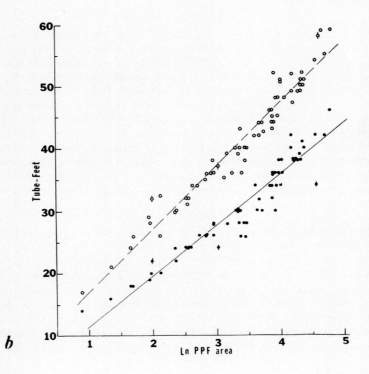

72

The Peristome

The peristome is situated anteriorly; its leading edge has a mean distance from the anterior end of the test of 25.05 ± 0.18 per cent of the test length (S.D. 1.34, C.V. 5.25). The variation is not significantly correlated with growth or depth. The peristome is crescent-shaped to oval in younger specimens, becoming more distinctly crescent-shaped in larger specimens.

The Peripetalous Fasciole

The peripetalous fasciole does not vary greatly during growth, other than becoming better defined and more angular. The widest parts are located at the ends of the petals and in the median area of interambulacra 1, 4, and 5. There is always a reentrant angle in interambulacra 2 and 3 so that the fasciole crosses plates 4 and 5 of the anterior plate-series. In the posterior series of interambulacrum 3, the fasciole is straight, crossing only plate number 5. In a few specimens, the lower edge of plate number 6 is also crossed by the fasciole. The path of the peripetalous fasciole is summarized in Table 12.

The proportional length of the peripetalous fasciole is 197.39 ± 1.99 per cent of the test length (S.D. 15.17, C.V. 7.67). This proportion increases slightly with growth and decreases slightly with increasing depth. In smaller specimens (test length *ca.* 10 mm) the proportion is 160 to 170 per cent of the test length and in larger specimens (test length 68 mm) the peripetalous fasciole is 220 per cent of the test length. The total area of the peripetalous fasciole increases logarithmically with increasing size. Figure 16*b* shows the natural log of the test length plotted against the natural log of the area of the peripetalous fasciole. The regression equation shown on the graph is:

$$LnY = 1.864 LnX - 2.94 \qquad Y = \text{Area of peripetalous}$$
$$S_{LnY.LnX} = \pm 0.383 \qquad\qquad \text{fasciole } (mm^2).$$
$$r = 0.918 \qquad\qquad X = \text{Test length (mm).}$$

As the urchin increases in size, its volume and the area of its peripetalous fasciole increase at an exponential rate. Thus, the peripetalous fasciole maintains a constant relationship with the volume of the animal. The relationship between the tube-feet and the peripetalous fasciole differs in being a semi-logarithmetic function, the number of tube-feet decreases

←

FIGURE 17. Tube-feet versus fasciolar area, and tunneling tube-feet per unit area of fasciole versus the test length in *Brissopsis elongata*. A, Decrease in number of tunneling tube-feet (ttf) per unit of peripetalous fasciole area (ppf, mm^2) with increase in test length (mm); both values expressed as their natural logarithms. Circles with a vertical bar indicate *B. elongata jarlii*.—B, Tube-feet versus natural logarithm of peripetalous fasciole area (PPF, mm^2); circles = pore-pairs in anterior and posterior paired petals, (IV, series b + V, series a); solid dots = functional tunneling tube-feet. Symbols with a vertical bar indicate *B. elongata jarlii*.

per unit of fasciole or unit of volume. When plotted against the natural logarithm of the peripetalous fasciole area the regression equation of the tunneling tube-feet is (Fig. 17b):

$$Y = 7.127 \text{LnX} + 6.384 \qquad Y = \text{Tunneling tube-feet.}$$
$$S_{Y.\text{LnX}} = \pm 1.01 \qquad\qquad X = \text{Area of peripetalous}$$
$$r = 0.902 \qquad\qquad\qquad\qquad \text{fasciole (mm}^2\text{).}$$

The respiratory tube-feet (a single series from both ambulacra IV and V), when plotted against the natural log of the peripetalous fasciole, have a regression equation of (Fig. 17b):

$$Y = 9.005 \text{ LnX} + 10.54 \qquad Y = \text{Pore-pairs, IVb, Va.}$$
$$S_{Y.\text{LnX}} = \pm 3.7 \qquad\qquad X = \text{Peripetalous fascicle}$$
$$r = 0.915 \qquad\qquad\qquad\qquad \text{area (mm}^2\text{).}$$

It is evident that the number of tube-feet is highly correlated with both the test length and the area of peripetalous fasciole and that their proportional number decreases steadily with respect to an increasing test length or fasciolar area. Thus, the number of tube-feet per unit of fasciole decreases (as is shown in Fig. 17a) with an increase in test length. The regression equation shown on the graph is:

$$\text{LnY} = 4.55 - 1.338 \text{ LnX} \qquad Y = \text{Tunneling tube-feet per unit}$$
$$S_{\text{LnY.LnX}} = \pm 0.046 \qquad\qquad\qquad \text{of fasciole (No./mm}^2\text{)}$$
$$r = 0.972 \qquad\qquad\qquad\qquad X = \text{Test length (mm).}$$

It is obvious from the high coefficient of correlation that there is little change in this relationship in specimens from different depths. The relationship of the fasciole, the tube-feet, and the test length is shown in Figure 7 and explained in the discussion of the fascioles of *B. atlantica*.

The peripetalous fasciole is indented between the paired petals (interambulacrum 1 and 4) to a mean distance from the apical system of 17.91 ± 0.19 per cent of the test length (S.D. 1.43, C.V. 7.98). This proportion shows a very slight decrease with growth but no change with depth. The distance from the apical system to the posterior portion of the peripetalous fasciole is 27.29 ± 0.33 per cent of the test length (S.D. 2.49, C.V. 9.15). This proportion shows a slight increase with growth but does not change significantly with depth. The distance from the apical system to the anterior portion of the peripetalous fasciole was discussed above (ambulacrum III).

The Subanal Fasciole

The subanal fasciole varies greatly in shape with an increase in size. In small specimens, test length 11 mm, the height of the fasciolar enclosure may be 69 per cent of its own width, and in larger specimens the height is reduced to 44 per cent of its width, becoming more distinctly bilobed. The mean height of the area enclosed by the subanal fasciole is

53.85 ± 0.85 per cent of its own width (S.D. 6.47, C.V. 12.00). Much of this variation can be attributed to allometry, but individual variation is also great for the character. The width of the area enclosed by the subanal fasciole is 42.54 ± 0.26 per cent of the test length (S.D. 1.95, C.V. 4.58). This proportion does not change significantly with growth or depth changes.

The proportional length of the subanal fasciole is 109.92 ± 0.75 per cent of the test length (S.D. 5.73, C.V. 5.23). This proportion increases slightly with growth (about a 20 per cent increase for a 60 mm increase in test length). The area of the subanal fasciole increases logarithmically with increasing size, keeping pace with the volume as does the peripetalous fasciole. In fact, the area of the peripetalous fasciole is normally almost the same as that of the subanal fasciole, particularly in the larger specimens. Figure 16b shows the natural log of the area of the subanal fasciole plotted against the natural log of the length. The regression equation is:

$$LnY = 1.755LnX - 2.465 \qquad Y = \text{Area of SAF (mm}^2)$$
$$S_{LnY.LnX} = 0.226 \qquad\qquad X = \text{Test length (mm)}.$$
$$r = 0.963$$

The plates crossed by this fasciole are summarized in Table 12, and discussed in the section on the posterior ambulacra. It is emphasized that there are normally five plates per ambulacrum within the subanal fasciole (numbers 7, 8, 9, 10, and 11).

The Spines and Pedicellariae

No significant differences were found between the spines of *B. elongata* and those of *B. atlantica*.

The pedicellariae have been accurately described by Mortensen (1907, 1951b) but it is worthwhile to give photographs of the globiferous and tridentate pedicellariae of the African and American subspecies to show the major similarities and differences. The globiferous pedicellariae of the African and American subspecies are alike except for the position of the thorns on the back of the valves. In *B. elongata* s.s., the thorns are on the midline of the back (Plate 18f,i) and in *B. elongata jarlii,* they are normally placed to one side or the other of the midline (Plate 17g,h,i). Some valves of both forms may have no thorns at all and the variable position of the thorns on *B. elongata jarlii* indicates that the position of the thorns is relatively unstable; they may be located near the midline in some valves. The tridentate pedicellariae of the American subspecies are different from the tridentate pedicellariae of the African subspecies but the differences are not as great as they appear at first glance. The valve shown in Plate 18g differs from those in Plate 17e,f in that the lateral projections of the blade are pointed upward and irregular in the former and angled outward and more symmetrical in the latter valves. Otherwise, they are

75

similar. The tridentate pedicellariae occur in a variety of forms in the same specimen, from the short-valved form (Plate 18*h*) to the long-valved form (Plate 18*g*), with numerous intermediate sizes. Apparently, the valves are subject to allometric variation and may change considerably as the individual pedicellaria matures.

The internal anatomy of *B. elongata* is similar to that of *B. atlantica*.

Lectotype.—Mortensen (1907) described this species from material collected off Puerto Cabello, Venezuela. Madsen has informed me (personal communication) that: "Mortensen marked the whole material of *Brissopsis elongata* from Puerto Cabello as types. The one shown in the photos, 1907 pl. 4 figs. 1, 4, 13 (the obvious lectotype) is preserved in alcohol and still in excellent condition. It is 44 mm long and thus slightly enlarged in the photo." This specimen is therefore designated as lectotype. It is deposited in the Universitetets Zoologiske Museum, Copenhagen, Denmark, as also is the holotype of *B. elongata jarlii*.

Type locality.—*B. elongata* s.s.: Off Puerto Cabello, Venezuela (*ca.* 11°N., 68°W.) in 22 to 27.5 m depth.

B. elongata jarlii: Off the Gold Coast of Africa, 46 m depth.

Distribution.—*B. elongata* s.s. is known from the South American coast from Venezuela to Panama. Mortensen (1907) refers the specimens from Puerto Rico (Clark, 1900 *B. lyrifera*) and one from ALBATROSS sta. 2145 (46 m, N.W. coast of Panama) to this species. It has thus been collected from 13 to 72 m depth and is a comparatively shallow water form of *Brissopsis*. *B. elongata jarlii* is known only from the Gulf of Guinea, from 37 to 59 m in depth.

Discussion.—Abnormalities: Various abnormalities have been discussed in the above description. The deformities of particular note are: the depressed aboral surface in some specimens from shallow stations; the pore-pairs continuing beyond the peripetalous fasciole in one specimen, and the variations in the number of plates inserted into the subanal fasciole being sometimes 4, sometimes 6, but normally 5.

Hybrid forms between *B. atlantica* and *B. elongata* are discussed under the former species.

Ecology: This is probably the only species of *Brissopsis* which could be studied easily in the field. There has been, however, no opportunity to do so and nothing definite is known of the animal's ecology other than what can be inferred by its similarity to *B. atlantica* and *B. alta*. It will be interesting to discover what environmental or behavioral differences exist between *B. elongata* and *B. atlantica* to account for the large difference in the number of tube-feet per unit of fasciole and per unit of test length.

Fossil History: *B. elongata* has not been recorded from the fossil record but the specimen from the Miocene of Costa Rica figured by Durham (1961) as *Brissopsis* sp. closely resembles the living *B. elongata*.

76

Comments: Both Mortensen (1951b) and Cherbonnier (1959) expressed doubts as to the specific status of the specimens from the Gulf of Guinea. While the location of the thorns on the back of the globiferous pedicellariae differs slightly in the transatlantic forms, this probably does not denote considerable genetic divergence and is not, in itself, sufficient to be considered of specific importance. It is entirely possible that there is genetic continuity between the African and American forms. As pointed out previously (Chesher, 1966) larval transport between Brazil and the Gulf of Guinea via the Equatorial Undercurrent is a very real possibility. If, as suggested by Metcalf et al. (1962) and Rinkel et al. (1966), the Equatorial Undercurrent flows at 2.9 or 1.8 knots, the journey from Brazil to the Gulf of Guinea would require only 43 to 70 days. It would, of course, be helpful to know the larval life-span of the American B. elongata but it is reasonable to expect that it could survive the voyage. As pointed out by Cherbonnier (1959), the posterior end of the test is overhanging in the African subspecies (Plate 17) and does not normally reach a vertical truncation in the American form. This is a character which changes with growth and it is possible that larger specimens of B. elongata s.s. will be found to have the posterior truncation over-hanging to the same degree as in the African form. B. elongata jarlii has slightly fewer tube-feet per unit of size (cf. Fig. 16) and more tube-feet per unit of fasciole (Fig. 17) than does the American form. All of the other characters are within the normal range of B. elongata s.s. Considering these characters with the known variation of B. elongata s.s. and the degree of differentiation of the other Brissopsis species (Table 2) I think the two forms conform to Mayr's (1953) definition of a subspecies.

The differences between the various species of Brissopsis are summarized in the key to the species, Table 2, and discussed in the section comparing sympatric species in the taxonomic conlusions.

Brissopsis mediterranea Mortensen, 1913
Figures 2, 3, 8, 18, 19; Plates 19, 20;
Tables 1, 2, 6, 12

Brissopsis lyrifera, A. Agassiz, 1883, p. 69, not B. lyrifera (Forbes) (part?)
Brissopsis atlantica, Mortensen, 1907, p. 162, pl. 3, fig. 17; pl. 19, figs. 8, 13, 14, 16, 22, 23, 30, 31 (part).
Brissopsis atlantica, Koehler, 1909, p. 238.
Brissopsis atlantica var. mediterranea, Mortensen, 1913, p. 29, pl. 3, figs. 1, 17; pl. 4, figs. 5, 19.
Brissopsis atlantica, H. L. Clark, 1917, p. 203 (part).
Brissopsis atlantica, Grieg, 1921, p. 44.
Brissopsis atlantica, H. L. Clark, 1925, p. 213 (part).
Brissopsis atlantica, Mortensen, 1927a, p. 338 (part).
Brissopsis atlantica, Mortensen, 1927b, p. 32.
Brissopsis atlantica, Kolosvary, 1937, p. 461.
Brissopsis atlantica, Mortensen, 1951a, p. 301, pl. 1, fig. 4; pl. 2, figs. 1, 2.

Brissopsis atlantica var. *mediterranea,* Mortensen, 1951b, p. 415, pl. 31, fig. 11; pl. 59, fig. 7, text fig. 199a.
Brissopsis atlantica var. *mediterranea,* Cherbonnier, 1959, p. 51, pl. 8, figs. M-O.
Brissopsis atlantica mediterranea, Chesher, 1966, p. 220.

Material examined.—3 specimens, 75 to 78 mm test length, PILLSBURY sta. P-34, off the Ivory Coast, 3°53'N., 2°33'W., 1984 - 1948 m, May, 1964.—14 specimens, 31.5 to 85 m test length, plus fragments, sta. P-53, off the Ivory Coast, 4°50'N., 4°58'W., 1579 to 1519 m, May, 1964.— 1 specimen, 76 mm test length; sta. P-76, off Liberia, 4°32'N., 9°42'W., 1556 - 1464 m, June, 1964. 1 specimen, 29 mm test length, sta. P-259, off Fernando Póo, 3°53'N., 8°55'E., 59 m, May 1965.—1 specimen, 22 mm test length, sta. P-260, off Cameroon, 3°45'N., 9°05'E., 46 m, May 1965.—Fragment, sta. P-309, off Nigeria, 4°15'N., 4°27'E., 1280 - 1318 m, May 1965.—3 specimens, 16.5 to 24.4 mm test length, GERDA sta. G-366, south of Florida Keys, 24°12'N., 81°17'W., 679—709 m, Sept. 1964.—1 specimen, 28.5 mm test length, sta G-362, south of Key West, Florida, 24°10'N., 81°42'W., 631 m, Sept. 1964.—1 specimen, 60 mm test length (fragmentary), sta. G-152, northern Florida Straits, 26°20'N., 79°39'W., 641 m, June 1963.—1 specimen, 16.5 mm test length (abnormal), sta. G-110, off Dry Tortugas, Florida, 24°21'N., 82°55'W., 183 m, June 1963.—3 specimens, ALBATROSS sta. 2748, E. of New Jersey, 39°31'N., 71°14.5'W., 2134 m, Sept. 1887.

Diagnosis.—Subanal fasciole distinct, crossing four ambulacral plates on either side, the first being plate 6. The peripetalous fasciole traverses plates 4 and 5 (sometimes 6) in series a of interambulacrum 3 and plate 5 in series b. Anal branches from the subanal fasciole, strongly developed, not reaching more than one-half the distance to the peripetalous fasciole (missing in some specimens). Posterior petals confluent proximally, diverging from about one-half their length. The anterior and posterior petals of each side form an even crescent shape. In small specimens, the posterior petals are almost parallel. The posterior end of the test vertical. Globiferous pedicellariae with two teeth surrounding the terminal opening (rarely with many teeth). Labrum not reaching past the first adjoining ambulacral plates.

Description.—The test is thin and fragile, with a broad, angular appearance. Its mean width is 88.11 ± 0.60 per cent of the test length (S.D. 2.53, C.V. 2.87), and its mean height is 60.27 ± 0.65 per cent of the test length (S.D. 2.43, C.V. 4.04). The width tends to increase slightly with growth. The specimens from the West Indies have the same relative width as those from Africa. The proportional height decreases slightly with increase in test length. Geographic variation is slight.

The posterior end of the test is vertically truncate. The truncated portion is set at an angle of 88 to 96 degrees with the plastron. The posterior truncation may be slightly concave and the area enclosed by the bilobed subanal fasciole built up into two projecting subanal snouts.

The dorsal interambulacral plates outside the peripetalous fasciole develop a raised node from which the tubercles radiate in a fairly regular series. In larger specimens, nodes of successive plates in interambulacra 1 and 4 form an irregular elevation from the peripetalous fasciole to the ambitus in both plate-series giving larger specimens a more angular appearance. The ventral side is evenly rounded, and the lowest point of the test is at the center of the plastron.

The highest point of the test is just posterior to the posterior portion of the peripetalous fasciole. From this point to the anterior portion of the peripetalous fasciole, the midline of the test is almost flat and is set at an angle of about 10° with the plastronal plane (Plate 19). In *B. atlantica,* this portion of the test is more convex and it is more or less parallel with the plastronal plane.

The Anterior Ambulacrum

The anterior ambulacrum is slightly sunken from the apical system to the peristome, creating a shallow notch in the anterior ambitus. The peripetalous fasciole crosses ambulacrum III at a mean distance from the apical system of 40.05 ± 0.34 per cent of the test length (S.D. 1.43, C.V. 3.57). This proportion does not vary allometrically or geographically.

Within the peripetalous fasciole, the frontal ambulacrum is divided into two areas, one nearest the apical system containing developing tube-feet and the other containing functional tunneling tube-feet. The number of functional tube-feet varies with growth from 18 or 19 (test length 16.5 mm) to 42 (test length 75 mm). The regression equation for the increase in tunneling tube-feet versus the test length is (Fig. 18):

$$Y = 18.393 LnX - 41.72 \qquad Y = \text{Tunneling tube-feet.}$$
$$S_{Y.LnX} = \pm\ 3.4 \text{ tube-feet} \qquad X = \text{Test length (mm).}$$
$$r = 0.882$$

The specimens from the Western Atlantic were not used in deriving this equation but are plotted on the graph. There is considerable individual variation in the production of these tube-feet. Specimens from the same station show as much variability in this character as specimens from the two sides of the Atlantic.

New plates are split off from the ocular plate as the urchin grows. These plates bear undeveloped, globular tube-feet situated over slit-like pores. The tube-feet progressively mature into tunneling podia with a terminal disc having 9 to 18 fringing digits. The discs are about 1.5 to 2 mm in diameter; their size increases slightly with age. The circumference is not deeply lobed. The supporting spicules are broad and well developed. These tube-feet issue from circular depressions near the dorsolateral edge of the ambulacral plates. The central portion of the peripodium is elevated to form a low, rounded support for the basal end of the podia. The pore-slit is located on the ventro-mesad portion of this projection. The pores are in a single series and demi-plates do not normally occur.

Ambulacrum III is widest near the peripetalous fasciole. Measurements of its width were taken from the outer edge of the pore series. The width varies with the size of the specimen; it is 10 per cent of the test length in a specimen 22 mm long and 4 per cent of the test length in an 85-mm specimen.

There are six plates per plate series from the peripetalous fasciole to the peristome. This number is constant and does not change with growth or geographic location. The mature urchin has five feeding tube-feet in the anterior phyllode. The pores of the feeding and sensory tube-feet are single and situated at the ventral edge of each ambulacral plate.

TABLE 6

STATISTICAL SUMMARY: *B. mediterranea* (GULF OF GUINEA)

Character	Mean	S.E.	S.D.	Range	N	C.V.
tl*	60.89	4.39	18.61	22-85	19	
tw	88.11	0.60	2.53	84-92	19	2.87
h	60.27	0.65	2.43	57-66	16	4.04
ax	44.94	0.49	2.01	39-48	18	4.50
pa	22.28	0.31	1.28	22-26	19	5.75
lp	71.00	0.79	2.49	66-74	11	3.51
ap	23.21	0.28	1.20	21-26	19	5.17
apw†	31.79	0.91	3.85	25-40	19	12.10
pp	19.79	0.37	1.58	17-23	19	8.00
ppw†	31.42	0.48	2.03	26-35	19	6.46
pp/ap‡	84.95	1.71	7.27	74-104	19	8.56
ff	40.05	0.34	1.43	37-43	19	3.57
pf	24.79	0.44	1.88	22-28	19	7.60
lf	11.74	0.24	1.02	10-14	19	8.90
pf/af‡	61.79	1.30	5.53	52-74	19	8.95
ppfl	170.74	1.84	7.81	160-186	19	4.58
ape	33.68	0.60	2.45	30-39	19	7.54
safw	42.92	1.16	3.86	35-48	12	9.00
safl	103.00	2.92	8.25	92-120	9	8.00
l	7.11	0.27	1.08	5.8-10	17	15.2
pl	50.90	1.32	3.96	43-55	10	7.80
b	13.92	0.56	1.94	11-17	13	13.90
c	24.31	0.80	2.78	21-30	13	11.40
d	34.91	1.01	3.20	31-41	11	9.20
aw	10.38	0.34	1.21	8.7-13	14	11.65
aw/ah‡	64.36	2.59	9.32	54-90	14	14.50

Data are expressed as percentages of test length unless otherwise indicated.
Character symbols as given in Figure 1.
*Test length (mm).
‡Ratio given as a percentage.
†Percentage of petal length.

The tuberculation of III can be seen in Plate 19 *a, f.* There is a conspicuous, single series of tubercles medially of the pore-series.

Ambulacra II and IV
(the anterior paired petals)

The peripetalous fasciole crosses ambulacrum IV on plates 9, 10, 11, or 12 of series a. The frequency of crossing on these plates is: 9 (4.3 per cent), 10 (30.4 per cent), 11 (61 per cent). The tuberculation outside the peripetalous fasciole varies considerably with growth and individual variation. In younger specimens, the ambulacra may be bare or have only a few large tubercles on each plate. In larger specimens one or two rows of tubercles border each plate leaving the midline naked to the peristome. The phyllode is fairly distinct and only slightly sunken. There are 8 to 9 feeding tube-feet per phyllode, each situated over a large, single pore located on the adoral edge of the plate. Sensory tube-feet are found in ambulacrum IV from the phyllode to plates 7a and 6 to 8b.

The petals are slightly sunken within the peripetalous fasciole. The two series of pore-pairs close distally. The anterior series of pore-pairs have 38 to 55 (mean 47.5) per cent of the apicalmost pore-pairs underdeveloped, with rudimentary, knob-like tube-feet. In the posterior pore-series, only two or three of the apicalmost tube-feet are underdeveloped. The total number of tube-feet (pore-pairs, or plates) increases logarithmically throughout growth. Figure 18 shows the pore-pairs of ambulacrum IV, series b, plotted against the natural log of the test length. The regression equation shown on the graph is:

$$Y = 6.927 LnX - 7.874$$
$$S_{LnY.LnX} = \pm 1.038$$
$$r = 0.935$$

Y = Pore-pairs, (IVb).
X = Test length (mm).

The specimens from the Western Atlantic were not used in calculating this equation, but they are plotted on Fig. 18. Only two small specimens vary significantly from the African specimens. There are only two or three tubercles on the ridge separating adjacent pore-pairs.

The anterior petals have a mean length of 23.21 ± 0.28 per cent of the test length (S.D. 1.20, C.V. 5.17). The mean width of the anterior petals is 31.79 ± 0.91 per cent of the petal length (S.D. 3.85, C.V. 12.10). The distance between the ends of the anterior petals is 33.68 ± 0.60 per cent of the test length (S.D. 2.54, C.V. 7.54). This proportion is significantly lower than the corresponding proportion in any of the other *Brissopsis* species investigated. This is an indication that the anterior petals are more confluent in *B. mediterranea;* the petals are not significantly shorter than in the other species.

In contrast to the other species of *Brissopsis* the anterior petals have a distinct posterior bend. The interporiferous zone and the posterior pore-series both curve posteriorly, forming a crescent shape with the anterior

81

pore-series and interporiferous zone of the posterior paired petals (Plate 19a). In *B. atlantica,* the crescent shape is obliterated by the relatively straight anterior petals.

Ambulacra I and V
(the posterior paired petals)

The peripetalous fasciole crosses ambulacrum V on plates 16, 17 or 18 of series a. The plates outside the peripetalous fasciole are heavily tuberculated to the ambitus, with only a narrow bare area on the lateral

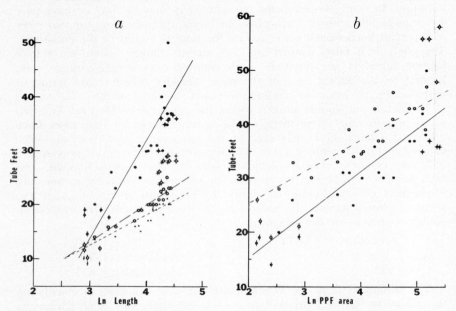

FIGURE 18. Tube-feet versus test length and versus peripetalous fasciole in *Brissopsis mediterranea* and *B. lyrifera capensis.* A, Increase in tube-feet with increasing test length (natural logarithm, mm): solid dots = *Brissopsis mediterranea,* Gulf of Guinea, tunneling tube-feet; solid dots with vertical bar = *B. mediterranea,* West Indies, tunneling tube-feet; solid dots with horizontal and vertical bars = *B. lyrifera capensis,* tunneling tube-feet; circles = *B. mediterranea,* Gulf of Guinea, pore-pairs IV, series b; circles with vertical bar = the same, West Indies; circles with vertical and horizontal bars = same, *B. lyrifera capensis;* triangles = pore-pairs posterior petal (V, series a), *B. mediterranea,* Gulf of Guinea; triangles with vertical bar = the same, West Indies; triangles with crossed bars = the same, *B. lyrifera capensis.*—B, Tube-feet versus natural logarithm of peripetalous fasciole (PPF, mm²): circles = pore-pairs IVb + Va, *B. mediterranea,* Gulf of Guinea; circles with vertical bars = the same, West Indies; circles with crossed bars = the same, *B. lyrifera capensis;* solid dots = tunneling tube-feet, *B. mediterranea;* solid dots with vertical bar = the same, West Indies; solid dots with crossed bars = the same, *B. lyrifera capensis.*

margin of the anterior plate series. The plates of these ambulacra are distinctly wider than adjacent plates of interambulacrum 5. Orally of the subanal fasciole the ambulacra are naked except for pedicellariae, sphaeridia, and small tertiary spines. Nearest the peristome, there are penicillate feeding tube-feet. In the adult, there are 7 feeding tube-feet per phyllode. Within the subanal fasciole, there are two to three subanal tube-feet per ambulacrum situated over double pore-pairs.

The petals are slightly sunken within the peripetalous fasciole. The pore-pairs close distally. The posterior series of pore-pairs have 46 to 65 per cent of their apicalmost pore-pairs reduced (mean 56.3). The number of plates in the petaloid portion of ambulacrum V increases throughout growth. Figure 18 shows the numbers of pore-pairs of ambulacrum Va plotted against the natural log of the test length. The regression equation is:

$$Y = 5.359 LnX - 3.55 \qquad Y = \text{Pore-pairs Va.}$$
$$S_{Y.LnX} = \pm 1.60 \qquad\qquad X = \text{Test length (mm).}$$
$$r = 0.791$$

The Western Atlantic specimens were not used in calculating this equation but are plotted on the graph for comparison. Their values fall below the values of the African specimens.

The mean length of the posterior petals is 19.79 ± 0.37 per cent of the test length (S.D. 1.58, C.V. 8.00) and 84.95 ± 1.71 per cent of the anterior petal length (S.D. 7.27, C.V. 8.56). The mean width is 31.42 ± 0.48 per cent of the posterior petal length (S.D. 2.03, C.V. 6.46). The posterior petal length varies allometrically, the proportional length increases with growth. The specimens from the Western Atlantic show no significant difference from the African specimens in the above proportions.

In small specimens (test length less than 25 mm) the posterior petals are confluent along their entire length (or at most diverge slightly), thus giving the young of this species a very characteristic appearance (Plate 20a). In large specimens, the petals diverge from about one-half their length and their general curvature matches that of the anterior petals.

The Interambulacra

The number of interambulacral plates from the peristome to the fascioles is a constant and important character which is discussed in the following section on fascioles.

The tuberculation is uniform in the interambulacra. The size of the tubercles increases on the oral side and within the peripetalous fasciole. There is a naked area along the midline of interambulacrum 5 from the apical system to the periproct. Interambulacral plates 1 are generally naked except for one or two large tubercles and a cluster of spines adjacent to the peristome. The clusters in interambulacra 1, 2, 3, and 4 are elevated in larger specimens and bear numerous tubercles resembling the bourrelets

83

of some cassiduloids (Plate 19*d*).

The plastron is shield-shaped, almost triangular, and convex. The mean length is 50.90 ± 1.32 per cent of the test length (S.D. 3.96, C. V. 1.32). This proportion increases with growth, and is 44 per cent in a specimen 22 mm in test length and 55 per cent in a 78-mm specimen. The width of the plastron (expressed as the per cent of the test length), measured at points B, C, and D is:

point	mean	S.E.M.	S.D.	C.V.
B	13.92	0.56	1.94	13.9
C	24.31	0.80	2.78	11.4
D	34.91	1.01	3.20	9.2

The extremely fragile test was broken on the oral side in most specimens. It was possible to measure the characters of the plastron in only 10 specimens.

The spines of the plastron radiate anteriorly from the midpoint of the posterior border of the plastron.

The labrum is short, not reaching back past the first adjoining ambulacral plates. No large tubercles are present on the labrum. Along the anterior edge is a line of tertiary tubercles which bear small, curved spines.

The Apical System

The apical system is ethmolytic, situated anteriorly on the dorsal surface at a mean distance from the anterior end of 44.94 ± 0.49 per cent of the test length (S.D. 2.01, C.V. 4.50). This proportion increases slightly with growth. As is evident from Plate 19, the apical system appears to be posterior of the center of the test. This illusion is also seen in the specimens themselves. When measured as described in the section on methods in the introduction, the apical system is found to be located on the anterior portion of the test.

There are four genital pores; the anterior two are only about half the size of the posterior pair. In smaller specimens, the posterior pair may be well developed before the anterior pair become distinct. Genital pores were present in all the specimens examined, even in the West Atlantic specimens 16.5 mm in test length. The madreporite passes between the posterior genital plates and oculars and widens distally to a varying degree.

The Periproct and Peristome

The periproct is situated high on the posterior end of the test, enclosed by interambulacral plates 5, 6, 7, 8. It is vertically elongate. The mean width of the periproct is 64.36 ± 2.59 per cent of its own height (S.D. 9.32, C.V. 14.5) and 10.38 ± 0.34 per cent of the test length (S.D. 1.21, C.V. 11.65). The proportional width is almost the same as in *B. atlantica* (allometric variation produces the discrepancy in the means) but *B. mediterranea* has a significantly higher periproct, particularly in the smaller specimens.

The pentagonal peristome is situated anteriorly; its leading edge has a mean distance from the anterior end of the test of 22.28 ± 0.31 per cent of the test length (S.D. 1.28, C.V. 5.75). The anterior edge of the labrum is 71.00 ± 0.79 per cent of the test length from the posterior end of the test (S.D. 2.49, C.V. 3.51). The labrum is very well developed and angular.

The Peripetalous Fasciole

The peripetalous fasciole is of nearly uniform width and follows an angular path over the test. The fasciole does not widen at the ends of the petals or the midline of the interambulacra. There is always a re-entrant angle in interambulacra 2 and 3 so that the fasciole crosses plates 4 and 5 of their anterior plate-series. The fasciole crosses the posterior plate-series high on plate 5. It does not cross plate 4 of this series as commonly found in *B. atlantica*. The path of the peripetalous fasciole across the various plates of the test is summarized in Table 12, and discussed in the sections on the ambulacra.

The proportional length of the peripetalous fasciole is 170.74 ± 1.84 per cent of the test length (S.D. 7.81, C.V. 4.78). The total area of the fasciole increases logarithmically with increasing size. Figure 19 shows the natural log of the area of the peripetalous fasciole plotted against the natural log of the test length. The regression equation is:

$$\text{Ln}Y = 1.86 \, \text{Ln}X - 3.35 \qquad Y = \text{Area (mm}^2\text{) of}$$
$$S_{\text{Ln}Y.\text{Ln}X} = \pm \, 0.311 \qquad\qquad\qquad \text{peripetalous fasciole.}$$
$$r = 0.918 \qquad\qquad\qquad X = \text{Test length (mm)}.$$

The specimens from the Western Atlantic were not used in calculating this equation but are plotted on the graph. Their values do not vary significantly from the values of the African specimens.

As the urchin increases in size, its volume and the area of the peripetalous fasciole increase at an exponential rate. Thus, the peripetalous fasciole maintains a constant relationship with the volume of the animal. The relationship between the tube-feet and peripetalous fasciole differs in being a semi-logarithmic function, the number of tube-feet decreases per unit of fasciole or unit of volume. When plotted against the natural logarithm of the peripetalous fasciole area, the regression equation of the tunneling tube-feet is (Fig. 18):

$$Y = 7.90 \, \text{Ln}X - 0.386 \qquad Y = \text{Tunneling tube-feet.}$$
$$S_{Y.\text{Ln}X} = \pm \, 3.7 \text{ tube-feet} \qquad X = \text{Area (mm}^2\text{) peripetalous}$$
$$r = 0.858. \qquad\qquad\qquad\qquad \text{fasciole.}$$

The Western Atlantic specimens were not used in calculating this equation, but it is evident from their values plotted on Fig. 18 that they do not differ significantly from the African specimens.

The regression equation of the numbers of respiratory tube-feet plotted against the peripetalous fasciole area is:

85

$$Y = 5.814 \ LnX + 13.9572$$
$$S_{Y.LnX} = \pm \ 2.72 \ \text{pore-pairs}$$
$$r = 0.860$$

$Y = $ Pore-pairs, (IVb, Va).
$X = $ Area (mm²). PPF.

and the equation of the tunneling tube-feet per unit area of fasciole plotted against the test length is shown in Figure 8.

$$LnY = 4.706 - 1.341LnX$$
$$S_{LnY.LnX} = \pm \ 0.283$$
$$r = 0.880$$

$Y = $ Tunneling tube-feet per unit area of P.P.F.
$X = $ Test length (mm).

The values for the specimens from the Western Atlantic are shown on the graphs. Only the number of respiratory tube-feet unit of fasciole differs significantly from the African specimens.

The peripetalous fasciole is indented between the paired petals (interambulacra 1 and 4) to a mean distance from the apical system of 11.74 $\pm$ 0.24 per cent of the test length (S.D. 1.02, C.V. 8.90). The distance from the apical system to the posterior portion of the peripetalous fasciole is 24.79 $\pm$ 0.44 per cent of the test length (S.D. 1.88, C.V. 7.60) and 61. 79 $\pm$ 1.30 per cent of the distance from the apical system to the anterior portion of the peripetalous fasciole (S.D. 5.53, C.V. 8.95).

The Subanal Fasciole

The subanal fasciole varies greatly in shape with an increase in size. In small specimens, 22 mm test length, the height of the fasciolar enclosure may be 74 per cent of its own width and in larger specimens, the height may be 24 or 25 per cent of its own width, becoming more distinctly bilobate. The width of the area enclosed by the subanal fasciole is 42.92 $\pm$ 1.16 per cent of the test length (S.D. 3.86, C.V. 9.00). This proportion increases allometrically. In small specimens (test length 22 mm) it may be 35 per cent of the test length. In larger specimens, the width of the area enclosed by the subanal fasciole is 45 to 48 per cent of the test length.

The proportional length of the subanal fasciole is 103.00 $\pm$ 2.92 per cent of the test length (S.D. 8.25, C.V. 8.00). This proportion does not increase significantly with growth. The Western Atlantic specimens average only 86.4 per cent and are thus somewhat smaller in this proportion. The area of subanal fasciole increases logarithmically with increasing size as does the peripetalous fasciole. The area of the subanal fasciole is almost the same as that of the peripetalous fasciole (Fig. 19). The regression equation for the increase in subanal fasciolar area with test length is:

$$Ln \ Y = 1.728 \ LnX - 2.87$$
$$S_{LnY.LnX} = \pm \ 0.291$$
$$r = 0.916$$

$Y = $ Area of SAF (mm²)
$X = $ Test length (mm)

The specimens from the Western Atlantic were not used in calculating this line but their values are plotted on Fig. 19, and it is evident that, although the proportional length of the fasciole is shorter in the specimens from the Western Atlantic, the area is not significantly different from the African specimens.

The plates crossed by the subanal fasciole are summarized in Table 12. Plates 6, 7, 8, and 9 of the posterior plate-series of ambulacra I and

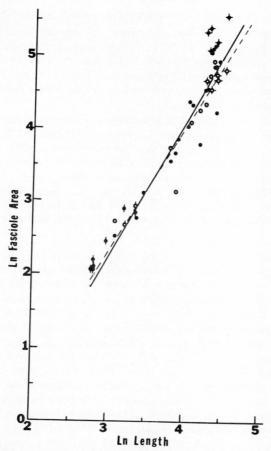

FIGURE 19. The fasciolar area versus the test length in *B. mediterranea* and *B. lyrifera capensis*. Increase in logarithm of fasciolar area (mm^2) with increasing test length (natural logarithm mm): solid dots = subanal fasciole area, *B. mediterranea*, Gulf of Guinea; solid dots with vertical bars = the same, West Indies; solid dots with crossed bars = the same, *B. lyrifera capensis*; circles = peripetalous fasciole area, *B. mediterranea*, Gulf of Guinea; circles with vertical bars = the same, West Indies; circles with crossed bars = the same, *B. lyrifera capensis*.

87

V are normally included within the fasciole. In the smaller specimens, plate 9 is almost excluded from the fasciole.

Branches from the subanal fasciole are well developed and extend along interambulacrum 5 about half way to the peripetalous fasciole. In the specimens from the Gulf of Guinea, these branches disappear with age.

The Spines and Pedicellariae

The spines do not differ significantly from other species of *Brissopsis*.

The pedicellariae have been described by Mortensen (1913, 1907, 1951b) and Cherbonnier (1959). Globiferous pedicellariae were not found in the specimens from the Gulf of Guinea. As mentioned in Chesher (1966), the valve figured by Cherbonnier (1959, pl. 8, fig. N) is not the globiferous pedicellaria of *Brissopsis* and probably comes from a specimen of *Eucidaris tribuloides africana*.

Plate 20 shows the valve of a globiferous pedicellaria and a tridentate pedicellaria from a specimen from the Western Atlantic. Mortensen (1913, 1951b) mentions that there are two forms of globiferous pedicellariae, both of which resemble corresponding forms in *B. atlantica*. The short form is apparently rare and the differences in these valves pointed out by Mortensen (1913) between this species and *B. atlantica* need to be investigated further. The short form does not appear to be identical with the globiferous pedicellariae of *B. alta;* the neck of the blade is shorter than in that species.

Lectotype.—The lectotype must be selected from the specimens from the Gulf of Naples described by Mortensen (1913). The specimen figured in pl. 3, fig. 8 should be selected as lectotype (the legend to the figures is in error as explained by Mortensen p. 29). The specimens are 20 to 27 mm long. The disposition of the specimens is unknown. At the time of description, Mortensen did not mention the similarity of these specimens and those from the Gulf of Guinea, off Nantucket and Cape Hatteras and from the TALISMAN (Mortensen 1951b). Had he mentioned in his description that the specimens from the Gulf of Naples were identical with the American "broad form" or the specimen (unnamed) from the TALISMAN described in his 1907 work, it would have been possible to designate one of these specimens as lectotype. This would have been preferable as the latter specimens are clearly illustrated (1907, pl. 3, figs. 1, 17; pl. 4, fig. 5; pl. 19, figs. 8, 13, 14, 16, 22, 23, 30, 31) and I have examined the specimens from ALBATROSS sta. 2748, including the specimen of pl. 3, fig. 17. From his remarks in the discussion on p. 416-419 (1951b) it is clear that Mortensen considered the specimens from the Gulf of Naples to be identical with the forms from the Gulf of Guinea and the Western Atlantic. Thus, the name *mediterranea* must be adopted for this species.

Type locality.—Gulf of Naples, 200 to 300 m.

Distribution.—*Brissopsis mediterranea* is distributed from the Mediterranean Sea along the African coast to the Gulf of Guinea including the Canary Islands. In the Western Atlantic, it is known from the Straits of Florida to Nantucket. Its bathymetric range is from 46 to 3200 meters.

Discussion.—Abnormalities: One specimen (sta. G-110) was found which is clearly abnormal. At first, the specimen was considered a hybrid of *B. alta* and *B. atlantica* both of which were also taken in the same trawl haul. *B. mediterranea* is known from deeper water nearby (G-362). The left, posterior genital pore is well developed but the others are not present. The specimen is abnormally high (70 per cent of the test length). Branches from the subanal fasciole are very well developed and reach almost to the peripetalous fasciole. Only four plates per ambulacrum enter the subanal fasciole. If the specimen is a hybrid, the general morphology indicates that it is a hybrid of *B. mediterranea* and *B. atlantica*. For example, the number of tunneling tube-feet for a 16.5-mm specimen is 14 in *B. alta,* 12 in *B. atlantica* and 19 in *B. mediterranea*. The number in the abnormal specimen is 18. If the specimen is a hybrid between *B. mediterranea* and *B. alta* the branches from the subanal fasciole should be poorly developed. The specimen, however, has branches which are characteristic of *B. mediterranea* in being broad and well developed and characteristic of *B. atlantica* in reaching closer to the fasciole than is normal for *B. mediterranea*. When specimens, about 16.5 mm test length, of all three species are simultaneously compared with the abnormal specimen, its greatest resemblance is to *B. mediterranea*. The specimen is, in my opinion, a hybrid between *B. atlantica* and *B. mediterranea*. The existence of such a hybrid does not detract from the hypothesis that *B. atlantica* and *B. mediterranea* are good species. Occasional hybrids are formed between *B. atlantica* and *B. elongata*. These hybrids (described in the discussion of *B. atlantica)* are not greatly deformed as is the *B. atlantica × mediterranea* specimen. The latter hybrid is a clear indication of the genetic independence of the two species in that the hybrids are clearly unable to compete with normal specimens of either species.

As with the specimen of *B. atlantica × elongata,* the *B. atlantica × mediterranea* specimen is higher than either of the parent species and the number of tunneling tube-feet is closer to the species with the higher number, viz. *B. mediterranea*. The span of the antreior petal ends is closer to that of *B. atlantica*. When plotted on Fig. 3, the specimen is seen to be closer to *B. mediterranea* in the key characters. Mortensen (1907, p. 162) states that *B. mediterranea* and *B. atlantica* may be found at the same station.

Fossil history: Mortensen (1951b, p. 420) indicates that *B. crescenticus* Wright, 1855, from the Miocene of Malta (fig. 181, a; p. 374) is probably the direct ancestor of *B. mediterranea*. Since Mortensen did not synonymize his var. *mediterranea* with the fossil species, and since I have not seen specimens of the fossil species, the specific name *B. mediterranea* is adopted here.

Comments: See the discussion under *B. atlantica*. Although the geographic ranges of the species B. *atlantica* and *B. mediterranea* overlap in the Western Atlantic, the bathymetric ranges seem to be distinct. Only two stations are reported with both species present. Although *B. mediterranea* is found in relatively shallow water in the eastern Atlantic and Mediterranean, it seems to be restricted to depths greater than 600 meters in the tropical Western Atlantic. The bathymetric and geographic overlap of the two species is uncertain, however, and requires further investigation.

The differences between this species and the other Atlantic species of *Brissopsis* are discussed under *B. atlantica* and *B. alta,* and are summarized in Table 2, Figures 2 and 3, and in the key to the species and subspecies of *Brissopsis.*

Brissopsis lyrifera capensis Mortensen, 1907

Figures 8, 18, 19; Plate 21; Tables 2, 7, 12

Brissopsis lyrifera, A. Agassiz, 1881, p. 189 (part).
Brissopsis lyrifera, Bell, 1904, p. 175.
Brissopsis lyrifera, Döderlein, 1906, p. 256, pl. 34, figs. 4-5; pl. 49, figs. 1-2.
Brissopsis lyrifera capensis, Mortensen, 1907, p. 157, pl. 18, figs. 3, 13; pl. 19, fig. 9.
Brissopsis lyrifera, Clark, 1917, p. 201.
Brissopsis lyrifera, Clark, 1923, p. 401.
Brissopsis lyrifera, Clark, 1924, p. 12.
Brissopsis lyrifera, Clark, 1925, p. 213.
Brissopsis lyrifera capensis, Mortensen, 1951b, p. 387.
Brissopsis caparti Cherbonnier, 1959, p. 51, pl. 9, figs. A-O.
Brissopsis lyrifera capensis, Chesher, 1966, p. 220.

Material examined.—6 specimens, 61 to 91 mm test length, Pillsbury sta. P.-256, off Cameroon, 3°45′N., 8°03′W., 409-485 m, May 1965.

Diagnosis.—Test high (over 60 per cent of the test length), posterior petals long (over 27 per cent of the test length); subanal fasciole present, variously developed, anal branches absent, peripetalous fasciole crossing plates 4a and 4b in interambulacrum 3; globiferous pedicellariae with two long end teeth at the terminal opening.

Description.—The test is thin and fragile, rounded and subglobular in appearance. Its mean width is 90 per cent of the test length (range, 87 to 95 per cent) and its mean height is 66 per cent of the test length (range 62 to 71 per cent). The highest point is between the posterior petal ends, from which point the test curves downward toward the anterior ambitus. The posterior end of the test is vertically truncate.

The dorsal interambulacral plates outside the peripetalous fasciole develop a raised node from which the tubercles radiate in a fairly regular series. The nodes of successive plates in interambulacra 1 and 4 form an

90

irregular elevation from the peripetalous fasciole to the ambitus in both plate series. The ventral side is evenly rounded; the lowest point of the test is at the posterior portion of the plastron (Plate 21).

The Anterior Ambulacrum

The anterior ambulacrum is slightly sunken from the apex to the peristome, forming a shallow notch in the anterior ambitus. The peripetalous fasciole crosses ambulacrum III on plate 5b at a mean distance from the apical system of 42 per cent of the test length (range: 42 to 44).

Within the peripetalous fasciole, the almost flat frontal ambulacrum is divided into two areas, one nearest the apical system containing developing tube-feet and the other containing functional, tunneling tube-feet. The tunneling tube-feet are plotted against the test length on Fig. 18. The

TABLE 7

Statistical Summary: *B. lyrifera capensis*

Character	Mean	Range	N
tl*	78	69-91	6
tw	90	87-95	6
h	66	62-71	6
ax	40	36-44	6
pa	22	20-24	6
lp	72	69-74	6
ap	34	31-36	6
apw†	29	22-33	6
pp	31	29-34	6
ppw†	30	25-34	6
pp/ap‡	91	84-96	6
wIII	6.3	5.7-7.0	6
ff	42	42-44	6
pf	32	30-36	6
lf	16	15-17	6
pf/af‡	75	70-80	6
ppfl	225	212-236	5
ape	51	46-54	6
safh/w‡	38	33-44	6
safw	47	46-49	6
safl	115	112-118	5
l	6.9	6.4-7.5	6
pl	50	47-54	6
b	14	9-18	6
c	25	19-30	6
d	34	30-39	6
aw	10	9-11	6
aw/ah‡	63	51-72	6

Data are expressed as percentages of test length unless otherwise indicated. Character symbols as given in Figure 1.
* Test length (mm).
†Percentage of petal length.
‡Ratio expressed as a percentage.

stalk of the tunneling tube-feet is lined with a thick layer of C-shaped spicules. The discs have *ca.* 9 to 18 fringing digits. The peripodia are small, circular, the muscle support not strongly developed. The single pores are oval and located at the ventro-mesal edge of the muscle support.

Ambulacrum III is widest near the peripetalous fasciole. Measurements of its width were taken from the outer edge of the pore series. The width averaged 6.3 per cent of the test length (5.7 to 7.0 per cent).

There are five feeding tube-feet in the anterior phyllode. The pores of these and the sensory tube-feet are single and placed at the adoral edge of each ambulacral plate.

The tuberculation of III is very similar to that found in *B. alta,* with a conspicuous series of tubercles medially of the pore series.

Ambulacra II and IV
(the anterior paired petals)

The peripetalous fasciole crosses ambulacrum IV on plate 9a. The tuberculation outside the peripetalous fasciole is continuous with the adjoining interambulacra leaving only a narrow median area naked. From the ambitus to the peristome the ambulacra are naked. The phyllode is flush with the test and contains 6 or 7 feeding tube-feet. The peripodia are small, with elongate, single pores and a poorly developed muscle support.

The petals are slightly sunken within the peripetalous fasciole. The two series of pore-pairs close distally. The pore-pairs of the anterior series decrease in size toward the apical system. About 30 per cent of the apicalmost pore-pairs are under-developed; the exact number is difficult to determine as the decrease in pore-pair size is not clearly delimited. In the posterior pore-series, only 3 or 4 of the apicalmost pore-pairs are underdeveloped. The total number of pore-pairs in IV, series b, is plotted against the test length in Fig. 18. There are numerous, very small tubercles on the ridge separating adjacent pore-pairs.

The anterior petals have a mean length of 34 per cent of the test length (range: 31 to 36 per cent) and a mean width of 24 per cent of the petal length (range: 22 to 33 per cent). The distance between the ends of the anterior petals averages 51 per cent of the test length (range: 46 to 54 per cent). The posterior pore-series and the interporiferous zone are straight. The anterior pore-series curves posteriorly, creating the illusion that the petals have a posterior bend.

Ambulacra I and V
(the posterior paired petals)

The peripetalous fasciole crosses ambulacrum V on plate 15a (16a in one specimen). The plates outside the peripetalous fasciole are completely covered with tubercles to plate 8 or 9 in the anterior series and plate 5

92

in the posterior series. In some larger specimens (cf. Mortensen 1951, pl. 30, fig. 13) there is a naked area along the anterior border of these ambulacra but it is never as pronounced as in *B. alta, B. atlantica* or *B. mediterranea*. The ambulacral plates between the ambitus and the peripetalous fasciole are about the same width as the adjoining interambulacral plates. In the adult, there are 6 or 7 feeding tube-feet per phyllode and 2 to 3 subanal tube-feet within the subanal fasciole.

The petals are slightly sunken within the peripetalous fasciole. The pore-pairs close distally. The posterior series of pore-pairs have 24 to 33 (mean 29) per cent of their apicalmost pore-pairs reduced. The number of pore pairs in the petaloid portion of Va are plotted against the natural log of the test length in Fig. 18. The mean length of the posterior petals is 31 per cent of the test length (range: 29 to 34 per cent) and 91 per cent of the anterior petal length (range: 84 to 96). The mean width of the posterior petals is 30 per cent of the petal length (range: 25 to 34 per cent).

The posterior petals are straight and diverge from the apical system even in small specimens (cf. Döderlein 1906, pl. 34, fig. 4). Mortensen (1951b, pl. 30, fig. 2) illustrates a specimen in which all the petals show a distinct curve similar to the condition in *B. mediterranea*. Mortensen (*op. cit.* p. 387) indicates that this condition is "a rare individual variation".

The Interambulacra

The number of interambulacral plates from the peristome to the fascioles is a constant and important character which is discussed in the following section on fascioles.

The tuberculation is uniform in the interambulacra. The size of the tubercles increases only slightly near the apex and along ambulacrum III. There is a naked area along the midline of interambulacrum 5 and a less distinct naked area along the midline of interambulacra 1 and 4 from the peripetalous fasciole to the ambitus. Interambulacral plates 1 of interambulacra 1, 4, and 5 are sparsely tuberculated or naked. The first plate of interambulacra 2 and 3 is tuberculated. The labrum does not extend back past the first adjoining ambulacral plates. The tubercles which line the anterior edge of the labrum are poorly developed. The mean length of the labrum is 6.9 per cent of the test length (range: 6.4 to 7.5).

The plastron is shield-shaped and slightly convex. Its mean length is 50 per cent of the test length (range: 47 to 54 per cent), and its width expressed as per cent of the test length measured at points B, C, and D, is:

point	mean	range
B	14	9 to 18
C	25	19 to 30
D	34	30 to 39

The spines of the plastron radiate in regular series from the raised node near the posterior, medial border of the plastron.

The Apical System

The apical system is ethmolytic, situated anteriorly on the dorsal surface at a mean distance from the anterior end of 40 per cent of the test length (range: 36 to 44 per cent). There are four genital pores, of which the anterior pair is slightly smaller than the posterior pair. The madreporite passes between the posterior genital and ocular plates and extends posteriorly to a point from the posterior genitals about equal to the distance from the outer edges of the anterior and posterior genital pores.

The Periproct and Peristome

The periproct is situated high on the posterior end of the test, enclosed by interambulacral plates 5, 6, and 7. It is vertically elongate. The mean width of the periproct is 10 per cent of the test length (range: 9 to 11 per cent) and 63 per cent of its own height (range: 51 to 72 per cent).

The peristome is situated anteriorly; its leading edge has a mean distance from the anterior end of the test of 22 per cent of the test length (range: 20 to 24 per cent). The anterior edge of the labrum is 72 per cent (range: 69 to 74 per cent) from the posterior end of the test. The labrum is well developed and crescent-shaped. The peristome is crescent-shaped to pentagonal.

The Peripetalous Fasciole

The peripetalous fasciole is of nearly uniform width and follows a sinuous path over the test. The fasciole widens very slightly at the ends of the petals and in the midlines of the lateral and posterior interambulacra. There is occasionally a re-entrant angle in interambulacra 2 and 3 so that the fasciole crosses plates 4 or 4 and 5 of the posterior series. The fasciole crosses only plate 4 of the anterior plate series. The path of the peripetalous fasciole over the various plates of the test is summarized in Table 12, and discussed in the sections on the ambulacra.

The proportional length of the peripetalous fasciole is 225 per cent of the test length (range: 212 to 236 per cent). The total area of the peripetalous fasciole is given in Fig. 19. The relation of the total area of the tunneling and respiratory tube-feet to the peripetalous fasciole area is given in Fig. 18, and the number of tunneling tube-feet per unit area of peripetalous fasciole is shown in Fig. 8. These graphs are discussed for *B. alta* and *B. atlantica*.

The peripetalous fasciole is indented between the paired petals (interambulacia 1 and 4) to a mean distance from the apical system of 16 per cent of the test length (range: 15 to 17 per cent). The distance from the apical system to the posterior portion of the peripetalous fasciole is 32 per cent of the test length (range: 30 to 36 per cent) and 75 per cent of the distance from the apical system to the anterior portion of the peripetalous fasciole (range: 70 to 80 per cent).

The Subanal Fasciole

The subanal fasciole varies greatly in its degree of development. In some specimens it is quite narrow (*ca.* 1 mm) but in others, it is wider (*ca.* 1.4 mm). In two of Cherbonnier's (1959, p. 53) specimens the adoral portion of the subanal fasciole is rudimentary or lacking. The fasciole is distinctly bilobed, the area enclosed is 47 per cent of the test length wide (range: 46 to 49 per cent) and the height of the fasciolar enclosure is 38 per cent of its own width (range: 33 to 44 per cent). The proportional length of the subanal fasciole is 115 per cent of the test length (range: 112 to 118). The area of the subanal fasciole is plotted against the test length in Fig. 19.

The plates crossed by the subanal fasciole are summarized in Table 12. Plates 6, 7, 8 and 9 of the posterior plate series of ambulacra I and V are included within the fasciole.

There are no anal branches from the subanal fasciole.

The Spines and Pedicellariae

The spines do not differ from those of the other species of *Brissopsis*.

The photographs and description of the pedicellariae given by Döderlein (1906, pl. 49, fig. 1) agree quite well with the few pedicellariae that were present on these specimens. Cherbonnier (*op. cit.* p. 53), in reference to var. *capensis* and the typical *B. lyrifera* and *B. evanescens,* states "Mais les pédicellaires tridactyles, trifoliés et rostrés diffèrent sensiblement de ceux que l'on trouve sur les espèces et variétés citées ci-dessus." His illustrations (pl. 9, figs. A-O) do not support this statement (compare with Döderlein, pl. 49, fig. 1) and the pedicellariae of the specimens at my disposal do not differ significantly from those of *B. lyrifera capensis*.

Syntypes.—Mortensen (1907) based his new "variety" on specimens from the CHALLENGER sta. 142 deposited in the British Museum of Natural History. Accordingly, one of these must be designated as lectotype.

Type locality.—Agulhas Bank, S. Africa; 35°41'S., 18°37'E., 275 m. Sand bottom.

Distribution.—*Brissopsis lyrifera capensis* is known from Agulhas Bank, South Africa, in *ca.* 275 m, to the Gulf of Guinea (east of Fernando Póo) in 409 to 485 m.

Discussion.—Abnormalities: As mentioned above, some large specimens may have curved petals and two are known with the ventral portion of the subanal fasciole incomplete.

Comments: Cherbonnier (1959) based his new species, *B. caparti,* on 18 specimens which were collected just south of the equator (0°15'S., 8°47'E) in 290 to 390 meters, not very far from where the Pillsbury specimens were collected. It is clear, from his description, that the Pillsbury specimens are from the same population as his specimens. His specimens measure 78 to 101 mm test length. Their mean width is 90 per cent of the test length, the mean height is 60.5 per cent of the test length, and the anterior petals and posterior petals are the same proportional length as the Pillsbury specimens. The length of the area enclosed by the peripetalous fasciole is about the same in both groups. Further, his description and drawings argue for the similarity of the Pillsbury specimens with his specimens. He distinguishes his specimens from the subspecies *B. lyrifera capensis* only on the basis of the development of the subanal fasciole, which showed considerable variability even in his material. Two of his specimens lack the ventral portion of the subanal fasciole. This is not an unusual abnormality in the genus *Brissopsis.* As mentioned above under *B. atlantica,* one specimen was found which lacked the entire subanal fasciole. Only a slight difference in the density of the tuberculation in the subanal area is present to show the path that the fasciole normally follows. Cherbonnier also mentions a difference in the pedicellariae which I am unable to substantiate in my specimens. Thus, there does not seem to be any significant difference between the subspecies *B. lyrifera capensis* and *B. caparti.* However, differences in the petal length seem to warrant subspecific separation of *B. lyrifera capensis* from *B. lyrifera* s.s. The difference in test height might be consistent for the population means, but there probably is considerable overlap in this character (Kongiel, 1962). There seem to be no differences in the number of tube-feet. In the specimens I have examined, I have found that the following characters differ between *B. lyrifera* s.s. and this subspecies: The length and width of the paired petals, the distance from the apical system to the posterior portion of the peripetalous fasciole, the proportional length of the peripetalous fasciole, the proportional width of the subanal fasciole enclosure, the proportional length of the subanal fasciole, and the proportional length of the labrum. Since none of these measurements for *B. lyrifera* s.s. is available in the literature, and since I have closely examined only three specimens from one locality, it is not possible to state which of the above differences are valid. Mortensen (1951b, p. 387) also mentions a difference in the location of the pedicellariae which may be important.

Brissopsis lyrifera s.s. is known from the European seas to the African west coast as far south as 8°N (Madsen, 1957). The two forms have never been found together, as far as is known. On the basis of the known distribution and differentiation, the South African form seems best to be described as a subspecies of *B. lyrifera.*

Genus *Plethotaenia* H. L. Clark

Plethotaenia H. L. Clark, 1917, p. 222.
Plethotaenia, Lambert and Thiery, 1924, p. 455.
Plethotaenia, H. L. Clark, 1925, p. 222.
Plethotaenia, Mortensen, 1951b, p. 484.
Meoma (Plethotaenia), Fischer, 1966, p. U592.

Diagnosis.—Peripetalous fasciole normally doubled or forming an irregular network. Frontal notch deep, but III a shallow groove or flush with the test apically of the peripetalous fasciole; pores of III single, no tunneling tube-feet. Subanal fasciole shield-shaped or oval, no anal branches. Paired petals closed distally. Apical system ethmolytic, genital pores 4.

Description.—Test nearly as wide as long (95 per cent) with a height of about 50 per cent of the test length, ambitus rounded to angular, adults reaching about 130 mm test length. Ambulacrum III broad and shallow from the apical system to the peripetalous fasciole, becoming a deep frontal notch, 7.2 to 16 per cent of the test length (subject to specific and allometric variation). Peristome anterior (*ca.* 25 per cent of the test length from the anterior end), sunken, phyllodes well developed, pores single, labrum prominent, not extending back past the first adjoining ambulacral plates. Plastron narrow (*ca.* 36 per cent of the test length fully tuberculated and straight sided; wider than the episternals; raised to a low keel. Subanal fasciole shield-shaped to oval, crossing plates 3, 4, and 5 of interambulacrum 5 and plates 6, 7, and 8 of the posterior ambulacra. Paired petals with a broad interporiferous zone flush with the test; pore-pairs small, conjugate, recessed; the series are closed distally. A few pore-pairs may continue outside the peripetalous fasciole. Primary tubercles well developed, with recessed auricles, scattered on the dorsal interambulacra primarily within the peripetalous fascioles and bordering ambulacrum III; primary spines short, (*ca.* 10 per cent of the test length), smooth, sharply pointed. Secondary tuberculation smooth, irregular, granular; secondary spines non-spatulate, hair-like. Peripetalous fasciole variously developed, from a rudimentary, single fasciole to a multiple or even a net-work of fascioles (see descriptions of the species); the primary fasciole crosses interambulacrum 3 on plates 7a and b and interambulacrum 4 on plates 7 or 8a and 9b and interambulacrum 5 on plates 11 or 12.

The tube-feet of the portion of III within the fasciole are non-penicillate, with single, slit-like pores. Subanal tube-feet poorly developed; pores double, but separating wall thin and ill-defined. Apical system ethmolytic, madreporite extending behind the posterior oculars, four genital pores of equal size, the system situated approximately centrally.

Periproct nearly round to horizontally elongate, the width about 11 per cent of the test length, situated subambitally on the obliquely truncated posterior end of the test so, in most specimens, it is visible from the oral side. Color in life purple to purple-brown.

Type-species.—*Plethotaenia spatangoides* (A. Agassiz 1883).

Discussion.—The original specimens of *Plethotaenia* were misidentified as *Spatangus purpureus* by A. Agassiz (1881), who subsequently allied the species with *Macropneustes.* Clark (1917) pointed out that the specimens clearly did not belong to *Macropneustes* and formulated the new generic name *Plethotaenia,* placing it in his large family Spatangidae. Lambert & Thiery (1924) placed *Plethotaenia* in their section *Rhabdobrissus,* which they characterized as follows: "Cette section comprend les *Brissoides* dont le fasciole sousanal montre des amorces de branches anales." *Plethotaenia,* however, shows no traces of anal branches from the subanal fasciole and has very little in common with *Plagiobrissus (Rhabdobrissus).* Fischer (1966) has considered the genus a subgenus of *Meoma.*

Were it not for the nebulous peripetalous fasciole, there is little doubt that Agassiz would have described these species as a new *Spatangus,* probably closely allied with *Spatangus paucituberculatus* A. Agassiz & H. L. Clark. (See, for example, Mortensen, 1951b, pl. 3, figs. 21 and 22). From the oral side, it is almost impossible to distinguish *Plethotaenia* from several species of the genus *Spatangus.* The generic description of *Spatangus* given by Mortensen (1951b, p. 7) would apply equally to *Plethotaenia* except the latter has a peripetalous fasciole. As already suggested by Clark (1917, p. 198), the absence of a peripetalous fasciole is not necessarily a primitive characteristic. It is well known that fascioles may be lost in ontogeny and recognized (even by Mortensen) that they may disappear in a phylogenetic lineage. There is no reason to suspect that the ancestors of *Spatangus* did not have a peripetalous fasciole. In fact, the characters of the paired petals would indicate that a peripetalous fasciole was present. It is also not unreasonable to assume that some phylogenetic lines closely related to *Spatangus* may not have lost the fasciole or may have regained the primitive character. The lack of expression of the peripetalous fasciole does not mean that its genetic basis is missing. The common reduction or total elimination of some fascioles with age indicates that the fasciolar system can be masked readily by inhibitor genes and that the absence of fascioles is no indication of the absence of the genetic constituents necessary to produce one.

The great similarity between *Plethotaenia* and *Spatangus* should not, therefore, be ignored simply because of the presence or absence of the peripetalous fasciole. The shape of the test, the spines, pedicellariae, ambulacra, apical system, phyllodes, subanal fasciole, internal anatomy and tube-feet are so similar that the close relationship between *Plethotaenia* and *Spatangus* is unquestionable. This does not mean they are congeneric or that *Plethotaenia* should be made a subgenus of *Spatangus.* The presence of the peripetalous fasciole in *Plethotaenia* might be an indication that it has been distinct from the species of *Spatangus* for a very long time and further investigations on the various species of *Spatangus* are needed before an objective conclusion can be reached. For further comments, see the section on sympatric species in the taxonomic conclusions.

Key to the Species of the Genus *Plethotaenia*

1. Labrum fully tuberculated, primary tubercles numerous on dorsal side, continuing outside fascioles in interambulacra 1 and 4. With 14 to 15 plates from the peristome to the petal in ambulacrum IV. Notch in anterior ambitus wider than deep, 7.2 to 12.8 per cent of the test length in depth .... *P. spatangoides.*
1. Labrum naked adjacent to plastron, primary tubercles not numerous on dorsal side, not continuing outside fascioles in interambulacrum 1 and 4. With 16 to 17 plates from the peristome to the petal in ambulacrum IV. Notch in anterior ambitus deeper than wide, 12.5 to 16 per cent of test length in depth .... *P. angularis.*

Plethotaenia spatangoides (A. Agassiz, 1883)
Figures 21-23; Plates 22, 23, 26 *b, e, h;* Tables 8, 12

Spatangus purpureus, A. Agassiz, 1880, p. 83; 1881, p. 171, not *Sp. purpureus* O. F. Müller.
Macropneustes spatangoides A. Agassiz, 1883, p. 64, pl. 27, figs. 1-5 (part).
Macropneustes spatangoides, Mortensen, 1907, p. 125, 127, 128, pl. 16, figs. 3, 4, 13, 14, 15, 20, 30, 33 (part).

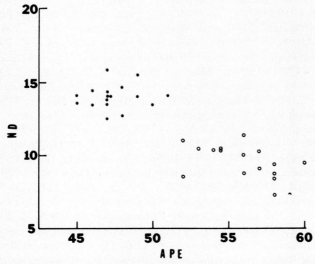

FIGURE 20. Identification diagram for *Plethotaenia angularis* (solid dots), and *P. spatangoides* (circles). ND = depth of anterior notch (percentage of test length); APE = span of the distal ends of the anterior petals (percentage of test length).

Plethotaenia spatangoides, H. L. Clark, 1917, p. 222 (part).
Plethotaenia spatangoides, Lambert & Thiery, 1924, p. 455 (part).
Plethotaenia spatangoides, H. L. Clark, 1925, p. 222 (part).
Plethotaenia spatangoides, H. L. Clark, 1941, p. 127 (part).
Not *Plethotaenia spatangoides,* Mortensen, 1951b, p. 485.

Material examined.—1 specimen, 66 mm test length, GERDA sta. G-273, off Riding Rocks, eastern Straits of Florida, 25°17'N., 79°14'W., 385 m, Jan. 1964.—3 specimens, 91 to 96 mm test length, sta. G-405, north of western end of Little Bahama Bank, 27°48'N., 79°00'W., 549 m, Sept. 1964.—1 specimen, 92.9 mm test length, sta. G-646, N.W. of Bimini, B.W.I., 25°49'N., 79°21'W., 439-531 m, July 1965.—5 specimens, 76 to 84 mm test length, sta. G-678, N.E. of Berry Islands, B.W.I., 25°57'N., 78°13'W., 540 m, July 1965.—2 specimens, 87 to 110 mm test length, sta. G-716, N.W. of Great Isaac, B.W.I., 26°08'N., 79°24'W., 544 m, Aug. 1965.—1 specimen, 95 mm test length, TURSIOPS sta. T-14, S.E. of Alligator Reef, Florida Keys, 161-183 m, June 1966.—1 specimen, 94.4 mm test length, R/V ATLANTIS, off Cuba; I.M.S. 42:40.—2 specimens, 111 to 112 mm test length, Coll. J. Moore, Gulf of Mexico off Florida, about 400 m, 1963.—6 specimens, 81.5 to 92.5 mm test length, ATLANTIS stas. 2983 and 2984, western end of Old Bahama Channel, off Cuba, 23°11'N., 79°08'W., 430-276 m, March 1938; M.C.Z. 7848.—2 specimens, 79 and 81.5 mm test length, ATLANTIS sta. 2983; B.M.N.H. 615.39-40.—2 specimens, 81.4 and 82 mm test length, ATLANTIS sta. 3467 and 3483, off Bahia de Matanzas, Cuba, 23°11.5'N., 81°26'W., 395-523 m, May 1938; M.C.Z. 7849.—3 specimens, 87 to 118 mm test length, ATLANTIS stas. 3434 and 3436, off Caibarien, Cuba (S.W. Cay Sal Bank), 23°10'N., 79°35'W., 467-476 m, May 1939; M.C.Z. 7850.— 1 specimen, 84.3 mm test length, CHALLENGER sta. 33, off Bermuda, 32°31'N., 64°43'W., 320 m, Mar. 1873; B.M.N.H. 1879 1.2.137.—8 specimens, 81.4 to 90 mm test length, SILVER BAY sta. 2443, north of Cay Sal Bank, Straits of Florida, 24°08'N., 80°09'W., 367 m; U.S.N.M. E-8360.—1 specimen, 89 mm test length, ALBATROSS sta. 2655, north of Little Bahama Bank, 27°22'N., 78°07.5'W., 619 m, May 1886; U.S.N.M. 14594.—1 specimen, 75 mm test length, FISH HAWK sta. 1097, off Marthas Vineyard, 39°54'N., 69°44'W., 290 m, Aug. 1881; U.S.N.M. 24596.—1 specimen, 85 mm test length, FISH HAWK sta. 1098, off Marthas Vineyard, 39°53'N., 69°43'W., 286 m, Aug. 1881; U.S.N.M. 5564.—1 specimen, 82 mm test length, PELICAN sta. 9; U.S.N.M. E-6684. —2 specimens, 89-105 mm test length, PELICAN sta. 9; U.S.N.M. E-6683. —Fragments, syntypic material of A. Agassiz, 1883, mixed lots containing both *P. spatangoides* and *P. angularis.*—M.C.Z. 3181, co-type fragments of both species, the larger *P. angularis,* the smaller, *P. spatangoides,* BLAKE sta. 291, off Barbados, 13°12'N., 59°41'W., Mar. 1879, 367 m.—M.C.Z. 3183, co-type fragments, mostly *P. spatangoides,* BLAKE sta. 300, off Barbados, 13°06.5'N., 59°39'W., March 1879, 150 m.—M.C.Z. 3182, co-type fragments of *P. spatangoides*, BLAKE sta. 134, off St. Cruz, 17°37′N., 64°48′W., 455 m.—Fragments, GERDA sta. G-377, off southern Florida Keys, 24°31′N., 81°11′W., 137 m, 17 Sept. 1964.

Diagnosis.—Primary tubercles numerous, even in the posterior, lateral interambulacra outside of the peripetalous fasciole. Tubercles continuing evenly from the plastron to the anterior edge of the labrum. Notch in anterior ambitus wider than deep, 7.2 to 12.8 per cent of the test length in depth. The portion of III enclosed by the peripetalous fasciole distinctly arched convexly. Ambitus rounded. 14 to 15 plates from the peristome to the petal in ambulacrum IV. Subanal fasciole normally broad and distinct. Plate 2b of interambulacrum 3 evenly covered with tubercles, no large naked areas.

TABLE 8
STATISTICAL SUMMARY: *Plethotaenia spatangoides*

Character	Mean	S.E.	S.D.	Range	N	C.V.
tl*	88.87	1.69	10.79	66-118.4	42	
tw	93.13	0.43	2.62	83-98	38	2.81
h	50.71	0.38	2.42	45-56	42	4.77
ax	44.38	0.43	1.94	40-47	21	4.38
pa	23.23	0.20	0.70	22-24	13	3.00
lp	73.17	0.34	1.14	71-75	12	1.55
ap	33.31	0.44	2.80	29-41	42	8.41
apw†	28.21	0.44	2.83	23-33	42	10.00
pp	30.36	0.56	3.58	23-39	42	11.70
ppw†	30.29	0.50	3.23	25-39	42	10.64
pp/ap‡	91.12	0.82	5.27	74-100	42	5.79
wIII	5.79	0.10	0.33	5.1-6.4	13	5.70
ff	36.65	0.66	3.10	32-43	23	8.45
pf	30.30	0.70	3.55	25-38	28	11.8
lf	30.04	0.73	3.64	24-38	26	11.9
pf/af‡	82.96	1.69	8.60	65-102	27	10.4
ppfl	425.07	25.05	93.72	247-660	15	22.2
ape	56.13	0.62	2.39	52-60	16	4.25
safh/w‡	70.35	1.39	6.52	58-85	23	9.3
safw	23.96	0.62	2.93	19-30	23	12.2
safl	64.42	2.32	7.70	55-76	12	11.9
ppe	34.44	0.47	1.84	33-37	16	5.3
pl	37.92	0.56	1.85	35-40	12	4.9
b	25.45	0.41	1.30	14-18	11	8.4
c	22.00	0.52	1.65	20-25	11	7.5
d	22.33	0.53	1.75	20-26	12	7.9
aw	11.54	0.22	1.10	9.3-13.4	25	9.5
aw/ah‡	76.04	1.41	6.91	62-94	25	11.0
nd/nw‡	56.10	1.91	11.95	36-88	40	21.2
nd	9.73	0.19	1.22	7.2-12.8	42	12.5

Data are expressed as percentages of test length unless otherwise indicated. Character symbols as given in Figure 1.
* Test length (mm).
† Percentage of petal length.
‡ Ratio expressed as a percentage.

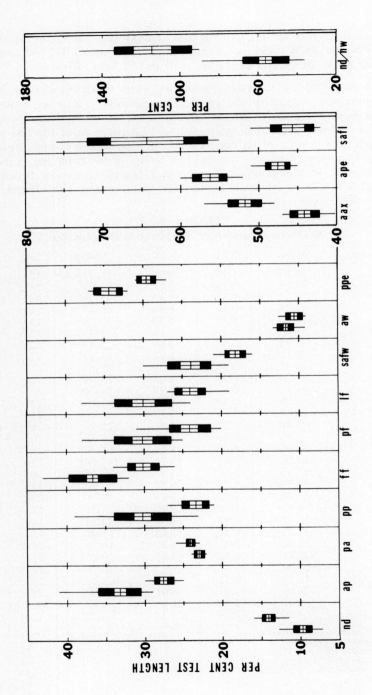

Description.—The test is evenly rounded, its oral side flat, rising centrally to a slight keel (Plate 23, *c, e*). The mean width is 93.13 ± 0.43 per cent of the test length (S. D. 2.62, C.V. 2.81). The mean height is 50.71 ± 0.38 per cent of the test length (S.D. 2.42, C.V. 4.77). No geographic or allometric variation was observed, but since the smallest specimen was 66 mm in test length, variation in these characters may occur in smaller specimens. The angle of the posterior truncation varies from 90° to 111° (measured with respect to the plastron and the dorsal portion of the periproct). The portion of the test enclosed by the subanal fasciole is raised to form a low snout (Plate 22, *b;* 23, *a*). The portion of the test from the subanal fasciole to the periproct is sunken (Plate 23, *c*).

The dorsal interambulacral plates outside the peripetalous fasciole have a slight median elevation which becomes more pronounced near the ambitus so as to flatten the almost circular outline in the interambulacra (Plate 22, *a, b*). The dorsal portions of interambulacra 2, 3, and 5 are so constructed that, viewed laterally, the specimens are nearly flat along their dorsal surface from between the posterior petal ends, past the apical system, to between the anterior petal ends (Plate 23, *a*). This flattened area is nearly parallel with the plastron.

The Anterior Ambulacrum

The anterior ambulacrum is flush with the test from the apical system through the area between the paired, anterior petals. From this point it
←

FIGURE 21. Variation diagram for *Plethotaenia spatangoides* (given first in each character comparison) and *P. angularis.* Abbreviations as given in Figure 1, except: aax = apical system to anterior end of test; safl = length of subanal fasciole; nd/nw = notch depth as a percentage of notch width. The variation diagrams (Hubbs & Perlmutter, 1942) are explained in Figure 11. The K value for each of the characters and the ratio of misclassification to all determinations (m) using each character alone (as shown in Figure 11) to separate the two species is:

Character	K	M
nd	8.3	1:46
ap	2.9	1:9
pa	0.86	1:3
pp	2.57	1:8
ff	2.86	1:9
pf	1.88	1:6
lf	1.91	1:6
safw	2.85	1:9
ppe	4.07	1:13
aax	6.97	1:35
ape	9.35	1:66
safl	5.96	1:24
nd/nw	7.10	1:36

Thus, when using the span of the distal ends of the anterior paired petals (ape) to separate the two species, there will probably be one misclassification for every 66 specimens examined.

103

becomes sunken, the depth of the groove becoming progressively greater toward the ambitus. The floor of the ambulacrum forms a half-circle, in cross section, from the peristome to the peripetalous fascioles. At the ambitus, the frontal notch has evenly sloping, rounded sides. The depth is 9.73 ± 0.19 per cent of the test length (S.D. 1.22, C.V. 12.5). It is wider than deep; the depth is 56.10 ± 1.91 per cent of the notch width (S.D. 11.95, C.V. 21.2). As indicated by the high coefficient of variation, this character shows considerable individual variation. The range of variation does not, however, overlap with the deeper notch of *P. angularis*. The anterior ambulacrum is sunken to the peristome.

The peripetalous fascioles cross the anterior ambulacrum at a mean distance from the apical system of 36.65 ± 0.66 per cent of the test length (S.D. 3.10, C.V. 8.45). Within the fasciolar area, the tube-feet are simple and non-penicillate. They are located over single, oval pores which are small, and set in the center of each ambulacral plate. These simple tube-feet are found at each pore except those of the phyllode, where typical spatangoid feeding tube-feet occur. There are four feeding tube-feet per plate series, situated over peripodia with conspicuous auricles and single pores.

The widest portion of III is within the frontal notch but the width was measured from the outer edges of the pore series at the point where the fasciole crosses the ambulacrum. The mean width of the frontal ambulacrum is 5.79 ± 0.10 per cent of the test length (S.D. 0.33, C.V. 5.70). This proportion decreases somewhat with growth.

The peripetalous fasciole is poorly developed on the plates of III and frequently it is missing completely, having ended on the adjoining interambulacral plates. When the fascioles do cross the plates of IIIb, they do so on plates 6, 7, 8, and 9 depending on the development of the interambulacral portions of the fascioles.

The tuberculation of III is small and granular. An irregular series of tubercles, intermediate in size between the primaries bordering the ambulacrum and the small tubercles of the interporiferous zone, is located along the poriferous zone. At the ambitus, the spines of the adjacent interambulacra and of III are slightly curved, forming a conspicuous tunnel (Plate 23, *f*). The inner edge of these spines is thorny (Plate 26, *h*). The exact function of this tunnel is unknown.

Ambulacra II and IV
(the anterior paired petals)

The peripetalous fasciole crosses ambulacrum IV on several plates from 9 to 16 or 17 of series a. The petaloid portion of IV begins on plates 14, 15, or 16 of series a. The percentage of the number of plates from the peristome to the petaloid area (indicated by the onset of double pores) in the specimens examined is: 14 (56 per cent), 15 (37 per cent), and 16 (6.5 per cent).

104

The tuberculation of the ambulacra is granular and evenly distributed. There are no naked areas with the exception of the phyllodes where only the interporiferous zone remains barren of tubercles. There are about 11 feeding tube-feet per phyllode, each situated over a large oval pore. The peripodia are raised slightly to form a concave auricle. The pores of the sensory tube-feet are also single, minute, situated near the center of the ambulacral plates, from the phyllode to the petaloid area of the ambulacra. The posterior plate series between the ambitus and the petal is wider than the corresponding anterior plate series (Plate 23, b).

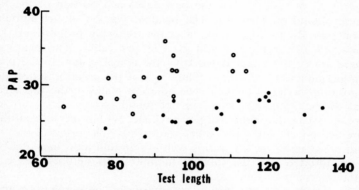

FIGURE 22. Number of pore-pairs (IV, series b) versus test length (mm) for *Plethotaenia spatangoides* (circles) and *P. angularis* (solid dots).

The petaloid area closely resembles that of *Spatangus*. The pore-series are closed distally, and may continue unaltered past the first portion of the peripetalous fasciole (Plate 23, g). The pore-pairs are slightly sunken; the interporiferous zone is flush with the test. Granular tuberculation covers all but the peripodia. There are 17 to 48 per cent of the apicalmost tube-feet of the anterior series underdeveloped; this percentage decreases allometrically. In the posterior series, only three or four undeveloped pore-pairs occur. The total number of tube-feet (pore-pairs, or plates) increases throughout growth. The lack of smaller specimens makes it impossible to conclude if the rate of increase is logarithmic or semi-logarithmic. Figure 22 shows the numbers of pore-pairs of ambulacrum IV, series b, plotted against the test length. The regression equation is:

$$\text{Ln}Y = 0.398 \, \text{Ln}X + 1.6275 \qquad Y = \text{Pore-pairs (IVb)}.$$
$$S_{\text{Ln}Y.\text{Ln}X} = \pm 0.184 \qquad X = \text{Test length (mm)}.$$

When smaller specimens are dredged, this relationship may be found to be semi-logarithmic but, at present, the above equation yields the highest coefficient of correlation.

The anterior petals have a mean length of 33.31 ± 0.44 per cent of

105

the test length (S.D. 2.80, C.V. 8.41). This proportion increases allometrically. The petals have a mean width of 28.21 ± 0.44 per cent of the petal length (S.D. 2.83, C.V. 10.00). This proportion decreases with an increase in test length. The petals are straight; their distal ends have a spread of 56.13 ± 0.62 per cent of the test length (S.D. 2.39, C.V. 4.25).

Ambulacra I and V
(the posterior paired petals)

The peripetalous fasciole crosses ambulacrum V on any of the plates from 18 to 25 of series a, but the best developed portion of the fasciole is normally found on plate 19. The petaloid portion of the ambulacrum begins on plate 18 to 20 of series a in the following proportions; 18 (50 per cent), 19 (19 per cent) and 20 (31 per cent). The plates of the ambulacra are evenly tuberculated from the apical system to the plastron; only the peripodia are left bare. Plates 1-4 of the anterior series and 1-5 of the posterior series are naked. The adjacent plates of the two series are of equal width. Occluded plates are not found.

There are six feeding tube-feet per phyllode. Within the subanal fasciole, there are two poorly developed subanal tube-feet. The pores of the subanal tube-feet are double; the separating wall is thin and indistinct. Plates 6, 7, and 8 are inserted into the subanal fasciole. This number was constant in all the specimens examined.

In the petaloid area, the five or six apicalmost pore-pairs are underdeveloped in both pore-series. The posterior petals have a mean length of 30.36 ± 0.56 per cent of the test length (S.D. 3.58, C.V. 11.70) and 91.12 ± 0.82 per cent of the anterior petal length (S.D. 5.27, C.V. 5.79). Their mean width is 30.29 ± 0.50 per cent of their length (S.D. 3.23, C.V. 10.84). All of these proportions vary allometrically, the length proportions increasing with growth, the width proportion decreasing with growth.

The ends of the posterior petals have a mean span of 34.44 ± 0.47 per cent of the test length (S.D. 1.84, C.V. 5.3). The petals are straight.

The Interambulacra

The number of interambulacral plates from the peristome to the fascioles varies due to the irregular development of the peripetalous fascioles and will be discussed in the section on fascioles.

The tuberculation of the interambulacra provides several valuable characters. The primary tubercles are arranged in V-shaped series on each interambulacral plate from the apical system to the ambitus in interambulacra 2 and 3. In interambulacra 1 and 4, these tubercles are located from the apex toward the ambitus to a point outside the peripetalous fascioles. The exact plate number on which the last series of tubercles occurs varies individually. In all specimens, primary tubercles are present

106

on plate 6 of the anterior series and plate 8 of the posterior series. In many specimens, the primary tubercles continued to plate 4 of the anterior series and 5 of the posterior series of interambulacra 1 and 4. In interambulacrum 5, the primary tubercles continue to the periproct. The secondary tuberculation of the dorsal surface is uniform and granular.

On the oral side, the size of the tubercles increases anteriorly. The tuberculation of the oral side is regularly distributed; the series of tubercles radiate from the raised nodes of the plates. Tuberculation continues unaltered from the plastron to the lip of the labrum. All of the interambulacra are inserted into the peristome and tuberculation continues to the edge of the peristome.

The plastron is straight-sided and wider than the episternals. Its mean length is 37.92 ± 0.56 per cent of the test length (S.D. 1.85, C.V. 4.9). The width of the plastron, measured at points B, C, and D is:

point	mean	S.E.	S.D.	C.V.
B	15.45	0.41	1.30	8.4
C	22.00	0.52	1.65	7.5
D	22.33	0.53	1.75	7.9

The plastron is elevated, its midline forming a low keel.

The labrum reaches to the middle of the first adjoining ambulacral plates. The lip is well developed.

The Apical System

The apical system is ethmolytic, situated slightly anteriorly on the dorsal surface at a mean distance from the anterior end of 44.38 ± 0.43 per cent of the test length (S.D. 1.94, C.V. 4.38). There are four circular genital pores of about equal size. The madreporite passes between the posterior genitals and oculars; its posterior prolongation is about equal to the distance between the outer edges of the posterior and anterior genital pores.

The female specimens tend to have larger genital pores than the males but the difference is not always apparent and too few specimens were available for a statistical analysis.

The Periproct and Peristome

The periproct is situated subambitally on the posterior end of the test (Plate 23), enclosed by interambulacral plates 5, 6, 7, and 8. It is finely tuberculated and surrounded by the larger spines of the anal tuft. The periproct is wider than high; its width is 131.2 ± 2.90 per cent of its height (S.D. 14.47, C.V. 11.0), and 11.54 ± 0.22 per cent of the test length (S.D. 1.10, C.V. 9.5).

The peristome is situated anteriorly; its leading edge has a mean distance from the anterior end of the test of 23.23 ± 0.20 per cent of the test length (S.D. 0.70, C.V. 3.00). The mean distance from the lip of the labrum to the posterior end of the test is 73.17 ± 0.34 per cent of the test length (S.D. 1.14, C.V. 1.55).

The Peripetalous Fascioles

The number of peripetalous fascioles varies considerably in the specimens examined. In general, there is only one fasciole which is continuous around the entire petaloid area. The complete fasciole is normally the most dorsal one. Secondary fascioles are found primarily in interambulacra 2 and 3 at the lower edge of the successive interambulacral plates, associated with the arrangement of primary tubercles of these same plates. The fasciole nearest the ambitus (plate 4) is the shortest and does not normally extend into the adjacent ambulacra. The fascioles of plates 5 and 6 may extend into the adjacent ambulacra and occasionally into the lateral interambulacra. They may also bend apically and merge with the primary fasciole. The fascioles of plates 7 and 8 are usually the best developed and may be divided several times, the branches either rejoining the primary fasciole or ending on a lateral interambulacral plate. In the majority of specimens examined, there were three or four fascioles in the anterior, lateral interambulacra. The posterior, unpaired interambulacrum normally has two fascioles but, again, these may be split into more or reduced to one. Plate number 12 normally has the best developed fasciole. In the posterolateral interambulacra, the fasciole may be found on plates 6 through 9. It is best developed on plate 7 of the anterior series and 9 of the posterior series.

The total proportional length of the fascioles has a mean length of 425 ± 25.05 per cent of the test length (S.D. 93.72, C.V. 22.2). The area of the fascioles is shown on Fig. 23 plotted against the test length.

The mean distance from the apical system to the lateral portions of the peripetalous fascioles is 30.04 ± 0.73 per cent of the test length (S.D. 3.64, C.V. 11.9). The mean distance from the apical system to the posterior portion of the peripetalous fascioles is 30.30 ± 0.70 per cent of the test length (S.D. 3.55, C.V. 11.8) and 82.96 ± 1.69 per cent of the distance from the apical system to the anterior portions of the fascioles (S.D. 8.60, C.V. 10.4).

The Subanal Fasciole

The subanal fasciole is oval in shape, and the width of the area enclosed by it has a mean of 23.69 ± 0.62 per cent of the test length (S.D. 2.93, C.V. 12.2). The height of the area enclosed by the subanal fasciole is 70.35 ± 1.39 per cent of the width (S.D. 6.52, C.V. 9.3). The proportional length of the subanal fasciole is 64.42 ± 2.32 per cent of the test length (S.D. 7.70, C.V. 11.9). This fasciole usually is broad and conspicuous. Its area is shown on Figure 23 plotted against the test length.

The plates crossed by this fasciole are constant. In interambulacrum 5, plates 3, 4, and 5 are crossed; in ambulacra I and V, plates 6, 7, and 8 are crossed.

The Spines and Pedicellariae

The spines are straight and nonspatulate except for those of the plastron which are slightly widened distally, and the spines within the frontal notch which may be curved and serrated along the inner margin. The secondary spines are small and hair-like. The primary spines are short, about 10 per cent of the test length, and sharply pointed. Their distribution is discussed in the above sections on the ambulacra and interambulacra.

The sphaeridia are not distinctive. They are set in shallow depressions surrounding the peristome.

There are two forms of tridentate pedicellariae: an elongate form (Plate 26, *e*) and a broad form (Plate 26, *b*). The size of the valves of both forms vary from small (*ca.* 0.4 mm) to large (*ca.* 1.0 mm). The pedicellariae resemble those of *Spatangus purpureus*. The valves of the broad form are rounded; the blade is nearly the same size as the auricles.

Internal Anatomy

Insufficient numbers of specimens were dissected to determine infraspecific differences in internal anatomy, but certain findings are important for the higher grouping of the spatangoid taxa. The internal anatomy of *Plethotaenia* is almost the same as described and illustrated for *Spatangus purpureus* (Koehler, 1883, pl. 1, figs. 1, 2 and 3). Of particular note is the presence of only one siphon. In the Brissidae, there are two. Hyman, 1955, fig. 199 A, indicates that *Meoma* has only one siphon but this is an error, as it has two distinct siphons. *Spatangus,* like *Plethotaenia,* has only one siphon. The internal, marginal vessel (Koehler, p. 84, pl. 1, fig. 1) of *Spatangus* joins the inferior loop of the intestine in a very characteristic way. This characteristic arrangement is also found in *Plethotaenia.* The drawing in Figure 24 was reproduced from a photographic tracing of the anatomy of *Plethotaenia angularis* and corresponds to Koehler's fig. 1, plate 1. Clearly, the anatomy of these two genera is sufficiently alike to establish the affinities of *Spatangus* and *Plethotaenia* even without the numerous other similarities.

There is only one caecum. The gonads are of the typical spatangoid type with the posterior two larger than the anterior two and the left anterior gonad divided into two lobes. The eggs, observed in the gonads of specimens from station G-405, September 1964, were quite small (*ca.* 0.3 to 0.4 mm in diameter) and were nucleate.

Types.—Agassiz described this species from fragmentary material which included portions of *P. angularis.* All fragments from BLAKE station 134, off St. Cruz, seem to be *P. spatangoides.* They are marked "cotype" and are deposited in the Museum of Comparative Zoology, catalogue no. 3182. It would, perhaps, be desirable to designate a neotype but there are no whole specimens from the type locality. There are a sufficient number of specimens available in various museums which are clearly *P. spatangoides*. These include: M.C.Z. 7849 and 7850; B.M.N.H. 1879 1.2.137, 6.15.39-40; U.S.N.M. E. 8360, E. 6684, 24594, 14594, E. 6683, E. 5564; and I.M.S. 42-40. Additional material, from I.M.S. collections will be deposited in the U.S.N.M.

Type locality.—BLAKE station 134, off St. Cruz, 17°37′N., 64°48′W., 455 m, coral sand, bottom temperature 12.5°C.

Distribution.—*P. spatangoides* is widely distributed in the western Atlantic from Martha's Vineyard to the Lesser Antillies in depths of 150 to 619 meters. Large populations are located just north of Cuba and just north of the Little Bahama Bank (see under Material Examined).

Discussion.—Ecology: The relatively deep water habitat has precluded direct ecological observation, and none of the specimens collected were able to survive in aquaria. *P. angularis* frequently is taken in the same haul with *P. spatangoides,* but the ratio of one form to the other is not constant and both may be found separately.

A specimen of *Montacuta,* a small erycinacean bivalve, was found attached to the spines bordering the frontal notch of *P. spatangoides.* Nothing is known of the details of this association. Specimens of the same bivalve also were found on the spines of *P. angularis.*

The type of substrate reported in the various dredging records conflicts with the evidence from the intestinal contents of the urchins. The records indicate substrates ranging from fine sand to coral rubble. The intestines, however, are filled with mud. It is probable that the mud was washed from the trawls on the return to the surface, the residual debris giving the impression that the bottom was rubble or sand.

The analysis of the gut contents showed a mean particle size of 0.102 mm with a sorting coefficient of 4.98, slightly above a normally sorted soil (Krumbein & Pettijohn, 1938). The mean percentage, by weight, of silt and clay was 47. Foraminifera and pteropods made up the majority of the larger particles. Small gastropods and lamellibranchs were also present.

Contamination from the urchins made organic analysis impossible.

Urchins which do not burrow as adults (i.e., *Palaeopneustes* and perhaps *Linopneustes*) are commonly dredged whole and alive. Urchins which burrow (*Brissopsis, Schizaster,* etc.) are more commonly dredged as dead tests or fragments than as whole, live specimens. *Plethotaenia* falls into the latter group and is more frequently dredged as fragments or dead tests than as live specimens. This fact, together with the general shape of the test, tends to indicate that *Plethotaenia* burrows in its natural habitat. Since this spatangoid has no tunneling tube-feet, it probably burrows with the apical tuft spines breaking the surface of the mud.

110

Fossil History: *Plethotaenia* is not known as a fossil. Its ancestors will probably be found among specimens identified as *Spatangus*.

Comments: Mortensen (1907, p. 129) indicated the possibility of two species of *Plethotaenia* in the Western Atlantic. In 1951b, however, he did not mention this possibility. It is unfortunate that the single specimen which he described in his monograph was *P. angularis*. A. Agassiz's (1883) description was based on both species, but in general was more descriptive of *P. spatangoides*.

For the differences between *P. spatangoides* and *P. angularis* see the discussion on the latter species.

Plethotaenia angularis, n. sp.
Figures 20-24; Plates 24-26; Tables 9, 12

Macropneustes spatangoides, A. Agassiz, 1883, p. 64, pl. 27, figs. 6-7 (part).
Macropneustes spatangoides, Mortensen, 1907, p. 125, 127, 128 (part).
Plethotaenia spatangoides, H. L. Clark, 1917, p. 222 (part).
Plethotaenia spatangoides, Lambert & Thiery, 1924, p. 455 (part).
Plethotaenia spatangoides, H. L. Clark, 1925, p. 222 (part).
Plethotaenia spatangoides, H. L. Clark, 1941, p. 127 (part).
Plethotaenia spatangoides, Mortensen, 1951b, p. 485, pl. 39, figs. 6, 10, 11; pl. 64, fig. 24.

Material examined.—1 specimen, 106 mm test length, GERDA sta. G-158, S.W. Grand Bahama Island, B.W.I., 26°27'N., 79°21'W., 540-531 m, June 1963.—7 specimens, 110 to 120 mm test length, sta. G-179, north of western end of Little Bahama Bank, 27°41'N., 79°11'W., 523 m, July 1963.—6 specimens, 77 to 112 mm test length, sta. G-405, north of western end of Little Bahama Bank, 27°48.5'N., 79°00'W., 540 m, Sept. 1964.—1 specimen, 134 mm test length, sta. G-666, north of western end of Little Bahama Bank, 27°48'N., 79°15'W., 524 m, July 1965.—1 specimen, 130 mm test length, sta. G-667, north of western end of Little Bahama Bank, 27°51'N., 79°15'W., 535 m, July 1965.—Fragments, sta. G-678, north of Little Bahama Bank, 27°57'N., 78°13'W., 540 m, July 1965.—1 specimen, 99.5 mm test length plus fragment, sta. G-694, south of Grand Bahama Island, 26°28'N., 78°40'W., 623 m, July 1965.—1 specimen, 92 mm test length, sta. G-695, south of Grand Bahama Island, 26°28'N., 78°37'W., 555 m, July 1965.—3 specimens, 87 to 95 mm test length, sta. G-707, south of Grand Bahama Island, 26°27'N., 78°40'W., 550 m, July 1965.—2 specimens, 96 and 117 mm test length, ATLANTIS sta. 2980 and 2981(b), western end of Old Bahama Channel, off Cuba, 22°47'N., 78°40'W., 457 m, March 1938; M.C.Z. 7847.—2 specimens, 86 and 85 mm test length, ATLANTIS sta. 2983, 2984, western end of Old Bahama Channel, off Cuba, 23°11'N., 79°08'W., 430-276 m, March 1938; M.C. Z. 7848 (mixed with *P. spatangoides*).—1 specimen, 77 mm test length, ALBATROSS sta. 2655-1, north of Little Bahama Bank, 27°22'N., 78°07.5'W., 619 m, May 1886; U.S.N.M.

111

TABLE 9

STATISTICAL SUMMARY: *Plethotaenia angularis*

Character	Mean	S.E.	S.D.	Range	N	C.V.
tl*	104.55	3.06	15.29	77-134	26	
tw	94.50	0.59	2.72	91-99	22	2.88
h	45.29	0.66	3.08	40-51	23	6.81
ax	51.77	0.41	2.01	48-57	25	3.88
pa	24.16	0.16	0.66	23-26	17	2.74
lp	71.92	0.37	1.23	70-74	12	1.70
ap	27.69	0.25	1.26	25-30	26	4.65
apw†	32.12	0.46	2.31	28-38	26	7.20
pp	23.48	0.38	1.88	21-27	25	8.00
ppw†	36.96	0.58	2.84	30-44	25	7.70
pp/ap‡	84.16	1.01	4.95	71-94	25	5.88
wIII	6.32	0.15	0.59	5.2-7.5	16	9.35
ff	30.17	0.51	2.09	26-34	18	6.94
pf	24.11	0.61	2.59	20-31	19	10.70
lf	24.10	0.46	2.00	19-27	20	8.30
pf/af‡	78.74	1.66	7.05	67-94	19	8.95
ppfl	183.47	9.77	39.09	149-292	17	21.30
ape	47.50	0.38	1.57	45-51	18	3.31
safh/w‡	71.45	1.10	4.78	65-84	20	6.71
safw	18.35	0.32	1.42	16-21	20	7.74
safl	45.63	0.70	2.71	42-51	16	5.94
ppe	29.53	0.33	1.33	27-31	17	4.50
pl	36.58	0.62	2.06	32-39	12	5.64
b	16.73	0.38	1.21	15-19	11	7.23
c	23.15	0.50	1.75	21-27	13	7.57
d	22.92	0.48	1.61	21-26	12	7.03
aw	10.53	0.25	1.04	9.1-12.6	19	9.87
aw/ah‡	119.47	3.78	16.04	102-157	19	13.45
nd/nw‡	114.14	4.43	20.32	90-152	23	17.80
nd	14.21	0.18	0.84	12.5-16	23	5.90

Data are expressed as percentages of test length unless otherwise indicated. Character symbols as given in Figure 1.
* Test length (mm).
† Percentage of petal length.
‡ Ratio expressed as a percentage.

14754.—Fragment, BLAKE sta. 291, off Barbados, 13°12′N., 59°41′W., 367 m, March 1879; M.C.Z. 3181 (with co-type *P. spatangoides*).— Fragment, BLAKE sta. 300, off Barbados, 13°06.5′N., 59°39′W., 150 m, March 1879; M.C.Z. 3183 (with co-type *P. spatangoides*).

Diagnosis.—Primary tubercles rarely found outside the peripetalous fasciole in the posterior, lateral interambulacra. Tubercles not continuing evenly from the plastron to the anterior edge of the labrum. Notch in anterior ambitus normally deeper than wide, 12.5 to 16 per cent of the test length in depth. The portion of III enclosed by the peripetalous fasciole almost straight, not distinctly arched. The ambitus low and angular. 16 to 17 plates from the peristome to the petal in ambulacrum IV. Subanal fasciole

112

thin, not strongly developed. Plate 2b of interambulacrum 3 with an area left free of tubercles from the distal end of the phyllode to about half the distance to the ambitus.

Description.—The test has a low, angular appearance, the oral side flat, rising centrally to a slight keel (Plates 24, 25). The mean test width is 94.60 ± 0.59 per cent of the test length (S.D. 2.72, C.V. 2.88). The mean height is 45.29 ± 0.66 per cent of the test length (S.D. 3.08, C.V. 6.81). The posterior portion of the test is obliquely truncated, the angle between the plastron and the truncated portion varying from 96° to 120°, with an average of 112°. The portion of the test enclosed by the subanal fasciole is raised to form a low snout (Plates 24, 25), the portion of the test from the fasciole to the periproct is concave.

The dorsal interambulacral plates are almost flat; only those nearest the ambitus develop raised nodes. The lateral and anterior portions of the ambitus are the only flattened portions of the otherwise circular outline.

The anterior lateral and posterior interambulacra are so constructed that the dorsal side of the specimens, viewed laterally, is evenly curved from the anterior to the posterior ambitus (Plate 25, *a*).

The Anterior Ambulacrum

The anterior ambulacrum is flush with the test from the apical system through the area enclosed by about one-half the length of the anterior paired petals. From this point the floor of the ambulacrum is curved gently toward the ambitus, becoming deeper near the ambitus. The degree of curvature increases rapidly near the ambitus and the ambulacrum forms a deep frontal notch. The walls of the frontal notch are nearly parallel and the outer edge is sharply set off from the ambitus. The frontal notch has a mean depth of 14.21 ± 0.18 per cent of the test length (S.D. 0.84, C.V. 5.9). It is deeper than it is wide, the depth being 114.14 ± 4.43 per cent of the notch width (S.D. 20.32, C.V. 17.8). This ratio increases with growth. In specimens smaller than 60 mm test length it may be difficult to use this character for specific identifications. In the smallest specimen examined, however, the ratio was much greater than found in *P. spatangoides*. The K value between the two species for this proportion is 7.1, indicating that there is one chance out of 36 that a specimen will be misclassified using this character alone (Fig. 21).

The anterior ambulacrum is only slightly sunken at the peristome.

The peripetalous fascioles are very poorly developed on ambulacrum III. They cross this ambulacrum at a mean distance from the apical system of 30.17 ± 0.51 per cent of the test length from the apical system (S.D. 2.09, C.V. 6.94) on plates number 8, 9 or 10. Within the fasciolar area, the tube-feet are simple, non-penicillate, and are located over single, slit-like pores which are small and set in the center of each ambulacral plate. These tube-feet continue to the feeding tube-feet of the phyllode and

113

are best developed within the deep frontal notch.

The widest portion of III is within the frontal notch, but the width was measured from the outer edges of the pore series at the point where the peripetalous fasciole crosses III. The mean width is 6.32 ± 0.15 per cent of the test length (S.D. 0.59, C.V. 9.35).

The phyllode is composed of four feeding tube-feet per plate-series. The pores are single, oval, and the peripodia do not have a pronounced muscle support.

The tuberculation of ambulacrum III is small and granular. Within the frontal notch the size of the tubercles increases slightly. The spines of these and adjacent interambulacral tubercles curve slightly and have a few thorns along their inner edge (Plate 26, g). The tunnel formed by the spines and the frontal notch is not as distinct as in *P. spatangoides* (Plate 25, f).

Ambulacra II and IV
(the anterior paired petals)

The peripetalous fasciole crosses ambulacrum IV on plates 15, 16, or 17, depending on the development of the accessory fascioles. The petaloid portion of the ambulacrum (marked by the onset of double pore-pairs) begins on plates 16 or 17; the percentages of the two plates are: 16 (53 per cent), 17 (47 per cent).

The tuberculation of the ambulacra is small and granular with the exception, in a few specimens, of an occasional primary tubercle on the interporiferous zone of the petals. The tuberculation continues almost to the phyllodes, which are naked. There are 11 or 12 feeding tube-feet per phyllode, each situated over a single, elongate pore. The peripodia do not have a well developed muscle support; the central elevation is rounded, not concave as in *P. spatangoides*. From the phyllode to the petals, there are sensory tube-foot pores which may be completely occluded in larger specimens. The posterior plate series from the ambitus to the petal is wider than the corresponding anterior plate series (Plate 25).

The petaloid area closely resembles that of *Spatangus*. The pore-series are closed distally and may continue unaltered past the first portion of the peripetalous fasciole. The pore-pairs are slightly sunken; the interporiferous zone is broad and flush with the test. In the anterior pore-series, 36 to 56 per cent of the apicalmost pore-pairs are undeveloped (mean 47.5 per cent). In larger specimens these pores may be completely occluded. In the posterior pore-series, only 4 to 7 pore-pairs remain undeveloped. The number of pore-pairs increases throughout growth. Figure 22 shows the number of pore-pairs of series b of ambulacrum IV plotted against the test length. The regression equation is:

$$\text{LnY} = 0.694 \text{ LnX} + 0.0318 \qquad Y = \text{Pore-pairs (IVb)}.$$
$$S_{\text{LnY.LnX}} = \pm 0.0233 \qquad X = \text{Test length (mm)}.$$

114

When smaller specimens become available, this relationship may prove to be semi-logarithmic but, at present, the above equation yields the highest coefficient of correlation.

The anterior petals have a mean length of 27.69 ± 0.25 per cent of the test length (S.D. 1.26, C.V. 4.65). This proportion increases allometrically. The petals have a mean width of 32.12 ± 0.46 per cent of the petal length (S.D. 2.31, C.V. 7.20). This proportion decreases with an increase in test length. The petals are straight, their distal ends having a spread of 47.50 ± 0.38 per cent of the test length (S.D. 1.57, C.V. 3.31). This proportion is much smaller than the corresponding proportion of *P. spatangoides* and the K factor of 9.35 indicates that only one specimen in 66 would be misclassified using this character alone (Fig. 21).

Ambulacra I and V
(the posterior paired petals)

The peripetalous fasciole crosses ambulacrum V on plates 19, 20, 21 or 22 of series a, the best developed portion is commonly found on plate 20a. The petaloid portion of the ambulacrum begins on plate 20 to 22 of series a in the following proportions; 20 (57 per cent), 21 (28.5 per cent), 22 (14.5 per cent). The plates of the ambulacra are evenly tuberculated from the apex to the plastron; only the peripodia are left bare. An occasional specimen may have one or two primary tubercles on the interporiferous zone of the petals. Plates 1-6 of the posterior series and 1-5 of the anterior series are naked. The adjacent plates of the two series are of equal width. Occluded plates are not present.

There are six feeding tube-feet per phyllode. Two poorly developed subanal tube-feet, absent in some specimens, occur within the subanal fasciole. The pores are small and double; the separating wall is thin and indistinct. Plates 6, 7, and 8 are inserted into the subanal fasciole. This number was constant in all the specimens examined.

In the posterior paired petals five to nine of the apicalmost tube-feet are undeveloped in both plate series. The posterior petals have a mean length of 23.48 ± 0.38 per cent of the test length (S.D. 1.88, C.V. 8.00) and 84.16 ± 1.01 per cent of the anterior petal length (S.D. 4.95, C.V. 5.88). The mean width of the posterior petals is 36.96 ± 0.58 per cent of the petal length (S.D. 2.84, C.V. 7.70). All of these proportions vary allometrically; the length proportions increase with growth and the width proportion decreases with growth.

The petals are straight; their distal ends have a span of 29.53 ± 0.33 per cent of the test length (S.D. 1.33, C.V. 4.50).

The Interambulacra

The number of interambulacral plates from the peristome to the fascioles varies due to the irregular development of the peripetalous

115

fascioles and will be discussed in the section on fascioles.

The tuberculation of the interambulacra provides several valuable characters. The primary tubercles are much less numerous than in *P. spatangoides,* and are only found within the peripetalous fasciole in the lateral interambulacra (1 and 4). Occasionally, one or two tubercles may be found in these areas outside of the peripetalous fasciole but never below plate 7 of the anterior plate series or plate 8 of the posterior plate series. In interambulacrum 5, primary tubercles continue along the midline to the periproct. In interambulacrum 2 and 3, primary tubercles are found adjacent to ambulacrum III from the apical system to the ambitus. These tubercles do not extend past the center of the posterior series of interambulacral plates. In *P. spatangoides,* the tubercles of this area extend from ambulacrum III to the anterior, lateral ambulacra. The secondary tuberculation of the dorsal surface is uniform and granular; the individual tubercles are almost microscopic.

On the oral side, the size of the tubercles increases anteriorly. The tuberculation is more regularly distributed; the series of tubercles radiate from the raised nodes of the plates. The auricles of the tubercles are not raised, even on the plastron, as is usual for most spatangoids. The labrum has only one or two tubercles; there is a distince separation of the tuberculation of the plastron and the edge of the labrum. Tuberculation is sparse on the plates which insert to the peristome. In most specimens, only a few tubercles are found adjacent to the peristome; the remainder of the first interambulacral plates are naked. In *P. spatangoides,* these plates are tuberculated.

An area devoid of tubercles extends from the distal end of the phyllodes (II and IV) anteriolaterally onto interambulacral plate 2 of the posterior plate series. This naked area extends about one half of the distance from the phyllode to the ambitus (Plate 24, *b;* 25, *g*). There is no obvious functional reason why this area should lack spines. This character is a reliable difference between the two species of *Plethotaenia.*

The plastron is straight-sided, wider than the episternals. Its mean length is 36.58 ± 0.62 per cent of the test length (S.D. 2.06, C.V. 5.64). The width of the plastron, measured at points B, C, and D is:

point	mean	S.E.	S.D.	C.V.
B	16.73	0.38	1.21	7.23
C	23.15	0.50	1.75	7.57
D	22.92	0.48	1.61	7.03

The plastron is elevated, its midline forming a low keel.

The labrum reaches to the middle of the first adjoining ambulacral plates. The lip is well developed.

The Apical System

The apical system is ethmolytic, situated centrally on the dorsal surface at a mean distance from the anterior end of the test of 51.77 ± 0.41 per cent of the test length (S.D. 2.01, C.V. 3.88). There are four circular genital pores of equal size. The madreporite passes between the posterior genitals and slightly past the posterior oculars.

The Periproct and Peristome

The periproct is situated subambitally on the posterior end of the test (Plate 25), enclosed by plates 5, 6, 7, and 8 of interambulacrum 5. It is finely tuberculated and surrounded by the large spines of the anal tuft. The periproct is wider than high; its width is 119 ± 3.78 per cent of its own height (S.D. 16.04, C.V. 13.45) and 10.53 ± 0.25 per cent of the test length (S. D. 1.04, C.V. 9.87).

The peristome is situated anteriorly, its leading edge having a mean distance from the anterior end of the test of 24.16 ± 0.16 per cent of the test length (S.D. 0.66, C.V. 2.74). The mean distance from the lip of the labrum to the posterior end of the test is 71.92 ± 0.37 per cent of the test length (S.D. 1.22, C.V. 1.70).

The Peripetalous Fascioles

The number of peripetalous fascioles varies considerably in the specimens examined. The fascioles are not as numerous or as well developed as in *P. spatangoides*. There is normally a primary fasciole which is continuous around the petaloid area. The complete fasciole is usually the dorsalmost one. The secondary fascioles are found primarily in interambulacra 2 and 3 at the lower edge of the successive interambulacral plates, on the adoral side of the primary tubercles of those plates. The fascioles nearest the ambitus are the least developed; the first ones are found on plate 6 or 7. These may reach almost to the adjoining ambulacra or may join the primary fasciole. Plate 8 usually has the best developed fasciole. The majority of specimens had only two fascioles in interambulacra 2 and 3. In interambulacra 1 and 4, there is usually only one fasciole. It crosses plate 8 (or 7) of the anterior plate series and 9 (or 8) of the posterior plate series. In interambulacrum 5, the peripetalous fasciole may be split but is single in the majority of the specimens examined and is located on plate 12 or 13.

The total proportional length of the fascioles is 183.47 ± 9.77 per cent of the test length (S.D. 39.09, C.V. 21.30). The area of the peripetalous fasciole is shown on Figure 23 plotted against the test length.

The mean distance from the apical system to the lateral portions of the peripetalous fascioles is 24.10 ± 0.46 per cent of the test length (S.D. 2.00, C.V. 8.3). The mean distance from the apical system to the posterior portions of the peripetalous fascioles is 24.11 ± 0.61 per cent of the test length (S.D. 2.59, C.V. 10.7) and 78.74 ± 1.66 per cent of the distance from the apical system to the anterior portions of the fascioles (S.D. 7.05,

C.V. 8.95). These fascioles may be very poorly developed and incomplete in various portions.

The Subanal Fasciole

The subanal fasciole is oval to heart-shaped; the width of the area enclosed by it has a mean of 18.35 ± 0.32 per cent of the test length (S.D. 1.42, C.V. 7.74). The height of the area enclosed by the subanal fasciole is 71.45 ± 1.10 per cent of its width (S.D. 4.78, C.V. 6.71).

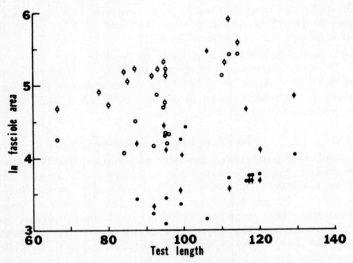

FIGURE 23. Area of the fascioles (mm²) versus test length (mm) for *Plethotaenia spatangoides* (circles) and *P. angularis* (solid dots). Symbol with a vertical bar = peripetalous fasciole; symbol without a vertical bar = subanal fasciole.

The length of the subanal fasciole is 45.63 ± 0.70 per cent of the test length (S.D. 2.71, C.V. 5.94). The fasciole is usually narrow and inconspicuous. Its area is shown on Figure 23 plotted against the test length.

The plates crossed by this fasciole are: interambulacrum 5, plates 3, 4, and 5, and ambulacra I and V, plates 6, 7, and 8.

The Spines and Pedicellariae

The spines are straight and nonspatulate except for the plastron spines which are distally widened. The spines within the frontal notch may have a few thorns along their inner margin. The secondary spines are small and hair-like. The primaries are short, about 8 to 10 per cent of the test length, and sharply pointed. Their distribution is discussed in the

118

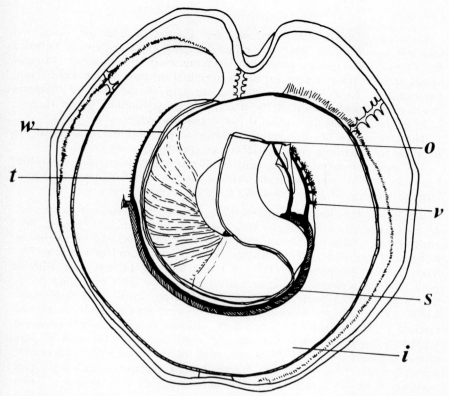

FIGURE 24. Anatomy of *Plethotaenia angularis: i* = lower loop of intestine; *o* = oesophagus; *s* = siphon; *t* = internal, marginal vessel, distal termination; *v* = internal, marginal vessel, termination at inferior loop of intestine; *w* = stone canal.

above sections on the ambulacra and interambulacra. The sphaeridia are not characteristic and are set in shallow depressions within the ambulacra of the oral side.

There are two forms of tridentate pedicellariae, one elongate (Plate 26, *d, f*), the other broad (Plate 26, *a, c*). The size of the valves of both forms varies from small (*ca.* 0.5 mm) to large (*ca.* 2 mm) for the elongate form in Plate 26, *d,* and *ca.* 1 mm long for the valve in Plate 26, *f*. The elongate type is similar to that of *P. spatangoides,* but the broad form shows some slight differences. In *P. angularis,* the distally widened portion of the valve is sharply set off from the neck and the basal portion of the valve is larger than the distal portion (Plate 26, *a, c*). Globiferous pedicellariae are rare.

Internal Anatomy

Concerning the internal anatomy see Figure 24 and the discussion under *P. spatangoides*. The only noticeable anatomical difference between the *Plethoteania* species is in the development of the internal marginal vessel and the relative position of the terminal opening of the siphon into the intestine. In *P. angularis,* the connection of the internal marginal vessel to the inferior loop of the intestine is proportionally longer than in *P. spatangoides,* and the siphon is proportionally longer.

The differences are not great, however, and additional dissections are required to determine their reliability as specific characters.

The eggs, observed in the gonads of specimens from station G-405, September 1964, were nucleate, with a diameter of 0.80 mm (twice as large as the eggs of *P. spatangoides* from the same station).

Holotype.— The holotype with spines attached is preserved in alcohol. Its measurements are: length, 106.2 mm; width, 98.6 mm; height, 46.7 mm; apical system to anterior end, 51.4 mm; anterior edge of peristome to anterior end of test, 25 mm; labrum to posterior end of the test, 75.3 mm; anterior, paired petal (IV) 29.1 mm long by 11 mm wide with 26 pore pairs in series b; posterior paired petal (V) 27.5 mm long by 11 mm wide with 23 pore pairs in series a; notch depth, 14.3 mm; notch width, 14 mm; length of subanal fasciole 46 mm, area enclosed by subanal fasciole 18 mm wide by 13.3 mm high; distance from the apical system to the peripetalous fascioles, anterior, 35 mm, posterior, 26 and 33 mm, lateral portions 21.5 and 27.3 mm; span of the petal ends, anterior 53 mm, posterior 33 mm; labrum length, 6 mm; plastron length 36.5 mm; plastron width, 24.5 mm (point C); anus width 11 mm, height 9.5 mm; peripetalous fasciole length, 310 mm.

The holotype is deposited in the United States National Museum along with three paratypes.

Type locality.—S.W. of Grand Bahama Island, 26°27'N., 79°21'W., 540 to 531 meters. June 1963, R/V GERDA sta. 158.

Distribution.—From the Straits of Florida to Barbados in depths of 150 to 623 meters. Relatively large populations are found just north of Cuba and just north of the Little Bahama Bank.

Discussion.—Ecology: The bathymetric range of this species has prevented direct ecological observations, and no collected specimens survived in aquaria.

Plethotaenia spatangoides is frequently taken in the same hauls with *P. angularis, Linopneustes longispinus* and *Paleopneustes cristatus.*

The substrate was discussed in the section on ecology under *P. spatangoides* above. *P. angularis* is also a fine sand or mud dweller.

As in *P. spatangoides,* a species of *Montacuta* is occasionally found attached to the spines of the frontal notch.

120

Comments: *Plethotaenia angularis* differs from *P. spatangoides* in many characters, the most obvious of which is the general difference in the shape of the test: *P. angularis* appears lower and more angular than *P. spatangoides*. The depth of the frontal notch, the distribution of the primary tubercles and the naked areas on the labrum and the anterolateral interambulacra offer excellent means of identification. Figure 21 shows the relationship of several characters between the two species. The K values and chances of a misclassification using any one of the characters are given in the legend to the chart. The span of the anterior petal ends, the depth of the notch and the depth of the notch compared to its width, the distance from the apical system to the anterior end of the test, the length of the subanal fasciole, the number of pore-pairs in the petals and the number of plates from the peristome to the petaloid portion of the anterior paired petals all offer useful characters for identification.

Plethotaenia is closely related to *Spatangus* but there is no difficulty in distinguishing between the two genera since *Spatangus* has no peripetalous fasciole. The fact that *Plethotaenia* has no close affinities with the Brissidae has been discussed in the generic discussion and under *P. spatangoides*.

Genus *Paleopneustes* A. Agassiz

Paleopneustes A. Agassiz, 1873, p. 188; 1874, p. 13; 1904, p. 178 (part).
Not *Paleopneustes*, Dames, 1877, p. 46 (= *Brissolampas*).
Palaeopneustes, Zittel, 1879, p. 536.
Paloeopneustes, Pomel, 1883, p. 30 (part).
Palaeopneustes, Duncan, 1889, p. 223.
Palaeopneustes, Wagner, 1903, p. 1 (part).
Palaeopneustes, Delage & Hérouard, 1903, p. 273.
Palaeopneustes, Meissner, 1904, p. 1389 (part).
Palaeopneustes, H. L. Clark, 1917, p. 143 (part); 1925, p. 196.
Paleopneustes, Lambert & Thiery, 1924, p. 446 (part).
Paleopneustes, Grant & Hertlein, 1938, p. 112 (part).
Palaeopneustes, Mortensen, 1950, p. 189.
Paleopneustes, Fischer, 1966, p. U624.

Diagnosis.—Ambulacrum III non-petaloid, flush with the test. Petals of lateral ambulacra flush with test or slightly sunken, open distally, interporiferous zone broad (*ca.* twice as wide as adjoining pore-pairs). Labrum extends posteriorly to third adjoining ambulacral plates. Marginal and peripetalous fasciole present in juveniles. Three genital pores.

Description.—Large spatangoids, reaching 130 to 150 mm in test length. The test is high and dome-shaped, flattened orally with the peristome and periproct slightly sunken. The ambulacra are flush with the test, petaloid; the interporiferous zone is broad and only slightly sunken in *P. cristatus*. The pore-series are open, with occluded plates at the distal ends (more common in *P. tholoformis*). The posterior ambulacra are naked from the ambitus to the peristome; the petals are about 40 per cent of the test length in the adults. The oral pore-pairs are double, the sensory pore-pairs

121

double or coalesced, and the respiratory pore-pairs double, only slightly conjugate. The tube-feet of ambulacrum III are simple; subanal tube-feet are present in the juveniles. The ambulacral plates between the plastron and posterior ambitus are not deformed as in species with a subanal fasciole.

The labrum is extended posteriorly to the third adjoining ambulacral plate. It is broad and fully tuberculated, well developed and extended anteriorly over the peristome. The plastron is short, *ca*. 30 per cent of the test length, narrower than the episternals. The periproct is above the ambitus in a slightly concave portion of the posterior end of the test, and is set obliquely in such a way as to be visible from below. The interambulacra 1 and 4 are not inserted into the peristome on the exterior of the test, internally produced into large calcite supports for the intestinal mesenteries; that of interambulacrum 1 smaller, non-functional. Interambulacra 2 and 3 are inserted to the peristome, internally produced into small, nonfunctional auricles. The plate structure of interambulacrum 1 is of great importance, the first interambulacral plate followed by a single plate, (plate 2a + 2b, cf. Loven 1883). The plate structure of interambulacrum 4 is of normal spatangoid type, the first plate followed by a pair of plates. The aboral plates evenly contoured, the test glossy, the tubercles easily dislodged (see under *P. tholoformis,* description of spines). The primary tubercles are small, their spines short, straight, fragile, thorny, irregularly scattered over the test.

Marginal fasciole present in younger specimens, crossing plates III (6b), 3 (3a and b), IV (10a or 9a), 4 (4a, 5b), V (11 or 12a), 5 (4 and 5). The peripetalous fasciole present in young specimens, crossing plates (the path not constant in 2, III, and 3) III (14), 3 (7 or 8 or both of both series), IV (17 to 20a), 4 (9 or 9 and 10 series a, 10 or 10 and 11 series b), V (20 to 23a), 5 (11 or 12).

Ophicephalous, tridentate, rostrate, triphyllous pedicellariae are present, the first very common all over the test.

Type-species.—*Paleopneustes cristatus* A. Agassiz, 1873.

Comments.—Mortensen (1950, p. 190) discussed the fossil specimens ascribed to this genus with the exception, of course, of the *Paleopneustes* from Japan (Morishita, 1953).

Mortensen was misled by Agassiz's (1883, p. 58) description of the young of this genus and, presumably, his insistence on the great similarity between this genus and *Linopneustes* is due to Agassiz's works of 1883 and 1904. Mortensen's entire family Paleopneustidae is not a natural grouping, as is pointed out by Mortensen (1950, p. 181). The majority of genera in this family are derived from, or are ancestral to, other families. The nonpetaloid or subpetaloid condition of the ambulacra is not necessarily a primitive state (as suspected by Clark, 1917 p. 99). *Paleopneustes* offers important evidence that, in this genus, the subpetaloid condition is a derived and not a primitive condition. Some of the oldest known fossil spatangoids have petaloid ambulacra (viz. the Toxasterids and Hemiasterids).

Since the fossil forms are poorly described, it is difficult to determine which fossil genera are closely related to *Paleopneustes*. There seem to be close affinities between *Paleopneustes* and *Pygospatangus* Cotteau, 1890 (Eocene of Spain), and *Prosostoma* Pomel, 1883 (Eocene or Miocene of Cuba). Of the living spatangoids, there are two closely allied genera, *Plesiozonus* de Meijere and *Pericosmus* L. Agassiz. The genus *Paleopneustes* differs from *Plesiozonus* in having a broader interporiferous zone and a better developed marginal fasciole. In addition, the petals of *Plesiozonus* are longer and the labrum reaches posteriorly to plate number two of the adjoining ambulacra. *Plesiozonus* is known from the Flores Sea (521 m) and off the Philippines (345 m). I have had the opportunity to examine specimens of *Pericosmus akabanus* (M.C.Z. 7400), *P. melanostomus* (U.S.N.M. type specimen) and *plesiozonus diodemae* (U.S.N.M.). I will give a brief comparative analysis of *Pericosmus akabanus, Plesiozonus,* and *Paleopneustes* to show the important similarities between the three genera. All three genera have (Table 13): the same general test shape; the peristome sunken with fairly well developed phyllodes and peripodia with double pore-pairs (Mortensen's 1950 text fig. 85 does not show the double pore-pairs, nor are they very clear in his pl. 15, fig. 6); a well developed labrum *ca.* 15 per cent of the test length, fully tuberculated, broad, extending posteriorly to the second adjoining ambulacral plate in *Per. akabanus* and *Pl. diodemae* and to the third in *Pal. cristatus;* a short plastron, *ca.* 30 to 35 per cent of the test length long and 22 per cent of the test length wide (narrower than the episternals); subanal tube-feet (only in the young of *Paleopneustes*), the ambulacral plates between the plastron and the ambitus not deformed; an anterior ambulacrum different from the lateral petals; the pore series of the paired petals open distally with occluded plates present; a marginal fasciole that crosses the same interambulacral plates; a peripetalous fasciole which is unstable on the anterior ambulacrum and the adjoining interambulacra, on plate 9 of series a interambulacrum 4, strongly indented between the petals and poorly developed (lacking in all the adults of *Paleopneustes* and in some adult *Plesiozonus*); small, evenly disrtibuted primary spines and tubercles, the spines thorny, straight, pointed; very similar pedicellariae (globiferous pedicellariae have not been found in *Paleopneustes,* and they are, according to Mortensen (1951b) quite rare in *Pericosmus*). Obviously, there are many similarities between the two genera which are characteristic of the entire order of Spatangoida and there is no point in listing these. There are, in addition to the characters mentioned above (particularly the oral peripodia, fascioles and plastron), three similarities which are of prime importance. The apical systems are very similar, ethmolytic with three genital pores of equal size. The structure of the test, described in the sec-

123

tion on the spines of *P. tholoformis* below, is alike in the three genera; the tests are glossy, with the tubercles easily dislodged leaving only a circular depression to indicate their former location. The third character is the most important: the first plate in interambulacrum 1 is followed by a single large plate. The plate of the posterior series which is normally adorally prolonged so as to touch or almost touch the first plate (as occurs on the opposite interambulacrum) is anteriorly truncated against the second plate. This is a fundamental change in the normal spatangoid asymmetry or "heteronomy" as described by Lovén (1883) and is identical in *Pericosmus, Plesiozonus,* and *Paleopneustes.* Thus, according to Lovén (1883, p. 14) and my own observations, the great majority of the spatangoids have plates 2a and 3a of interambulacrum 1 formed into a compound plate, (2 + 3a). In a few genera, however, plates 2a and 2b of interambulacrum 1 are united to form a compound plate (2a + 2b). This unusual formation is not easily overlooked. It is also found in two other recent genera; *Protenaster* (= *Desoria*) and *Faorina.* Lovén (1874) finds a similar condition in some of the Cretaceous genera of the family Holasteridae. *Protenaster* is not closely related to *Pericosmus* or *Paleopneustes.* It is probable that the 2 + 2 heteronomy is secondarily derived in *Protenaster* as it is in the genus *Brissus* where plate 1 is followed by only a single plate in both interambulacrum 1 and 4 but plates 2b and 3b are still united in interambulacrum 1 and separate in interambulacrum 4.

Faorina, because the type species supposedly has a latero-anal fasciole, was placed in the family Schizasteridae (Mortensen, 1951b, p. 245) along with a statement that this genus is probably most closely related to *Plesiozonus* (family Paleopneustidae). The fasciole is poorly developed, however, and does not connect with the peripetalous fasciole. It is, in fact, present only under the anal system where it could be either a marginal or a latero-anal fasciole. The typical schizasterid latero-anal fasciole joins the peripetalous fasciole on plate 5a of interambulacrum 4. In *Faorina,* the peripetalous fasciole is not found on plate 5a or even 6a and could not have met a hypothetical latero-anal fasciole on plate 5a. *Faorina,* therefore, has a peripetalous and a marginal fasciole as do species of the genera *Pericosmus, Plesiozonus,* and *Paleopneustes.* Re-examination of the type specimens of *Faorina chinensis* Gray, 1851 (B.M.N.H. 47.6.18.5 and 51.3.12.66), uncovered many other taxonomic characters shared by *Faorina, Pericosmus, Paleopneustes,* and *Plesiozonus.* All four genera have: plate 1 of interambulacrum 1 followed by a single plate; oral peripodia with double pores; interambulacra 1 and 4 excluded from the peristome; subanal tubefeet; an ethmolytic apical system with three gonopores; the peripetalous fasciole unstable on interambulacra 2 and 3; a high, domed test with a flattened oral surface; a well developed, fully tuberculated labrum; a short, broad plastron; occluded plates at the distal ends of the petals; open poreseries in the petals; purple coloration; and very similar tuberculation. Considering these numerous similarities, it is clear that these genera, and

124

probably *Prosostoma,* belong to the same large, and probably very old, branch of the amphisternous spatangoids.

To summarize, *Paleopneustes* is more closely related to *Plesiozonus* than to any other spatangoid genus. The loss of fascioles and the change from an advanced, burrowing spatangoid to a surface-dwelling urchin during ontogeny can lead to two conclusions. The first is that the adult characters of *Paleopneustes* are a condition derived from forms with distinct fascioles and petals (such as *Pericosmus*) and that *Paleopneustes* is a specialized form of spatangoid, adapted to survive as an adult on the surface of the substrate. The second possible conclusion is that *Paleopneustes* is ancestral to more specialized spatangoids (such as *Pericosmus* and *Faorina*) and that the young stages are evidence that evolution in the spatangoids progresses by neoteny. Arguments can be given for both conclusions and fossil evidence can be offered to support both views. In my opinion, the best conclusion is that *Paleopneustes* is a secondary derivation, hence the first hypothesis is probably correct. This view is strengthened by the fact that other unrelated urchins have derived the same general shape (i.e., *Conolampas,* a cassiduloid). Probably the dome-shaped test, sub-petaloid ambulacra, and marginal periproct are all adaptations for large irregular urchins which live on the surface of the deep-sea sediments.

Key to the Recent Species of the Genus
Paleopneustes

1. Paired petals with a bare interporiferous zone, 17 or 18 plates from the peristome to the petal in ambulacrum IV, 19 to 21 in ambulacrum V .... *P. cristatus*
1. Paired petals with interporiferous zone tuberculated, 19 or 20 plates from the peristome to the petal in ambulacrum IV, 21 to 23 in ambulacrum V .... *P. tholoformis*

Paleopneustes tholoformis, n. sp.
Figure 25; Plates 27, 28*e, f,* 29*a, f;* Tables 10, 12

Paleopneustes cristatus A. Agassiz, 1873, p. 188 (part).
Paleopneustes cristatus, A. Agassiz, 1874, p. 14 (part).
Paleopneustes cristatus, A. Agassiz, 1878, p. 192 (part).
Paleopneustes cristatus, A. Agassiz, 1880, p. 81 (part).
Paleopneustes cristatus, A. Agassiz, 1883, p. 58 (part).
Paleopneustes cristatus, Rathbun, 1885, p. 615 (part).
Paleopneustes cristatus, Rathbun, 1886, p. 287 (part).
Palaeopneustes cristatus, Wagner, 1903, p. 1 (part).
Palaeopneustes cristatus, A. Agassiz, 1904, p. 179 (part).
Palaeopneustes cristatus, Meissner, 1904, p. 1389 (part).
Palaeopneustes cristatus, Mortensen, 1910, p. 99 (part).
Palaeopneustes cristatus, H. L. Clark, 1917, p. 144 (part).
Palaeopneustes cristalus, Lambert & Thiery, 1924, p. 446 (part).
Palaeopneustes cristatus, H. L. Clark, 1925, p. 196 (part).

Palaeopneustes cristatus, H. L. Clark, 1945, p. 124 (part).
Palaeopneustes cristatus, Mortensen, 1950, p. 191 (part).
Paleopneustes cristatus, Fischer, 1966, p. U624 (part).

Material examined.—32 specimens, 125 to 150 mm test length, GERDA
sta. G-239, eastern Straits of Florida off Browns Cay, 25°20′N., 79°15′W.,
348-256 m, January 1964.—5 specimens, 119 to 144 mm test length, sta.
G-272, eastern Straits of Florida off Cat Cay, 25°28′N., 79°18′W., 384-

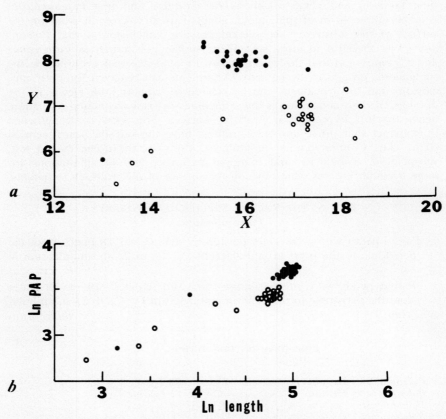

FIGURE 25. *A,* Identification diagram for species of *Paleopneustes: X =* width
of plastron (point A, percentage of test length) + width width of anterior
petal (percentage of anterior petal length) + ine-half the length of posterior
petal (percentage of anterior petal length) + one-half the span of the distal
ends of anterior petals (percentage of test length) + span of the distal ends of
posterior petals (percentage of test length) all divided by 10; *Y =* pores in
an anterior petal (IV, series b) + plates from peristome to petals (IVa + Va)
all divided by 10.—*B,* Graph showing relation of respiratory pore-pairs to
test length: natural logarithm of number of pores in anterior petal (PAP) (IV,
series b) versus natural logarithm of test length (mm).

126

357 m, March 1964.—1 specimen, 143 mm test length, sta. G-508, eastern Straits of Florida off Great Isaac, 26°02'N., 79°18'W., 403 m, March 1965.—1 specimen, 144 mm test length, sta. G-523, N.W. Providence Channel, 26°13'N., 78°50'W., 512 m, March 1965.—2 specimens, 23.5 and 50 mm test length, PILLSBURY sta. P-372, off N.W. Colombia, 9°45'N., 76°12'W., 525 m, July 1966.—1 specimen from Montserrat, 161 m; B.M.N.H. 1892.2.25.25.—1 specimen, 135 mm test length, 183 m, off Barbados; M.C.Z. 2808.—2 specimens, 122 and 130 mm test length, off Frederikstad, 330 m; M.C.Z. 2700.—2 specimens, 125 mm test length, off Barbados, 133 to 155 m; M.C.Z. 2810.—1 specimen, 129 mm test length; U.S.N.M. 6828.

Diagnosis.—Tubercles evenly distributed on dorsal surface, interporiferous zone of petals tuberculated and flush with surface of test. There are 19 or 20 plates from the peristome to the anterior petal (IVa), 21 to 23 plates to the posterior petal (Va). Tridentate pedicellariae small (*ca.* 1.8 mm valve length), distal end of blade not sharply set off from neck (See also Fig. 25).

Description.—The test is high and dome-shaped, rising to a peak in some specimens, with an oval outline (Plate 27). The ventral side is flat, with the anteriorly placed peristome sunken. The periproct is on a slightly concave portion of the posterior and of the test. The test has a mean width of 85.24±0.20 per cent of the test length (S.D. 1.31, C.V. 1.54) and a mean height of 64.12±0.46 per cent of the test length (S. D. 2.95, C. V. 4.60). The proportional width decreases slightly with growth, and the height increases its proportion with growth. Individual variation, however, is greater than the allometric changes. No geographic variation was found; the greatest variation occurs in the specimens from sta. G-239. The shape of the test, viewed laterally, varies considerably with growth. The apical system becomes more peaked, the oral side flatter, and the anal system more hooded and much smaller in the larger specimens. The ambitus, which is slightly rounded in small specimens, becomes sharply defined in larger specimens.

The dorsal interambulacral plates rise toward their midlines forming a low and indistinct elevation from the apical system to the ambitus in each plate series (except in interambulacrum 5). These elevations are visible in a specimen 50 mm in test length but not in one 23.5 mm in test length.

The Anterior Ambulacrum

The anterior ambulacrum is flush with the test from the apical system to the ambitus and is slightly sunken below the ambitus to the peristome. The plates of III show a transformation in shape adjoining interambulacral plate 6. Below this point, to the ambitus, the plates are about twice as broad as high. Above this point, to the apical system, the plates are distinctly higher, almost as high as wide. The peripetalous fasciole, which

127

disappears with growth, crosses interambulacrum 3 on plate 7 or 8 of series a. The change in the ambulacral plate structure just described probably indicates the area delimited by the peripetalous fasciole in the juvenile.

The tube-feet of ambulacrum III are simple and non-penicillate, and are situated over microscopic, double pores located in the center of each plate. The pore-pairs are best developed near the apical system and at the ambitus. At the apical system, the pores are separated by a well developed, projecting muscle support. Below the ambitus, the pore-pairs increase in

TABLE 10

STATISTICAL SUMMARY: *Palaeopneustes tholoformis*

Character	Mean	S.E.	S.D.	Range	N	C.V.
tl*	139.18	1.25	8.02	119-158	42	
tw	85.24	0.20	1.31	82-88	42	1.54
h	64.12	0.46	2.95	57-71	42	4.60
ax	46.79	0.17	1.06	45-50	38	2.26
pa	19.86	0.13	0.78	18-21	37	3.93
lp	77.11	0.23	1.37	74-80	37	1.78
ap	43.07	0.32	2.05	38-47	42	4.70
ap†	16.60	0.24	1.56	14-22	42	9.40
pp	40.24	0.36	2.29	36-45	42	5.70
ppw†	19.38	0.26	1.66	16-22	42	8.57
aipz†	8.23	0.22	1.33	5.5-11	38	16.20
pipz†	10.78	0.27	1.62	6.6-15	38	15.00
pp/ap‡	93.33	0.49	3.14	88-100	42	3.37
pl	31.91	0.45	2.62	29-46	35	8.21
a	10.32	0.19	1.09	8.2-12	34	10.50
b	17.74	0.18	1.08	16-20	35	6.10
c	21.20	0.14	0.82	20-23	35	3.86
ape	69.97	0.35	2.16	66-74	38	3.09
ppe	50.79	0.41	2.47	46-57	38	4.87
aw/ah‡	87.31	0.87	5.60	75-100	42	6.41
ah	14.00	0.16	1.02	11-16	42	7.30
l	13.74	0.10	0.60	12-15	35	4.36

Data are expressed as percentages of test length unless otherwise indicated. Character symbols are given in Figure 1; others are: aipz = width of interporiferous zone of anterior petal. pipz = width of interporiferous zone of posterior petal.
*Test length (mm).
‡Ratio expressed as a percentage.
†Percentage of respective petal length.

size and are located on the oral side of each plate. The phyllode is sunken and fairly well developed, with ten feeding tube-feet. The peripodia are recessed and circular. The central portion consists of a high, flat muscle support which separates the pores, leaving one anterior and one posterior pore. The pores unite before reaching the interior of the test. Occasionally, the muscle supports do not meet over the pores, leaving a single bilobed pore, and occasionally the anteriormost pore is poorly formed or closed.

The tuberculation of ambulacrum III is continuous with that of the adjoining interambulacra, except at the phyllode which lacks primary tubercles.

Ambulacra II and IV
(the anterior paired petals)

The tuberculation of the anterior, paired ambulacra is continuous with that of the adjoining interambulacra except in the poriferous zone of the petals and the interporiferous zone of the phyllodes. The interporiferous zone of the paired petals is flush with the test and has many primary tubercles (normally one per ambulacral plate) (Plate 27). The number of plates from the peristome to the first petaloid plates (marked by the onset of respiratory tube-foot pore-pairs) is either 19 or 20 in series a of ambulacrum IV. The percentage of occurrence of these numbers of plates in the specimens examined is: 19 (54 per cent) and 20 (46 per cent). A single specimen was found with only 18 plates in this series.

There are 15 or 16 feeding tube-feet per phyllode. These tube-feet are situated over peripodia similar to those found in the anterior phyllode. The double pore-pairs, however, are not oriented one anterior, one posterior, but instead are one adoral, one aboral. Again, it is the inner pore-pair which is best developed and the aboral pore-pair may become reduced or obliterated in some peripodia of older specimens.

Sensory podia are located from the phyllode to the petaloid area. The pores are single and situated on the adoral edge of the plate near and below the ambitus and in the center of the plate near the petaloid area. These podia are not well developed and may be lacking entirely from the ambitus to the petal.

The two pore-series of the petals are open distally and are normally straight. The inner pore of the pore-pair is rounded and smaller than the tear-drop-shaped outer pore. The last two to four pore-pairs may be on occuluded plates (i.e., the plates do not reach the adjoining interambulacral border) (Plate 27f). At least one or two occluded plates are found at the distal ends of all the petals in all specimens. One or two specimens were found with no occluded plates on one of the petals but had normal development on the other three petals.

The number of pore-pairs increases logarithmically with growth. Figure 25 shows the natural log of the pore-pairs (IV, series a) plotted against the natural log of the length. The apicalmost pore-pairs are underdeveloped (2 to 4 in each pore series) and each pore is separated from the other by a projecting ridge. These apicalmost pore-pairs bear podia similar to those of the anterior ambulacrum. The pore-pairs of the aboral half of each petal are situated on the lateral portion of each ambulacral plate. On the adoral half of the petal, the pore-pairs are in the center of the plates and primary tubercles are situated on the plates lateral to the pore-pairs.

The length of the petal (IV) has a mean of 43.07 ± 0.32 per cent of the

129

test length (S.D. 2.05, C.V. 4.70). This proportion increases with growth; it is only 30 per cent of the test length in a specimen 50 mm long and 23 per cent of the test length in a 23.5 mm specimen. The width of the petal is 16.60±0.24 per cent of the petal length (S.D. 1.56, C.V. 9.40). The interporiferous zone has a mean width of 8.23±0.22 per cent of the petal length (S. D. 1.33, C. V. 16.2). The distance between the anterior petal ends is 69.97±0.35 per cent of the test length (S. D. 2.16, C. V. 3.09). This proportion increases with growth. It is 54 per cent in a specimen 50 mm in test length and 43 per cent in a specimen 23.5 mm in test length.

Ambulacra I and V
(the posterior paired petals)

The tuberculation of the posterior, paired ambulacra is continuous with that of the adjoining interambulacra from the apical system to the ambitus. The areas adjacent to the plastron are naked from the ambitus to the peristome with the exception of secondary tubercles and a series of primary tubercles which encroach on the lateral edges of the plates.

The interporiferous zone is flush with the test with one primary tubercle per plate. The number of plates from the peristome to the petaloid portion of the ambulacra (V) varies from 21 to 23 plates in the following percentages: 21 (5 per cent), 22 (71 per cent), 23 (24 per cent). There are 8 feeding tube-feet per phyllode in the large specimens. The peripodia are like those of the other phyllodes. The sensory podia are located over small, V-shaped pores at the adoral edge of each plate from the phyllode to the ambitus, except in the smaller specimens (and a few large ones), where penicillate subanal tube-feet occur in the posterior plate series from the posterior end of the plastron to the ambitus. These subanal tube-feet are situated over double pores at the adoral edge of plates 7, 8, 9, and 10. The plates are not distorted so as to curve in behind the plastron as is normal with those spatangoids with a subanal fasciole. The subanal tube-feet are very poorly developed in the adults and only moderately developed in the juveniles.

The petaloid area is similar to the anterior paired petals with the exception that there may be one or two pore-pairs per series difference (either plus or minus). The mean length of the posterior petal (V) is 40.24±0.36 per cent of the test length (S. D. 2.29, C. V. 5.70) and 93.33±0.49 per cent of the anterior petal length (S. D. 3.14, C. V. 3.37). Both of these proportions increase with growth. The width of the posterior paired petal is 19.38±0.26 per cent of its own length (S. D. 1.66, C. V. 8.57).

The posterior paired petals are straight and divergent from the apical system. Their distal ends span a distance of 50.79±0.41 per cent of the test length (S. D. 2.47, C. V. 4.87). The interporiferous zone is 10.78±0.27 per cent of the petal length (S. D. 1.62, C. V. 15.0).

130

The Interambulacra

The number of interambulacral plates from the peristome to the fascioles is discussed in the section on fascioles.

The primary tuberculation of the interambulacra is sparse and irregularly scattered over the dorsal surface (the tubercles themselves are discussed in the section on spines). Secondary tubercles, also sparse and irregularly distributed on the dorsal surface, show no relationship with the primary tubercles. At, and below, the ambitus, tuberculation becomes fairly dense but shows no indication of regularity except on the plastron where the tubercles are arranged pinnately from the midline of the plastron.

The first plates of interambulacra 1 and 4 are excluded from the peristome on the exterior of the test. On the interior of the test, they are built up to form supports for the intestinal mesenteries. The "perignathic apophysis" (Gordon 1926) on the left side of the animal is well developed and projects posteriorly, forming a broad, flattened support. The projection of interambulacrum 1 is not functional and is non-spatulate. The first plates of interambulacra 2 and 3 are inserted to the peristome. These plates are also built up on the interior of the test, forming small, non-functional auricles. The labrum is fully tuberculated and projects posteriorly to the middle of the third adjoining ambulacral plate. It is strongly developed, with the anterior edge crescent-shaped. Its length is 13.74±0.10 per cent of the test length (S.D. 0.60, C.V. 4.36).

The plastron has a mean length of 31.91±0.45 per cent of the test length. Its width, measured at points A, B, and C, is:

point	mean	S.E.	S.D.	C.V.
A	10.32	0.19	1.09	10.5
B	17.74	0.18	1.08	6.1
C	21.20	0.14	0.82	3.86

The plastron is proportionally larger in younger specimens (36 per cent in a specimen 50 mm in test length) and is proportionally wider in the smaller specimens (at point C, the width is 26 per cent of the test length in a 50 mm specimen).

The Apical System

The apical system is ethmolytic, situated anteriorly on the dorsal surface at a mean distance from the anterior end of 46.79±0.17 per cent of the test length (S.D. 1.06, C.V. 2.26). During growth, the apical system shifts to a slightly more posterior position. There are 3 genital pores of equal size; the right, anterior pore is lacking in all the specimens. The pores are not present in a specimen 50 mm in test length. The madreporic plate projects slightly past the posterior oculars. It is broad and slightly elevated.

The Periproct and Peristome

The periproct is situated just above the ambitus on the posterior end

131

of the test (Plate 27). The dorsal portion of the periproct extends posteriorly farther than the ventral portion. The periproct is enclosed by interambulacral plates 4, 5, 6, and 7. It is oval, with the longer diameter vertical. The mean width of the periproct is 14.00 ± 0.16 per cent of the test length (S.D. 1.02, C.V. 7.3), and 87.31 ± 0.87 per cent of the periproct height (S.D. 5.60, C.V. 6.41).

The peristome is situated anteriorly, its leading edge having a mean distance from the anterior end of the test of 19.86 ± 0.13 per cent of the test length (S.D. 0.78, C.V. 3.93). The anterior edge of the labrum has a mean distance from the posterior end of the test of 77.11 ± 0.23 per cent of the test length (S.D. 1.37, C.V. 1.78). The peristome is crescent-shaped.

The Fascioles

The marginal fasciole disappears completely with growth. In one specimen 119 mm in test length, faint traces are still visible. The marginal fasciole is still present in a specimen 50 mm in test length. The marginal fasciole crosses the following plates: III (6b), 3 (3a and b), IV (10a), 4 (4a, 5b), V (12), 5 (4 and 5). This fasciole passes under the periproct exactly as it does in *Pericosmus*. Its course is just above the ambitus around the circumference of the test except at the posterior end. The length of the marginal fasciole is 300 per cent of the test length.

The peripetalous fasciole also disappears completely with growth. In the specimen 50 mm in test length it is still faintly visible. It crosses the following plates: III (ca. 14), 3 (7 or 8 of both series), IV (19 or 20), 4 (9 and 10 of series a, 10 series b), V (22a), 5 (11 and 12a). The length of the peripetalous fasciole is 140 per cent of the test length in the 50-mm specimen. The development of this fasciole on interambulacra 2 and 3 and ambulacrum III is irregular and in these areas the fasciole seems to follow no set course.

The Spines

The spines are serrated (Plate 29f) and fragile. Mortensen (1950, text fig. 144a) illustrated the cross section of a spine from *P. cristatus*. The spines are sharply pointed except on the plastron where they are somewhat spatulate. There is an anal and apical tuft of spines. The spines are shorter and thinner than those of *P. cristatus*. The primary tubercles are peculiar in that they are set on the surface of the test, not at all recessed, and can be easily dislodged leaving only a circular depression to mark their former location. This is the result of the peculiar calcite structure of the test, which, as in most spatangoids, is made up of an outer, dense layer and an inner, porous layer. In most spatangoids, the outer layer is fairly thick and is continuous with the calcite of the tubercles. In *Paleopneustes,* however, the outer layer is extremely thin and forms a dense, glossy surface on which the tubercles and their auricles are set. Perhaps the best description of this condition would be: test glossy, tubercles easily dislodged.

132

The Sphaeridia and Pedicellariae

The sphaeridia are set in shallow depressions near the feeding tube-feet and in the center of each ambulacral plate from the phyllode to the posterior ambitus.

The pedicellariae are not strikingly different from those found in *P. cristatus*. The large form of the tridentate pedicellariae does not, however, reach as large a size as in *P. cristatus*. The maximum valve length is about 1.8 mm. The distal end of the blade is not sharply set off from the neck and the auricles are not as low and angular as in *P. cristatus* (Plate 32 *e, f*). In *P. tholoformis*, the raised calcite ridges of the blade are better developed. The other pedicellariae (Plate 29) do not offer any constant specific characters. As in *P. cristatus*, the ophicephalous pedicellariae are almost as abundant as the secondary spines.

Internal Anatomy

No characters of specific value were found in the internal anatomy of this species. It might be mentioned, however, that there are two siphons and one caecum. The right, anterior gonad is missing entirely and the left anterior gonad is bilobed in the usual spatangoid pattern.

Holotype.—The holotype is a specimen 133.6 mm in test length (Plate 27), dried and denuded of spines. The test has been sprayed with a thin layer of lacquer in preparation for photography and to strengthen it. Dimensions, given as percentages of the test length, are: width, 85; height, 66; apical system to anterior end, 47; peristome to anterior end, 19; labrum to posterior end, 76; length of anterior petal, 42; length of posterior petal, 39; plastron, 31; plastron width, A, 12, B, 19, C, 21; span of the distal ends of the anterior paired petals, 70; span of the posterior paired petals, 50; periproct width, 15; labrum length, 13. The width of the anterior petal is 18 per cent of its length and that of the interporiferous zone 10 per cent of its length. The width of the posterior petal is 21 per cent of its length. The posterior petal is 93 per cent of the anterior petal. There are 20 plates to the petal in ambulacrum IVa and 22 plates to the posterior petal (Va). Seven paratypes, 136 to 148 mm test length, were also selected from the type locality. The specimens are deposited in the Museum of Comparative Zoology.

Type locality.—The holotype and paratypes are from R/V GERDA station 239 off Browns Cay in the eastern Straits of Florida (25°20′N., 79°15′W., 348 to 256 m, January 1964). The substrate is a fine, white sand; median particle size, 0.25 mm, silt and clay fraction 19.9 per cent by weight. The sand has a sorting coefficient of 10, indicating a well mixed substrate.

Distribution.—*Paleopneustes tholoformis* is known from Barbados to the northern end of the Straits of Florida. It has also been taken from Colom-

133

bia and the Gulf of Mexico, indicating a wide distribution in the tropical western Atlantic. Depth range: 133 to 525 meters.

Discussion.—Abnormalities: no pronounced abnormalities were found.

Ecology: Nothing is known of the ecology of this species. The general shape of the test would indicate that the species does not burrow as an adult. This is supported by the large numbers of live adults captured by surface trawls in an unbroken condition. The young specimens are rarely taken whole or alive. The presence of fascioles and the general shape of the younger specimens indicate that they burrow. The color in life is dark purple.

Comments: This species is frequently found at the same station with *P. cristatus.* A. Agassiz's syntypes in the M.C.Z. consist of one specimen of *P. cristatus* and one of *P. tholoformis,* both in the same container. It is clear that Agassiz believed the two forms to be polytypic members of the same species. As with the two sympatric species of *Plethotaenia,* the two forms may be dredged separately, with no representatives of the other type, or together in no definite proportion. No intermediate specimens occur, and the characters mentioned in the diagnosis seem constant. These two facts make the polytypic species concept less acceptable, but do not rule out the possibility. For a continuation of this argument, see the section on sympatric species in the taxonomic conclusions. The young specimens are more difficult to identify, as the tuberculation of the petaloid area does not develop until after the fascioles have faded (probably about 60 mm test length) and insufficient numbers of small specimens have been captured to produce a satisfactory series. The number of plates from the peristome to the petals seems to hold good for the small specimens as well as the larger ones as do the characters of Fig. 25.

Paleopneustes cristatus A. Agassiz, 1873
Figure 25; Plates 28*a-d,* 29*b-e, g,* 30, 31*a-f,* 32*a-d, g;* Tables 10, 12

Paleopneustes cristatus A. Agassiz, 1873, p. 188 (part).
Paleopneustes cristatus, A. Agsasiz, 1874, p. 14 (part), pl. 4, figs. 1-3.
Paleopneustes cristatus, A. Agassiz, 1878, p. 192 (part).
Paleopneustes cristatus, A. Agassiz, 1880, p. 81 (part).
Paleopneustes cristatus, A. Agassiz, 1883, p. 58, pl. 21 (part).
Paleopneustes cristatus, Rathbun, 1885, p. 615 (part).
Paleopneustes cristatus, Rathbun, 1886, p. 287 (part).
Palaeopneustes cristatus, Wagner, 1903, p. 1 (part).
Palaeopneustes cristatus, A. Agassiz, 1904, p. 179 (part), pls. 95, 96, text figs. 261, 265, 266, 269.
Palaeopneustes cristatus, Meissner, 1904, p. 1389 (part).
Palaeopneustes cristatus, Mortensen, 1910, p. 99 (part).
Palaeopneustes cristatus, H. L. Clark, 1917, p. 144, pl. 145, 13-19 (part).
Palaeopneustes cristalus, Lambert & Thiery, 1924, p. 446 (part).
Palaeopneustes cristatus, H. L. Clark, 1925, p. 196 (part).
Paleopneustes cristatus, Grant & Hertlein, 1938, p. 112, pl. 24.
Palaeopneustes cristatus, H. L. Clark, 1945, p. 124 (part).

134

Palaeopneustes cristatus, Mortensen, 1950, p. 191 (part), pl. 4, fig. 2, pl. 8, fig. 1, pl. 22, figs. 7, 9-12, 18, 19, pl. 23, figs. 11,12, 20.
?*Palaeopneustes* cf. *cristatus,* Morishita, 1953, p. 27, pl. 3, fig. 1 (= *Plesiozonus?*).
Paleopneustes cristatus, Fischer, 1966, p. U624 (part), fig. 509.

Material examined.—Fragments, GERDA sta. G-199, middle of the Straits of Florida, off Miami, 25°47′N., 79°47′W., 805 m, September 1963.— 1 specimen, 65.4 mm test length, sta. G-393, N.W. of Little Bahama Bank, 27°22′N., 79°11′W., 165 m, rubble bottom, September 1964.—1 specimen, 107 mm test length, sta. G-405, north of western end of Little Bahama Bank, 27°48.5′N., 79°00′W., 549 m, September 1964.—2 specimens, 106 and 114 mm test length, sta. G-523, N.W. Providence Channel, 26°13′N., 78°50′W., 512 m, March 1965.—fragment, sta. G-695, south of Grand Bahama Island, 26°28′N., 78°37′W., 555-575 m, July 1965.—2 specimens, *ca.* 50 and 60 mm test length (broken), sta. G-698, south of Grand Bahama Island, 26°28′N., 78°42′W., 329-165 m, July 1965.—1 specimen, 51 mm test length, sta. G-683, north of Berry Islands, 25°52′N., 77°54′W., 227 m, July 1965.—11 specimens, 112 to 130 mm test length, G-722, south of Grand Bahama Island, 26°15′N., 78°57′W., 393 m, August 1965.—1 specimen, 115 mm test length; ATLANTIS, off Cuba; I.M.S. 42.37.—1 specimen 33.8 mm test length, PILLSBURY sta. P-372, off N.W. Colombia, 9°45′N., 76°12′W., 525 m, July 1966.—2 specimens, 29.5 and 16.7 mm test length, sta. P-392, off N.W. Colombia, 9°45′N., 76°09′W., 76 m, July 1966.—1 specimen, 43 mm test length, off Barbados, 103 m; M.C.Z. 2807.—1 specimen, 105 mm test length, off Martinique, 384 m; B.M.N.H. 1892.2.25.26.—1 specimen, 88 mm test length, BLAKE, off Barbados, 150 m; Zool. Mus. Amsterdam.—2 specimens, 121 and 125 mm test length, ATLANTIS sta. 3000, off Cuba, 21°23′N., 81°29′W., 467 m, March 1938; M.C.Z. 7819. —1 specimen, 82 mm test length, off Dominica, 367 m; M.C.Z. 2806.— 1 specimen, 104 mm test length, off Barbados, 183 m; M.C.Z. 2808.— 1 specimen, 110 mm test length, off Martinique, 385 m; M.C.Z. 2809.— 1 specimen, 124 mm test length, off Dominica, 172 m; M.C.Z. 2804.— 1 specimen, 115 mm test length, off Montserrat, B.W.I., 220 m; M.C.Z. 2793.—11 specimens, 77 to 119 mm test length, ATLANTIS sta. 3386, Old Bahama Channel off Cuba, 22°33′N., 78°11′W., 403 m, April 1939; M.C.Z. 7820.—6 specimens, 106 to 117 mm test length, ATLANTIS sta. 2982d, Old Bahama Channel, off Cuba, 22°44.5′N., 78°41′W., 330 m, March 1938; M.C.Z. 7818.

Diagnosis.—Primary tubercles not present in interporiferous zone of petals or along midline of interambulacrum 5 or in interporiferous zone of III. There are 17 or 18 plates from peristome to anterior petal (IVa), 19 to 21 plates to posterior petal (Va). Tridentate pedicellariae large (*ca.* 2 to 3 mm valve length), with long neck, distal end sharply set off from neck, auricles low and angular. See also Fig. 25.

135

Description.—The test is high and dome-shaped, the outline oval, the ventral side flat. The periproct is on a slightly concave portion of the posterior end of the test. The test has a mean width of 87.17 ± 0.39 per cent of the test length (S.D. 2.46, C.V. 2.82) and a mean height of 61.61 ± 0.54 per cent of the test length (S.D. 3.43, C.V. 5.56). The width, which becomes proportionally less with growth, is 95 per cent of the test length in a specimen with a test length of 16.7 mm. The height shows much individual variation but no definite allometric trend. The shape of the test, viewed laterally, varies considerably with growth. The aboral surface becomes more dome-shaped, the periproct proportionally smaller and more hooded, and the oral side much flatter. The ambitus, slightly rounded in small specimens, becomes sharply defined in larger specimens (Plates 27, 28*a-d*, 30*a-f*).

The dorsal interambulacral plates rise toward their midlines to form a low and indistinct elevation from the apical system to the ambitus in each plate series. These elevations are visible in the smallest specimen (16.7 mm) but may be missing entirely in some larger specimens.

TABLE 11

STATISTICAL SUMMARY: *Paleopneustes cristatus*

Character	Mean	S.E.	S.D.	Range	N	C.V.
tl*	111.19	1.90	12.19	77-130	42	
tw	87.17	0.39	2.46	81-94	41	2.82
h	61.61	0.54	3.43	53-71	41	5.56
ax	47.67	0.43	1.62	44-51	15	3.40
pa	20.67	0.19	0.70	20-22	15	3.38
lp	76.07	0.27	1.00	74-78	15	1.31
ap	41.62	0.33	2.09	38-47	42	5.02
apw†	21.05	0.42	2.64	16-28	41	12.5
pp	40.45	0.34	2.18	35-46	42	5.40
ppw†	23.51	0.42	2.64	19-31	41	11.21
aipz†	10.21	0.45	1.74	6.5-12	16	17.00
pipz†	12.32	0.54	2.10	7.1-15	16	17.00
pp/ap‡	97.21	0.52	3.36	87-106	42	3.46
pl	32.56	0.52	2.03	30-38	16	6.24
a	13.47	0.45	1.67	11-18	16	12.4
b	19.69	0.30	1.16	18-22	16	5.90
c	22.94	0.25	0.97	21-24	16	4.23
ape	72.33	0.57	2.15	69-76	15	2.98
ppe	54.73	0.77	2.89	52-61	15	5.29
aw/ah‡	93.62	1.75	11.18	75-122	42	12.6
ah	13.10	0.22	1.38	10-16	42	10.5
l	15.56	0.18	0.70	14-17	16	4.5

Data are expressed as percentages of test length unless otherwise indicated. Character symbols are as given in Figure 1, except: aipz = width of interporiferous zone of anterior petal. pipz = width of interporiferous zone of posterior petal.
*Test length (mm).
†Percentage of respective petal length.
‡Ratio expressed as a percentage.

The Anterior Ambulacrum

The anterior ambulacrum is flush with the test from the apical system to the ambitus where it becomes slightly sunken to the peristome. The plates show a transformation in shape adjoining interambulacral plate 6. Below this point, to the ambitus, the plates are about twice as wide as high. Above this point, to the apical system, the plates are distinctly higher, almost as high as wide. The peripetalous fasciole, which disappears with growth, crosses interambulacrum 3 on plate 7 or 8 of series a. The change in the ambulacral plate structure just described probably indicates the area delimited by the peripetalous fasciole in the juvenile.

The tube-feet of ambulacrum III are simple and non-penicillate. They are situated over microscopic double pores located in the center of each plate. The pores are best developed near the apical system and at the ambitus. Nearest the apex, the pores are single and fairly large. Below the ambitus, the pores increase in size and are located on the oral side of each plate. The phyllode is sunken and well developed with 10 feeding tube-feet. The peripodia are recessed and oval. The auricle is broad, extending antero-laterally from the large pore. The pore is double in most peripodia with a low, poorly developed muscle support. The muscle support is very well formed in the smaller specimens, projecting high above the peripodia. In some of the larger specimens, some of the peripodia have the muscle support resorbed leaving only a single pore (Plate 30f).

The tuberculation of ambulacrum III is continuous with that of the adjoining interambulacra except along the interporiferous zone of the upper portion of the ambulacrum and at the phyllode. There is a single series of large primary tubercles in the interporiferous zone close to the apical system which is continuous to the large tubercles of the adjoining interambulacra. Together, these tubercles, with their spines, produce the apical tuft of spines.

Ambulacra II and IV
(the anterior paired petals)

The tuberculation of the anterior, paired ambulacra is continuous with that of the adjoining interambulacra from the petal to just below the ambitus. The petaloid portion of the ambulacra has no primary tubercles (Plate 30d). The phyllodes are also naked. The number of plates from the peristome to the first petaloid plates (marked by the appearance of respiratory tube-foot pore-pairs) is 17 or 18 in series a of ambulacrum IV. Of the specimens examined, 50 per cent had 17 plates and 50 percent had 18.

There are 15 to 16 feeding tube-feet per phyllode. These tube-feet are situated over peripodia similar to those found in the anterior phyllode.

Sensory podia are located from the phyllode to the petaloid area. The pores are single and situated on the adoral edge of the plate near and below the ambitus and in the center of the plate near the petaloid area.

137

The two pore-series of the petaloid portion are open distally and are normally straight. The inner pore of the pore-pair is smaller and rounder than the outer pore. Occluded plates are not frequently found at the ends of the petals. When they are present, there is usually only one occluded plate per pore-series. The pore-pairs are distinctly larger in this species than in *P. tholoformis*. The interporiferous zone, in addition to being naked, is slightly sunken below the level of the test. The respiratory tube-feet are shown in Plate 31*d*.

The number of pore-pairs increases logarithmically with growth. Figure 25 shows the natural log of the pore-pairs (IV, series a) plotted against the natural log of the length. The apicalmost 5 to 8 pore-pairs are underdeveloped. The wall separating these pore-pairs is not built up to form a muscle support. The pore-pairs are situated on the lateral portion of each ambulacral plate. They are not placed in the center of the plates except in the last few plates of each series.

The length of the petaloid portion of ambulacrum IV has a mean of 41.62 ± 0.33 per cent of the test length (S.D. 2.09, C.V. 5.02). This proportion increases logarithmically with growth, and is only 18 per cent of the test length in a specimen 16.7 mm in test length. The width of the petal is 21.05 ± 0.42 per cent of the petal length (S.D. 2.64, C.V. 12.5). This proportion shows much individual variation but does not seem to change greatly with growth. In a specimen 16.7 mm in test length the width of the petal is 27 per cent of the test length, just as in a specimen 107 mm in test length. The interporiferous zone has a mean width of 10.21 ± 0.45 per cent of the petal length (S.D. 1.74, C.V. 17.0). The large variation in this character is primarily individual variation. The distance between the anterior petal ends is 72.33 ± 0.57 per cent of the test length (S.D. 2.15, C.V. 2.98). This proportion increases with growth, and is only 42 per cent in a specimen 16.7 mm in test length.

Ambulacra I and V
(the posterior paired petals)

The tuberculation of the posterior, paired ambulacra is continuous with that of the adjoining interambulacra from the petaloid area to the ambitus. The petals and the areas adjacent to the plastron are naked with the exception of a few primary tubercles that may be found on the lateral edges of the ambulacral plates just below the ambitus.

The interporiferous zone of the petals is slightly sunken and naked. The number of plates from the peristome to the petaloid portion of ambulacrum V varies from 18 to 21 in the following percentages: 18 (5 per cent), 19 (10 per cent), 20 (50 per cent), 21 (35 per cent). There are 8 feeding tube-feet per phyllode. The peripodia are like those of the other phyllodes. The sensory podia are located over small, oval pores at the adoral edge of the plates from the phyllode to the ambitus except in the smaller specimens, where subanal tube-feet occur in the posterior

138

plate series from the posterior end of the plastron to the ambitus. These subanal tube-feet are situated over poorly developed double pores, at the adoral edge of plates 7, 8, 9, and 10. The plates are not distorted so as to curve in behind the plastron as is normal with those spatangoids with a subanal fasciole. The subanal tube-feet were not found in the adults.

The petaloid area is similar to the anterior paired petals with the exception that there often is a difference of one or two (either plus or minus) pore-pairs per series. The mean length of the posterior petal (V) is 40.45 ± 0.34 per cent of the test length (S.D. 2.18, C.V. 5.40), and 97.21 ± 0.52 per cent of the anterior petal length (S.D. 3.36, C.V. 3.46). Both of these proportions increase with growth, being 16 and 90 per cent respectively, in a 16.7 mm test length specimen. The width of the posterior paired petal is 23.51 ± 0.42 per cent of its own length (S.D. 2.64, C.V. 11.21). The posterior petals are straight and diverge from the apical system. Their distal ends span a distance of 54.73 ± 0.77 per cent of the test length (S.D. 2.89, C.V. 5.29). This proportion increases greatly with growth, and is only 25 per cent of the test length in a specimen 16.7 mm in test length. The interporiferous zone is 12.32 ± 0.54 per cent of the posterior petal length (S.D. 2.10, C.V. 17.0).

The Interambulacra

The number of interambulacral plates from the peristome to the fascioles is discussed in the section on fascioles.

The primary tuberculation of the interambulacra is sparse and irregularly scattered over the dorsal surface; only the interporiferous zones of the petals and the sutures of the plates are naked. Secondary tubercles are also very sparse and irregularly distributed. At, and below the ambitus, the tuberculation becomes fairly dense but shows no indication of regularity except on the plastron and epiplastron where the tubercles radiate pinnately from the midline of the posterior interambulacrum.

The first plates of interambulacra 1 and 4 are excluded from the peristome on the exterior of the test except in the smallest specimen. On the interior of the test, they are built up to form supports for the intestinal mesentaries. The perignathic apophysis (Gordon, 1926) of the left side of the animal is the best developed, projecting posteriorly to form a broad, flattened support. The projection of interambulacrum 1 is not functional and is non-spatulate. The first plates of interambulacra 2 and 3 are inserted to the peristome. These plates are also built up on the interior of the test and form small, non-functional auricles.

The labrum is fully tuberculated and projects posteriorly to the middle of the third adjoining ambulacral plate. It is strongly developed, with the anterior edge crescent-shaped. Its length is 15.56 ± 0.18 per cent of the test length (S.D. 0.70, C.V. 4.5). The plastron has a mean length of 32.56 ± 0.52 per cent of the test length (S.D. 2.03, C.V. 6.24). Its width, measured at points A, B, C is (per cent of the test length):

point	mean	S.E.	S.D.	C.V.
A	13.47	0.45	1.67	12.4
B	19.69	0.30	1.16	5.90
C	22.94	0.25	0.97	4.23

The plastron is proportionally longer in small specimens and is 37 per cent of the test length in the 16.7-mm specimen.

The Apical System

The apical system is ethmolytic, situated anteriorly on the dorsal surface at a mean distance from the anterior end of 47.67 ± 0.43 per cent of the test length (S.D. 1.62, C.V. 3.40). During growth, the apical system shifts to a slightly more posterior position. In a specimen 16.7 mm in test length, the distance from the anterior end of the test is 41 per cent of the test length.

There are 3 genital pores of equal size; the right anterior pore is lacking in all the specimens. The genital pores first appear at about 45 or 50 mm test length. They are fully developed at 65 mm test length. The madreporic plate projects slightly past the posterior oculars. It is broad and, in many specimens, strongly convex.

The Periproct and Peristome

The periproct is situated just above the ambitus on the posterior end of the test. The dorsal portion of the periproct extends posteriorly further than the ventral portion giving it a hooded appearance. The periproct is enclosed by interambulacral plates 4, 5, 6, and 7. It is oval to round, with the longer diameter either vertical or horizontal. The mean width of the periproct is 13.10 ± 0.22 per cent of the test length (S.D. 1.38, C.V. 10.5) and 93.62 ± 1.75 per cent of the periproct height (S.D. 11.18, C.V. 12.6).

The peristome is situated anteriorly; its leading edge has a mean distance from the anterior end of the test of 20.67 ± 0.19 per cent of the test length (S.D. 0.70, C.V. 3.38). The anterior edge of the labrum has a mean distance from the posterior end of the test of 76.07 ± 0.27 per cent of the test length (S.D. 1.00, C.V. 1.31). This percentage increases with growth, and is 73 per cent of the test length in a 16.7-mm specimen. The peristome is crescent-shaped and, along with the phyllodes, conspicuously sunken below the level of the oral side of the test.

The Fascioles

The marginal fasciole disappears completely with growth at about 100 mm test length. There is considerable variation in the time of resorption; the fasciole is present in one specimen 125 mm in test length and absent in one 88 mm in test length. Of particular interest are two broken specimens, *ca.* 50 and 60 mm test length, which have not the slightest indica-

140

tion of a marginal or peripetalous fasciole. From the distribution of the tubercles in the vicinity of the ambitus it is clear that these specimens probably never had fascioles. In addition, they have no subanal tubefeet.

The marginal fasciole crosses the following plates: III (6b), 3 (3a and b), IV (10a), 4 (4a, 5b), V (12a), 5 (4 and 5). This fasciole passes under the periproct. Agassiz (1883, p. 58, 59; pl. 21, fig. 7) made an error in his description on the young stages of *P. cristatus*. He stated that the marginal fasciole passes over the periproct just as in *Linopneustes* and discussed this phenomenon at some length. I have examined the specimen he described and include a photograph of it here (Plate 31 *e, f*) to show that the marginal fasciole passes under the periproct. The same specimen, as Clark pointed out (1917, p. 144), has a peripetalous fasciole. The combination of a marginal and peripetalous fasciole is, of course, typical of Pericosmids. When the path of the fascioles in *Paleopneustes* is compared with that of *Pericosmus akabanus* they are found to be very similar. Many other similarities also indicate a much closer relationship between *Paleopneustes* and *Pericosmus* than between *Paleopneustes* and *Linopneustes* or *Archeopneustes*.

The proportional length of the marginal fasciole varies from 285 to 311 per cent of the test length and becomes proportionally shorter in the larger specimens.

The peripetalous fasciole also disappears completely with growth. Its development is even more tenuous than that of the marginal fasciole (Plates 28 *b, d;* 32 *g*) and is only two or three tubercles wide on most specimens. It is still clearly visible in the specimen 65 mm in test length (Plate 31 *a-c*). This fasciole crosses the following plates: III (14), 3 (7 or 8 or both of both series), IV (17 or 18a), 4 (9 or 9 and 10 series a, 10 or 10 and 11 series b), V (20 or 21), 5 (12 or 11 and 12). The length of the peripetalous fasciole varies from 126 per cent of the test length in a specimen 16.7 mm in test length to 187 per cent of the test length in a specimen 65 mm in test length.

The Spines

The spines are thorny (Plate 29*e*) and sharply pointed. Mortensen (1950 text fig. 144a) illustrated the cross section of a spine from this species. The spines of the plastron are only slightly spatulate. The apical tuft spines are long and fairly sturdy (*ca.* 13 to 16 mm long in a specimen 100 mm in test length). The primary tubercles are larger than in *P. tholoformis* and secured more firmly to the glossy surface of the test. Still, they are easily dislodged, leaving only a circular depression to indicate their former presence.

The Sphaeridia and Pedicellariae

The sphaeridia are similar to those of *P. tholoformis* but they are not set into depressions.

The pedicellariae are similar to those of *P. tholoformis*. Rostrate, tridentate and ophicephalous pedicellariae are present. The large form of tridentate pedicellariae differs from that found in *P. tholoformis* in being larger (2 to 3 mm valve length) and in having a thin neck with the distal portion of the blade sharply set off from the neck. The auricles are lower and more angular (Plate 29c, g). The ophicephalous pedicellariae are almost as abundant as the secondary spines (Plates 9b; 31d).

The internal anatomy is discussed in the comments under *P. tholoformis*.

Lectotype.—Agassiz's type material is a composite of both *P. cristatus* and *P. tholoformis*. The container with his "cotypes" contains one specimen of each species. The smaller of the two specimens, 104 mm in test length, is selected as the lectotype. Its dimensions are: length, 104 mm, width 9 mm, height 63 mm. The specimen is in alcohol with the spines intact. It is deposited in the M.C.Z., number 2808.

Four paralectotypes are also deposited in the Museum of Comparative Zoology. They are the specimens listed under material examined that have been assigned M.C.Z. numbers 2793, 2804, 2806, and 2809.

Type locality.—The lectotype was collected off Barbados in 183 m by the HASSLER.

Distribution.—*Paleopneustes cristatus* is known from Barbados to the northern end of the Straits of Florida. It has also been taken from Colombia and the Gulf of Mexico, indicating a wide distribution in the tropical western Atlantic. Its range coincides with that of *P. tholoformis*. Depth: 76 to 805 meters.

Discussion.—Abnormalities: No pronounced abnormalities were found.

Ecology: Nothing is known of the ecology of this species. It has been taken on a variety of substrates from coral rubble to mud. As discussed under *P. tholoformis,* the adults of this species probably do not burrow, but the young specimens probably do. The coloration in life tends to be a lighter shade of purple than in *P. tholoformis*.

Comments: The naked petals and the number of plates from the peristome to the petals separate this species from *P. tholoformis*. The possibility that this is a polytypic species is discussed under *P. tholoformis* and in the section on taxonomic conclusions.

In addition to the comments given under *P. tholoformis,* it should be mentioned that the sexes of both species were identified by gonad smears.

Genus *Saviniaster* Lambert, 1911

Saviniaster Lambert, 1911, p. 33.
Saviniaster, Lambert & Thiery, 1924, p. 431 (Aeropsidae).
Saviniaster, Mortensen, 1951b, p. 351 (Schizasteridae).
Prenaster (Saviniaster), Fischer, 1966, p. U576.

low, barely projecting above the level of the surrounding test. Sphaeridia (Plate 35) are located at the base of the feeding tube-feet. They are ovoid and not noticeably recessed; their stalk is attached to a smooth and flush area of the test.

Large and small tridentate, rostrate, and globiferous pedicellariae are located in ambulacrum III and are most numerous below the marginal fasciole.

Ambulacra II and IV
(the anterior paired petals)

The peripetalous fasciole does not cross ambulacra II and IV. The marginal fasciole crosses ambulacrum IV on plate 7a and 7b and the pore-pairs for the respiratory tube-feet (the double pore-pairs) begin on plate 18a and 15b.

Orally of the marginal fasciole, tuberculation is evenly scattered, leaving only the phyllode naked (Plate 33c). The adoral tube-feet are developed into feeding tube-feet (6 in the anterior series and 5 in the posterior series). The pores of the phyllodes are large, oval, single, and situated on the adoral edge of the smooth, oval peripodia. The muscle support is central, smooth, and projects only slightly above the surrounding test.

Apically of the marginal fasciole, the tuberculation is scattered evenly over ambulacra and interambulacra alike, with no naked areas (Plate 33a, 34e). The tubercles in the petaloid areas are only slightly smaller than those in the adjoining interambulacra. From plates 7a and 7b to plates 18a and 15b (ambulacrum IV), the pores are small, vertical slits situated near the adoral edge of the plate. A small sensory tube-foot is situated over each of these pores.

The petals are 35.5 per cent of the test length in length, flush with the test and flexed slightly anteriorly. From the apical system, the anterior paired petals diverge from each other at an angle of 160° for a short distance then angle outward, diverging at an angle of nearly 180°. At about one-third of their length, they curve gently forward, resuming the 160° divergence. The ends of the petals are 68.5 per cent of the test length from each other.

The pore-series are open distally. The anterior pore-series is poorly developed. The pores are double, situated on the adoral portion of the plates, and angled so the distal pore is ventrolateral to the medial pore. The ridge separating the pores of each pore-pair is raised to form a central projection (Plate 34 a, e). There are eight underdeveloped tube-feet near the apical system, followed by 13 small, but apparently functional, respiratory tube-feet.

The posterior pore-series is better developed and longer than the anterior pore-series. There are eight undeveloped pore-pairs and 17 respiratory tube-feet.

The petals are narrow; their width is only 9.3 per cent of the petal

145

length. The largest pore-pairs of the anterior pore-series are 0.5 mm across their longest diameter. The pores of the posterior pore-series are 0.7 mm across their longest diameter.

Ambulacra I and V
(the posterior paired petals)

The peripetalous fasciole crosses ambulacrum V just below the end of the posterior petal on plate 20a, 37.8 per cent of the test length from the apical system. The marginal fasciole crosses plates 10a and 9b of ambulacrum V. The phyllode is only slightly sunken. There are three feeding tube-feet in each pore-series. The tuberculation is evenly scattered with only the first three plates of both plate-series naked. Plate 3b extends two-thirds of the distance of the plastron and thus, the areas adjacent to the plastron are naked. Posterior to plate 3b, a narrow area adjacent to the plastron is free of spines almost to the marginal fasciole.

There are two sensory tube-feet posterior to the oral tube-feet in both plate-series. Plates 6, 7, 8, and 9 of the posterior plate-series have subanal tube-feet which are penicillate and situated over large, single or partially divided pores (Plate 34c). There are no tube-feet between the marginal fasciole and the semiperipetalous fasciole.

The posterior petals are flush with the test and flexed slightly posteriorly. They diverge from the apical system at an angle of 56° and bend gently inward at about two-thirds of their length. Their distal ends diverge at an angle of about 45°. The distal ends of the posterior petals are 34.3 per cent of the test length apart. The pore-series are open and are the same length. The pore-pairs of the anterior series are slightly smaller than those of the posterior series. The pore-pairs are angled so the distal pore is ventrolateral of the medial pore. The ridge between the pores of each pore-pair is elevated as in the anterior petal.

There are nine underdeveloped tube-feet and 16 respiratory tube-feet in the anterior series and six underveloped and 18 respiratory tube-feet in the posterior series. Like the anterior petals, the width of the posterior petals is only 9.3 per cent of the petal length. The pore-pairs are about 0.7 mm across their longest diameter.

The Interambulacra

The number of interambulacral plates from the peristome to the marginal and peripetalous fascioles is given in the section on those fascioles. The tuberculation is evenly and irregularly scattered, increasing in size along the anterior ambulacrum and below the marginal fasciole. The largest spines (tubercles) are located along the anterior ambitus and on the plastron.

The plastron is large and broad; its length is 53.3 per cent of the test length and its width is 37.5 per cent of the test length. The labrum is short, crescent-shaped, and does not extend more than half-way down the first adjoining ambulacral plate. Its length is 4.34 per cent of the test length. A row of fine, curved spines is located along the anterior edge of the labrum.

Plates 2 and 3 of interambulacrum 1 are coalesced to form one large plate (2 + 3a) which, in the holotype, does not quite reach plate number 1.

The Apical System

The apical system is ethmolytic, situated anteriorly on the dorsal surface of the test at a distance from the anterior end of 24 per cent of the test length. This position is directly above the peristome. There are 4 very small (*ca.* 0.1 mm in diameter) genital pores of equal size. The madreporite extends past the posterior genitals about as far as from its anterior margin to the posterior genitals (Plate 34*d*).

The oculars are pentagonal, large, and deeply recessed into the test, giving the illusion that the genitals are raised. The pores in the ocular plates are about the same size as the genital pores.

The apical system is not coalesced but is so small and symmetrical that it gives the appearance that the plates are fused. Sutures are, however, still visible.

The Periproct and Peristome

The periproct is enormous (Plate 33*b*); 28.4 per cent of the test length high and 16.7 per cent of the test length wide. The posterior interambulacrum (plates 4, 5, 6, 7, and 8) is smoothly contoured and forms the lateral and dorsal walls of the posterior portion of the test. The periproct forms almost all of the posterior portion of the test and has a hooded, sunken appearance. The anus is situated in the upper central portion of the periproct. The small plates surrounding the anus have numerous finger-like projections directed posteriorly (Plate 35*i*). These projections have a thick epithelial layer which is ciliated and probably assists in removing debris from the anus as in other spatangoids.

The peristome is situated anteriorly; its leading edge is located 22.7 per cent of the test length from the anterior end of the test. The anterior edge of the labrum is 67.5 per cent of the test length from the posterior end of the test. Tertiary spines, rostrate, globiferous, and tridentate pedicellariae are found on the peristome. The peristome is sunken and crescent-shaped; its width is 21.7 per cent of the test length.

The Fascioles

The semiperipetalous fasciole is poorly developed. In most areas it is only two clavulae wide (Plates 33*a*, 34*e*). It is evenly curved along most of its length, angling downward along the ridge of nodes of the anterior plate series in interambulacra 1 and 4. The fasciole has an area of 11.4 mm^2 and its length is 125 per cent of the test length. The anterior ends terminate on plate 6 of the anterior plate-series in interambulacra 1 and 4 and do not reach the marginal fasciole which crosses this plate-series on plate 4. The distance from the apical system to the semiperipetalous fasciole, along the midline of interambulacrum 4, is 37.5 per cent of the test length. The fasciole crosses the posterior interambulacrum at a point 41.2 per cent of the test length from the apical system.

The path of the semiperipetalous fasciole over the plates of the test is summarized in Table 12.

The marginal fasciole circumscribes the entire ambitus, passing under the periproct in interambulacrum 5. It is found on plates: III (3b), 3 (3a, 3b), IV (7a, 7b), 4 (4a, 5b), V (10a, 9b), 5 (4 and 5a). Its length is 308 per cent of the test length and it has a total area of 111 mm^2. The anterior portion of the marginal fasciole is 47.5 per cent of the test length from the apical system. The distance along the midline of interambulacrum 4, from the apical system to the marginal fasciole, is 61.5 per cent of the test length. The use of the terms "semiperipetalous" and "marginal" for the types of fascioles discussed here was suggested by Lambert (1924) and rejected by Mortensen (1951b). For a discussion of this matter, see the section on fascioles in the taxonomic conclusions.

The Spines and Pedicellariae

The spines are smooth, hollow, exactly like those of other spatangoids. Plate 33 shows the relative size and shape of the spines. There are no prominent anal, subanal or apical tufts of spines. The larger spines are located on the plastron, anterior to the peristome, and adjacent to ambulacrum III. The plastronal spines are spatulate.

The tubercles are moderately crenulate and perforated, with very small auricles except on the plastron where the auricles are better developed. The spines are evenly and seemingly randomly distributed. No primaries are present, secondary spines are uniform in size, straight and sharply pointed. Tertiary spines are numerous and evenly distributed.

Globiferous, tridentate, and rostrate pedicellariae are abundant all over the test. Ophicephalous pedicellariae were not observed. The globiferous pedicellariae (*ca.* 1 mm in valve length) surmount thin, limbless stalks with no muscular neck. The valves are short and broad, the neck terminating in a distal pore with 7 or 8 small teeth surrounding it (Plate 35*d, e*). Several types of tridentate pedicellariae are present, ranging from short, spoonshaped forms to large, elongate forms with a terminal disc (Plate 35*f; ca.* 2.0 mm in valve length). Some tridentate valves are strongly toothed (Plate 35*a; ca.* 1.9 mm in valve length). The rostrate pedicellariae (Plate 35*b; ca.* 0.7 mm in valve length) are not different from those of other spatangoids.

Holotype.—The only known example is a specimen 60 mm in test length, deposited in the U.S. National Museum. It is dried, with the spines re-

148

moved from the left side. The test is broken on the left side and has been repaired with water-soluble glue.

Type locality.—South of Grand Bahama Island, 26°29'N., 78°40'W., 366 meters depth, GERDA sta. 704.

Discussion.—Habitat: The specimen was dredged from a brown mud bottom. Presumably this species burrows as do other spatangoids. Since the specimen was damaged by the dredge, nothing could be learned of its habits.

Coloration: In life, *Saviniaster enodatus* is light brown. Only the tube-feet are pigmented a darker brownish-red. The test is a darker brown than the spines. The cleaned test is white.

Fossil history: *Saviniaster* is known from a single species, *S. miqueli* Lambert, 1911, found in the Eocene deposits of France. Lambert's specimens were poorly preserved and it is difficult to make any comparison with the Recent species. The labrum is poorly developed in the Eocene specimens and this may afford a distinguishing character. The anterior pore-series of the anterior paired petals do not seem as reduced in the fossil species as in *S. enodatus*. Other differences between the two forms may be detected when specimens of both become available for study.

Comments: For a discussion of the terminology of the fascioles see the section on fascioles in the taxonomic conclusions.

There are no other known species of *Saviniaster* except the fossil *S. miqueli* discussed above under fossil history.

TAXONOMIC CONCLUSIONS

Sympatric species.—The analysis of the sympatric species of *Brissopsis, Plethotaenia,* and *Paleopneustes* has provided some interesting insights into the genetics of spatangoids. The species of each pair differ from each other in a similar fashion. In each genus, there is a high form and a low form. The high form has more plates in its ambulacra than the low form, it has a denser tuberculation, and the fascioles are better developed. One of the two forms generally grows to a larger size than the other and there is usually a difference in the posterior truncation of the test; one is vertical and the other oblique. This peculiar arrangement of sympatric species is not limited to the Straits of Florida or to the Recent era. Fell (1963) described a sympatric species pair of *Spatangus* from New Zealand. They differ from one another in almost exactly the same way as do the species of *Plethotaenia*. From deeper water off New Zealand, a third *Spatangus* is known. The comparison of this form, *Spatangus multispinus* Mortensen, 1925, with *Spatangus thor* Fell, 1963, is even more like the *Plethotaenia* species pair. *P. angularis* and *S. thor* are more angular, more obliquely truncated posteriorly, have a deeper frontal notch, and broader petaloid areas than *P. spatangoides* and *S. multispinus*. There is a difference in the

149

subanal fascioles of the species but it is reversed. *S. multispinus* and *P. angularis* have poorly developed subanal fascioles compared to their respective partners.

Kermack (1954), Rowe (1899) and Nichols (1959) have provided another set of species pairs from the Cretaceous deposits of southern England. *Micraster coranguinum* differs from *M. senonensis* in being lower, with a deeper frontal notch, a more pronounced "posterior rise," fewer respiratory tube-feet, finer tuberculation, and a more oblique posterior portion of the test. This is exactly the same in the two species of *Plethotaenia*. Like the *Spatangus* pair from New Zealand, the higher form has a poorly developed subanal fasciole compared to the lower form. Nichols (1959) indicates that a parallel species pair is found in *Micraster glyphus* and *M. stolleyi*, from the Cretaceous deposits of Northern England.

In the genus *Brissopsis, B. oldhami* differs from *B. luzonica* as *B. mediterranea* differs from *B. atlantica*. The first pair is found in the Indian Ocean, the second in the Atlantic Ocean. In each pair there is a broad, high form (*B. mediterranea, B. oldhami*) with crescent shaped petals, a vertical posterior truncation, and four ambulacral plates entering the subanal fasciole, and a narrow, lower form (*B. atlantica, B. luzonica*) with more angular petals, a more oblique posterior truncation, and 5 ambulacral plates entering the subanal fasciole.

In the Pacific species *Plesiozonus diomedeae,* there is a form with a high test and one with a low test. The high form has wider petals and more ambulacral plates than the lower, more angular form. Mortensen (1951b) states that all stages of intermediates exist and that the two forms are the same species. *Pericosmus,* which is closely related to *Paleopneustes* and probably to *Plesiozonus,* has no less than four sympatric species reported from Mauritius (Mortensen, 1951b, p. 174). The differences between these sympatric species are, however, poorly known.

The above data have two possible interpretations. The first is that the species are polymorphic and the second, that evolution in the spatangoids follows a remarkably constant pattern.

Genetic polymorphism has been defined (Ford 1965) as "The occurrence together in the same habitat of two or more discontinuous forms, or 'phases', of a species in such proportions that the rarest of them cannot be maintained merely by recurrent mutation." The numerous differences in the pairs of spatangoids would indicate that if the species are polymorphic, the mechanism is complex and similar to sexual polymorphism except that it is not sex-linked. The chromosomes of spatangoids are not long and complex, but are short and numerous (*ca.* 48 or 50 diploid). It is not difficult to think of one of these chromosomes (or a portion of one) being lost or gained during meiosis, particularly if there is an unpaired portion such as the X-Y chromosomes. Sex-linked dimorphisms are known in the few spatangoids which brood their young. In the females of these species, the ambulacra are deeply sunken as brood pouches.

150

in the two forms (see Fig. 21.) While such a situation is possible in a polymorphic species it is not common and indicates that the two sympatric forms are really two species.

If the two forms were polymorphic phases of a single species, each major population would be expected to have both forms represented. In most polymorphic species there is a common form and a rare form. While the rare form may be absent from any particular population, the common form is not. In the spatangoids, however, large populations of each form are found. Thus, only *Paleopneustes cristatus* was found at sta. G-722 and only *P. tholoformis* was found at sta. G-239.

Plethotaenia spatangoides is distributed from the Caribbean to the New England coasts but *P. angularis* is known only in the southern portion of this distribution. The two forms occur together at some stations, but both forms occur separately at other stations. *Brissopsis mediterranea* has a broad distribution which extends from the Gulf of Guinea and Mediterranean to the east coast of the United States. *B. atlantica* is found in the Florida and Caribbean area. *B. alta* is only known from the Gulf of Mexico and Florida. All three species are sympatric in the Cuba to Florida area. *B. alta* and *B. atlantica* are commonly found together but *B. atlantica* is also found alone or burrowing with *B. elongata* or *B. mediterranea*. It is possible that *B. alta* is a polymorph of *B. atlantica*. It is also possible that *B. atlantica* is a polymorph of *B. mediterranea*. A much more likely explanation is that these forms are distinct species with overlapping geographic ranges.

The fact that the two forms live together in the same mud is contrary to the well-known "Gause's Hypothesis" that two closely related species can not share the same ecological niche. There is, however, little interspecific competition involved. The ecological niche (mud) is so large that there is no shortage of space or deteritus.

As shown by the studies of Kermack (1954), Nichols (1959), and in this paper, a slight shift in one character will result in the corresponding shift of related characters to maintain a constant internal and external equilibrium. Thus, one factor might change due to an ecological selective pressure and the other factors would shift in the required direction to maintain homeostasis. Since all of the spatangoids have a similar genetic background and are reacting to environmental pressures related to their burrowing habits (and particularly to their respiration), it is to be expected that different genera would form sibling species which differ similarly from one another. The environmental stress that produces the new form does not have to be the same. The selective pressure could be temperature, siltation, increased water movement, predation, or any ecological change. The response of the spatangoids will be to burrow deeper or shallower or faster or slower and, if the conditions persist, the selective pressure will produce a low, angular urchin or a high rounded one. Once the selective pressure is eliminated, the two forms will, if possible, come together again.

If reproductive isolation has occurred (perhaps by a change in spawning time) the two forms will remain distinct. The changes in siltation and temperature associated with the ice ages might possibly have some relation to the numerous sympatric spatangoid species found in the Straits of Florida.

On the basis of the paleontological evidence, the zoogeographic distribution, and the study of sympatric species of other groups, the most logical conclusion is that the coexisting forms are separate species.

The Variability of Characters

Tables 1-12 and the descriptions of the various species give information on the variability of each character. The characters which are variable in one species or genus may not be plastic in another. The relative ease with which characters may be lost, geographic variability, and allometric changes make the use of single, key characters unsuitable for drawing phylogenetic conclusions between species or genera. It is evident that reaching phylogenetic conclusions, even on an interspecific level, is difficult as many characters vary together forming a "grade of organization," and key characters such as globiferous pedicellariae or fascioles may disappear and even reappear in a direct phylogenetic lineage—as was observed also by Kermack (1954, p. 423) in the geologic series of *Micraster*.

In future zoogeographic studies on spatangoids, caution must be used in applying the superspecies (and the subgeneric) concept. There are several species of *Brissopsis* in the Indian and Atlantic Oceans and it might be concluded, from existing evidence, that two or three superspecies are involved. These would be a *B. oldhami—mediterranea* superspecies, a *B. luzonica—atlantica* superspecies, and a *B. elongata—obliqua* superspecies. In view of the parallel evolution discussed in the foregoing section on sympatric species, and considering the work of Koehler (1914) and Mortensen (1951b), it is more likely that there are two distinct groups involved: one group which evolved in the Atlantic and another which developed independently in the Indo-Pacific area. Both groups were probably derived from the same stock (possibly *B. crescenticus*). A close examination of the Indo-Pacific and fossil *Brissopsis* species might produce conclusive evidence as to which process is taking place.

As might be expected in animals with pelagic larvae living in relatively deep water, there is little geographic variation in the species described in this study. *B. lyrifera,* along the eastern Atlantic, shows some geographic variation as does *B. atlantica* between Florida and Colombia. The characters that change geographically are discussed within the description of each species and summarized in Table 1 and Figure 11.

The Fascioles

The fascioles are bands of small ciliated spines which aid spatangoid

154

burrowing movements. They act as a valve, dividing the various parts of the burrow into respiratory, movement and feeding, and drainage areas. Their ciliation aids in pumping water from the surface of the sediment into the burrow and out into the sand behind the animal. The function is further explained in the description of *B. alta.* There are several types of fascioles in the spatangoids and their presence in any one form may be of great phylogenetic interest. Some fascioles can be found on the same interambulacral plates throughout whole families and knowledge of the course of these structures is important for understanding intergeneric relations. The path of the fascioles on the ambulacral plates is more variable and is of interspecific importance. Fascioles are often resorbed during ontogeny or lost during phylogeny so that their absence is of little taxonomic value. Often, the plate structure of the test will indicate if a fasciole has been present in the phylogeny of any particular group. The fascioles have an obvious and important relation to the tuberculation, plate structure, and pore-pair structure of the test. The growth of the ambulacral plates is inhibited by the fascioles, the restricted growth can form smaller plates and occluded plates in the petaloid, respiratory areas. The respiratory tube-feet and pore-pairs are normally developed only within the fasciole. Primary tuberculation increases in size within the confines of a fasciole. The plates of the posterior ambulacra (usually plates 6 are the first) are prolonged toward the anal system when a subanal fasciole is (or was) present. The various types of fascioles found in spatangoids and their path over the interambulacra plates are:

Subanal fasciole (SA.F.): Interambulacrum 5, plates 3, 4, 5, and occasionally 6. Ambulacral plate 6 of the adjoining ambulacra is normally the first plate to enter the subanal fasciole. In *B. elongata,* plate 7 is the first.

Marginal fasciole (M.F.): Circumscribes the ambitus, passing under the anal system. The marginal fasciole crosses interambulacral plates: 3 (3a and b), 4 (4a, 5b), 5 (4 and 5).

Peripetalous fasciole (PP.F): Circumscribes the ends of the petals; its development is not as constant as the fascioles previously mentioned. Its path over the various plates of the test may be of specific, generic, or familial value depending on the group. In general, this fasciole is unstable on and near ambulacrum III, but is frequently found on plate 4a of interambulacrum 3. There seem to be two types of peripetalous fascioles (parallel or convergent evolution); one evolving from the marginal fasciole (schizasterids), the other apparently unrelated to the marginal fasciole (Brissidae). There is still some doubt about this, however, as the path over the plates is often nearly identical in genera of the two families.

The above fascioles are, as pointed out by Lambert (1924, p. 41), the primary fascioles. Modifications of these are:

Latero-anal fasciole (L.F.): Passes under the anus on plates 4 and 5,

155

TABLE 12

Path of the Fascioles over the Plates of the Test

Species	Fasciole	III a	3 a	3 b	IV a	4 a	4 b	V a	5 a
Brissopsis *atlantica*	PP.F.	6	4&5	4&5	9-13	6&7 (6,7,8)	7&8	16-18	10(11)
	SA.F.	—	—	—	—	—	—	6-10	3-5
Brissopsis *mediterranea*	PP.F.	6	4&5 (4,5,6)	5	9-12	6&7 (6,7,8)	7 (7&8)	16-18	10(11)
	SA.F.	—	—	—	—	—	—	6-9	3-5
Brissopsis *elongata* s.s.	PP.F.	6 (7)	4&5	5	9-12	6&7	7&8 (7)	17-19	11(10)
	SA.F.	—	—	—	—	—	—	7-11 (7-10)	3-5
B. elongata *jarlii*	PP.F.	7	4-6 (4&5)	5	12	6&7 (6,7,8)	7&8 (7,8,9)	19	12
	SA.F.	—	—	—	—	—	—	7-11	3-5
Brissopsis *alta*	PP.F.	6	4	4	9-10	6&7	7&8 (7)	17-19	10(11)
	SA.F.	—	—	—	—	—	—	6-9	3-5

Species	Fasciole								
Brissopsis lyrifera s.s.	PP.F.	5 (6?)	4	4 (4&5)	9-10	6&7	7	14-15	10
	SA.F.	5	—	—	—	—	—	6-9	3-5
B. lyrifera capensis	PP.F.	5	4	4 (4&5)	9	6&7 (6,7,8)	7&8	15-16	9
	SA.F.	—	—	—	—	—	—	6-9	3-5
Plethotaenia spatangoides	PP.F.	6-9	4-8	4-8	9-17	6-9	8-9	18-25	12-14
	SA.F.	—	—	—	—	—	—	6-8	3-5
Plethotaenia angularis	PP.F.	8-10	6-8	6-8	15-17	8 (7)	9 (8)	19-22	12-13
	SA.F.	—	—	—	—	—	—	6-8	3-5
Paleopneustes cristatus	PP.F.	14	7&8	7&8	17-18	9&10 (9)	10&11 (10)	20-21	11&12 (12)
	M.F.	6	3	3	10	4	5	12	4&5
Paleopneustes tholoformis	PP.F.	14	7&8	7&8	19-20	9&10	10	22	11&12
	M.F.	6	3	3	10	4	5	12	4&5
Saviniaster enodatus	S-PP.F.	3	—	—	—	6&7	8	20	11
	M.F.	3	3	3	7	4	5	9&10	4&5

Plate numbering follows Lovén (1874). Abbreviations for fascioles as given on pp. 155 and 158. The numbers in parentheses indicate a less common condition. For further analysis, see the descriptions of the species.

over the flanks of the urchin on plates 5a and 5b of interambulacra 1 and 4, and joins the peripetalous fasciole on plate 5a. Mortensen (1951b, p. 207) points out that in schizasterid juveniles, a marginal fasciole appears first from which a branch is later developed which passes between the anal system and the posterior paired petals. This branch, together with the anterior portion of the marginal fasciole, forms the peripetalous fasciole in the adult. The posterior portion of the marginal fasciole becomes the latero-anal fasciole.

Semiperipetalous fasciole (S-PP.F): Mortensen (1951b) insisted that this terminology is unnecessary in view of his studies on the development of the fascioles in the schizasterids. The semiperipetalous fasciole is, he believed, the incomplete peripetalous fasciole of the juvenile, and to call the fascioles of *Agassizia, Prenaster,* and *Saviniaster* marginal and semi-peripetalous only obscures their true affinities with the other schizasterids. I do not agree. In the schizasterids, the marginal fasciole of the juvenile (and the peripetalous fasciole of the adult) passes over plate 4a and b of interambulacrum 2 and 3 and plate 5a of interambulacrum 1 and 4. In the genera with a semiperipetalous fasciole, the marginal fasciole is not found on these plates, but on plates 3a and b of interambulacrum 2 and 3, and plate 4a of interambulacrum 1 and 4. The typical schizasterid condition may be derived from the *Agassizia* condition, but they are not the same in the two groups. Other differences in the morphology of the two groups of genera support the usage of a different terminology for this condition.

Anal branches (A.B.): From either side of the subanal fasciole of some genera, a branch is developed on interambulacrum 5 which might extend as far as the peripetalous fasciole. There is evidence to indicate that these branches might have evolved separately in different spatangoid groups. In some genera (i.e., *Echinocardium, Plagiobrissus*) these branches are not connected to the subanal fasciole but join together under the periproct. In other genera *(Brissopsis)* they arise from the subanal fasciole.

Internal fasciole (I.F.): The internal fasciole encloses the apical system and the petaloid portion of ambulacrum III. This fasciole may be found with or without a peripetalous fasciole and may have developed in different groups separately.

The paths of the fascioles over the plates of the test are summarized in Table 12.

THE HIGHER CLASSIFICATION OF SPATANGOIDS

Mortensen (1950, 1951b) has provided echinologists with an invaluable catalogue of all the known spatangoids. However, the arrangement of the taxa into various families is in some instances not very satisfactory. In the discussion of the genus *Paleopneustes,* four genera are brought together which Mortensen has placed in three separate families. In the interest of a better understanding of the phylogeny of spatangoids, and also

158

for ease of identification of recent and fossil forms which may lose the fascioles during growth, it seems desirable to group these genera into a family Paleopneustidae which may be diagnosed as follows: Amphisternous spatangoids with a compound plate representing 2a + 2b in interambulacrumcrum 1. Three genital pores; apical system ethmolytic. Test normally flat ventrally, highly arched dorsally. Ambulacra subpetaloid to petaloid. Marginal and peripetalous fascioles present, vanishing with age in some species. Test glossy, the tubercles easily dislodged. Plastron short, *ca.* 30 to 40 per cent of test length. Labrum well developed. Phyllodes with double pore-pairs.

The genera known to belong to this family are: *Paleopneustes, Pericosmus, Faorina,* and *Plesiozonus.* Possibly *Prosotoma* and *Pygospatangus* belong to this group also. The similarities between these genera are summarized in Table 13 and discussed above under the genus *Paleopneustes.*

Paleopneustidae is an unfortunate name in that there is nothing primitive about its petals. However, the family Paleopneustidae was established in 1904 and the Pericosmidae in 1905, so the family as now constituted must be known under the older synonym, Paleopneustidae. Some of the genera in Mortensen's (1950) Paleopneustidae actually appear to be primitive. Others (i.e., *Linopneustes*) are not primitive at all and their correct relationships must be established. Since the true relationships of many of these genera are unknown, they are left in the polyphyletic family suggested by Fischer (1966), the Asterostomatidae. *Paleopneustes* is the type genus of the revised family Paleopneustidae containing the genera *Pericosmus, Faorina, Plesiozonus,* and *Paleopneustes;* Pericosmidae is considered a junior synonym of Paleopneustidae.

The genus *Plethotaenia* is placed in the family Spatangidae on the basis of the evidence presented in the discussions of *Plethotaenia* and its species. Fell (1963) has already shown that Mortensen's diagnosis and description of the family Spatangidae are in error by the discovery of a multiple internal fasciole in some specimens of *Paramaretia peloria.* The addition of *Plethotaenia* to the Spatangidae will not add any new error into the familial description. It is not clear whether the family Spatangidae is a natural assemblage of genera or not. Whatever the disposition of the other genera in the Spatangidae, it is absolutely certain that *Plethotaenia* and *Spatangus* belong to the same family and that they are not near relations of the Brissidae.

Biological and Ecological Conclusions

It is difficult to reach many conclusions about the biology of the species described in this paper because all are from poorly known habitats. *Brissopsis atlantica* and *B. alta* were examined alive in the laboratory and the results are presented in the discussions of those species. It is interesting to note that the species-pairs live together in the same substrate and that although the substrate may vary from one locality to the next,

TABLE 13

SIMILARITIES OF PALEOPNEUSTID GENERA

	Plesiozonus diomedeae	*Paleopneustes* (both spp.)	*Pericosmus akabanus*	*Faorina chinensis*
Genital pores	3	3	3	3
Madreporite ethmolytic	×	×	×	×
IA. 1 (only) meridoplacus	×	×	×	×
Pastron (% of test length)	34	32	36	38
Labrum (% of test length)	16	14	15	13
Plastron width (% of test length)	28	22	21	23
Shape (L × W × H as % of test length)	100 × 98 × 68	100 × 85 × 64	100 × 95 × 69	100 × 93 × 72
Marginal fasciole on IA plates (3a, b; 4a, b; 5a)	3, 3; 4, 5; 4 & 5 (vanishes with age)	same (vanishes with age)	same (present on adults)	missing on IA 3 & 4 as adult; same on IA 5a
Peripetalous fasciole on IA plates (as above)	8 & 9 & 10, 9; 8 & 9 & 10, 9 & 10; 10 & 11 (vanishes with age)	7 & 8, 7 & 8; 9 & 10, 10 & 11; 11 & 12 (vanishes with age)	7 & 8 & 9, 7 & 8; 7 & 8 & 9, 8 & 9; 10 & 11 (present on adults)	5 & 6, 5 & 6 & 7 & 8; 7, 8; 10 & 11 (present on adults)
Oral pore-pairs double	×	×	×	×
Occluded plates in petals of IV and V	×	×	×	×
Number of amb. plates adjacent to labrum	2	3	2	2

the morphology of the urchins remains the same. The difference in the morphology of the two forms of each species-pair does not seem to be related to a change in the ecological niche. Both species of *Brissopsis* burrow, and both species of *Paleopneustes* probably do not. The major difference between the two species of *Brissopsis* studied in the laboratory was in the rate of movement. *B. atlantica* moves faster than *B. alta*. Shallow water investigations have shown that two species of spatangoids burrowing in the same substrate have different behavioral patterns (Chesher, in preparation), and that the differences in behavior are reflected in the various characters of the test. In general, it may be stated that the higher forms are slower than the lower forms. Although *Meoma ventricosa* and *Plagiobrissus grandis* are not congeneric, they both inhabit the same substrate and show some interesting parallels with the *Brissopsis alta—B. atlantica* pair. Briefly, *Meoma ventricosa* and *B. alta* are slower and have higher tests than *Plagiobrissus* and *B. atlantica*. In addition, the former species have commensals (a pinnotherid crab in *Meoma* and an erycinacean bivalve in *B. alta*) whereas the faster moving species do not have these associated organisms. This lends weight to the laboratory observations on the *Brissopsis* species.

The examination of the gonads of the various species of the deeper water revealed that one member of each species pair had smaller eggs than the other. It is not known whether the difference in size is due to different spawning seasons or to a difference in size of the mature eggs. No ripe females were found.

SUMMARY

The analysis of the genera *Brissopsis, Plethotaenia,* and *Paleopneustes* indicates that in the West Indian area each genus has two species which live sympatrically. The species-pairs share the same ecological niche, and hybridization between members of the pairs is rare. The differences between the two species of each pair are surprisingly constant in the various genera. Basically, there is a form with a high and rounded test which differs from its low, angular counterpart in having more ambulacral plates, heavier tuberculation, a more vertically truncated posterior end, and a less developed fasciolar system. These species pairs are not restricted to the genera of this study or to the West Indies. Similar pairs of species are found all over the world and in the fossil record. Evidence from shallow water spatangoids and from *Brissopsis* indicates that the morphological differences are correlated with the rate of movement of the animals and not with the depth to which they burrow. The higher forms move more slowly than the lower forms.

The possibility that these species-pairs represent a non-sex-linked dimorphism is rejected on the basis of the known variability and geographic distribution of the forms.

The study of the taxonomic characters of these genera indicate a

161

strong genetic control which is not greatly influenced by substrate changes or geographic distance. The path of the fascioles over the plates of the test is shown to be a constant and valuable character within the Spatangoida. The absence of fascioles in any particular group is not always an important character as these structures may be resorbed during ontogeny or lost during phylogeny. There is evidence to indicate the presence of inhibitor genes which prevent the phenotypic expression of epidermal characters, including the fasciolar system and the pedicellariae.

Lovén's (1874, 1883) discovery of alternate states in the plate symmetry of interambulacrum 1 may have significant value in spatangoid taxonomy. Based on similarities in this and other features, the genera *Paleopneustes, Pericosmus, Faorina, Plesiozonus* and probably *Prosostoma* and *Pygospatangus,* are considered a natural phylogenetic family Paleopneustidae.

The genera *Plethotaenia* and *Spatangus* are closely related. The internal anatomy, tuberculation, subanal fasciole, labrum, plastron, ambulacra, and general shape of the test indicate a definite affinity between these two genera, an affinity which they do not share with the Brissidae. *Plethotaenia* is, therefore, removed from the Brissidae and placed in the Spatangidae.

The genus *Plethotaenia* has two sympatric species. *Plethotaenia spatangoides* A. Agassiz is the type species and is distributed from the New England coasts through the West Indies. *Plethotaenia angularis,* n.sp., is known only from the West Indian area.

The genus *Paleopneustes* has two sympatric species. The type species is *Paleopneustes cristatus* A. Agassiz. The distribution of *Paleopneustes tholoformis,* n.sp., conforms to that of *P. cristatus.* They are restricted to the West Indian area from the Straits of Florida to Barbados.

The following species and subspecies of *Brissopsis* are recognized in the Atlantic: *B.mediterranea, B. atlantica, B. elongata, B. elongata jarlii, B. lyrifera, B. lyrifera capensis, B. alta, B. evanescens. B. atlantica* has been found burrowing with *B. alta, B. mediterranea,* and *B. elongata.* Hybrids may occur between *B. atlantica* and *B. elongata* or *B. mediterranea.*

Saviniaster enodatus, n.sp., was discovered south of Grand Bahama Island in 366 meters of water. The genus was known previously from one species in the Eocene deposits of France. *Saviniaster* is related to the fossil genus *Prenaster* and the Recent genus *Agassizia.*

The system of measurements used in this paper has been devised as a step toward the establishment of a standardized system of measurements for spatangoid taxonomy.

162

LITERATURE CITED

AGASSIZ, ALEXANDER
1869. Preliminary report on the Echini and star-fishes dredged in deep water between Cuba and the Florida Reef, by L. F. de Pourtales. Bull. Mus. Comp. Zool., *1* (9): 253-308.
1872-1873. Revision of the Echini. Ill. Cat. Mus. Comp. Zool., *7* (1-3): 1-628.
1873. The Echini collected on the Hassler Expedition. Bull. Mus. Comp. Zool., *3* (8): 187-190.
1878. Report on the Echini. Reports on the results of dredging . . . by the United States Coast Survey steamer "Blake" 2. Bull. Mus. Comp. Zool., *5* (9): 181-195, pls. 1-5.
1880. Preliminary report on the Echini. Reports on the results of dredging . . . by the U. S. Coast Survey steamer "Blake." Bull. Mus. Comp. Zool., *8* (2):69-84.
1881. Report on the Echinoidea, dredged by H.M.S. Challenger during the years 1873-1876. The Voyage of H.M.S. Challenger, Zoology, *3* (part 9): 318 pp, 45 pls.
1883. Report on the Echini. Reports on the results of dredging . . . by the U. S. Coast Survey steamer "Blake." Mem. Mus. Comp. Zool., *10* (1): 94 pp, 32 pls.
1904. The Panamic deep sea Echini. Mem. Mus. Comp. Zool., *31:* 243 pp, 112 pls.

AGASSIZ, ALEXANDER AND L. F. DE POURTALÈS
1874. Echini, crinoids, and corals. Zoological results of the Hassler Expedition, *1*. Ill. Cat. Mus. Comp. Zool., *8:* 1-54.

AGASSIZ, LOUIS
1840. Catalogus systematicus Ectyporum Echinodermatum fossilium Musei Neocomensis. Petitpierre, Neocomi Helvetorum. 20 pp.

AGASSIZ, LOUIS AND E. DESOR
1847. Catalogue raisonné des espèces, des genres et des familles d'Échinides. Ann. Sci. Nat., Zoologique, sér. 3, *8:* 4-35.

BELL, F. J.
1904. The Echinoderma found off the coast of South Africa. *1*, Echinoidea. Marine Investigations in South Africa, *3:* 167-175.

BRATTSTRÖM, H.
1946. Observations on *Brissopis lyrifera* (Forbes) in the Gullmar Fjord. Ark. Zool., *37* A (18): 1-27.

BUCHANAN, J. B.
1966. The biology of *Echinocardium cordatum* (Echinodermata: Spatangoidea) from different habitats. J. mar. biol. Ass. U.K., *46* (1): 97-114.

CHERBONNIER, G.
1959. Échinides. Expédition Océanographique Belge dans les Eaux Côtières Africaines de l'Atlantique Sud, *3* (6): 37-59, 10 pls.

CHESHER, RICHARD H.
1963. The morphology and function of the frontal ambulacrum of *Moira atropos* (Echinoidea: Spatangoida). Bull. Mar. Sci. Gulf and Carib., *13* (4): 549-573.

1966. Report on the Echinoidea collected by R/V Pillsbury in the Gulf of Guinea. *In* The R/V *Pillsbury* Deep-Sea Biological Expedition to the Gulf of Guinea, 1964-1965. Stud. trop. Oceanogr. Miami, *4* (Part 1): 209-223.

CLARK, HUBERT LYMAN
1901. The echinoderms of Porto Rico. Bull. U. S. Fish Comm., 1900 (Part 2): 231-263, pls. 14-17.
1917. Hawaiian and other Pacific echini. The Echinoneidae . . . and Spatangidae. Mem. Mus. Comp. Zool., *46* (2): 85-267, pls. 144-161.
1923. The echinoderm fauna of South Africa. Ann. S. Afr. Mus., *13* (7): 221-435, pls. 8-23.
1924. Echinoderms from the South African fisheries and marine biological survey. Sea Urchins (Echinoidea). Rep. Fish. Mar. Biol. Surv. S. Afr., 4 (1): 1-16, 4 pls.
1925. A catalogue of the Recent sea-urchins (Echinoidea) in the collection of the British Museum (Natural History). Oxford Univ. Press, London. 250 pp, 12 pls.
1933. A handbook of the littoral echinoderms of Porto Rico and the other West Indian islands. Sci. Surv., N. Y. Acad. Sci., *16* (1): 1-147, 7 pls.
1941. The echinoderms (other than holothurians). Reports on the scientific results of the Atlantis Expeditions to the West Indies.. Mem. Soc. Cubana Hist. Nat., *15* (1): 1-154, 10 pls.

CLARKE, B.
1962. Balanced polymorphism and the diversity of sympatric species. Syst. Ass. Publ., 4: 47-70.

COKER, R. E.
1939. The problem of cyclomorphosis in Daphnia. Quart. Rev. Biol., *14:* 137-148.

COOKE, C. WYTHE
1952. Cenozoic irregular echinoids of Eastern United States. J. Paleont., *16* (1): 1-62, pls. 1-8.

DAMES, A.
1877. Die Echiniden der Vicentinischen und Veronesischen Tertiarablagerungen. Palaontographica, N.F. *1* (25): 99 pp, pls. 1-11.

DELAGE, Y. AND E. HÉROUARD
1903. Traité de zoologie concrète. *3,* Les échinodermes. Schleicher, Paris. 495 pp, 53 pls, 565 text figs.

DE MEIJERE, J. C. H.
1904. Die Echinoidea der Siboga-Expedition. Siboga Exped. Monogr. *43:* 251 pp, 23 pls.

DESOR, E.
1858. Synopsis des échinides fossiles. Paris. 490 pp, 44 pls.

DÖDERLEIN, LUDWIG
1906. Die Echinoiden der deutschen Tiefsee Expedition. Wissenschaftliche Ergebnisse der deutschen Tiefsee Expedition auf dem Dampfer "Valdivia" 1898-1899, *5:* 61-290, figs. 1-46, pls. 9-50.

DUNCAN, P. M.
1889. A revision of the genera and great groups of the *Echinoidea*. J. Linn. Soc. London, *23* (141): 1-311.

Durham, J. Wyatt
1961. Miocene echinoids from the Valle Central, Costa Rica. J. Paleont., *35* (3): 480-488, pls. 67-68, 2 text figs.

Fell, H. Barraclough
1963. The spatangid echinoids of New Zealand. Zool. Pub. Vict. Univ. Wgton., 32: 1-8, 6 pls.

Fischer, A. G.
1966. Spatangoids. *In* Moore's Treatise on Invertebrate Paleontology, part U, Echinodermata 3 vol. 2: U543-U628.

Forbes, E.
1841. A history of British starfishes, and other animals of the class Echinodermata. London. 270 pp.

Ford, E. B.
1965. Genetic polymorphism. M.I.T. Press, Cambridge, Mass. 101 pp.

Gage, J.
1966. Observations on the bivalves *Montacuta substriata* and *M. ferruginosa,* "commensals" with spatangoids. J. Mar. biol. Ass. U.K., *46* (1): 49-70.

Gordon, Isabella
1926. The development of the calcareous test of *Echinocardium cordatum.* Phil. Trans. B, *215:* 255-313.

Grant, U. S. IV, and L. G. Hertlein
1938. The West American Cenozoic Echinoidea. Univ. Calif. Publ. Math. Phys. Sci., *2:* 225 pp, 30 pls.

Grieg, J. A.
1921. Echinodermata. "Michael Sars" North Atlantic Deep-Sea Expedition, *3* (2): 1-44.

Hayward, J. F.
1943. An application of the principles of allometry to the study of English Senonian *Echinocorys.* Nature, Lond., *151:* 617.

Heywood, V. H. and J. McNeill
1964. Phenetic and phylogenetic classification. Syst. Ass. Publ., 6: 164 pp.

Hubbs, C. L. and A. Perlmutter
1943. Biometric comparision of several samples with particular reference to racial investigations. Amer. Nat., *76:* 582-592.

Hyman, Libbie H.
1955. The invertebrates: Echinodermata. The coelomate Bilateria. Volume 4. McGraw-Hill, New York. 763 pp.

Jackson, R. T.
1922. Fossil Echini of the West Indies. Carnegie Inst. Washington Publ., *306:* 103 pp. 18 pls.

Kermack, K. A.
1954. A biometrical study of *Micraster coranguinum* and *M. (Isomicraster) senonensis.* Phil. Trans. B, *237* (649): 375-428, pls. 24-26.

Kier, Porter M.
1956. Separation of interambulacral columns from the apical system in Echinoidea. J. Paleont., *30* (4): 971-974.

KOEHLER, R.
1883. Recherches sur les Échinides des côtes de Provence. Ann. Mus. d'Hist. Nat. Marseille, Zoologie 1, Mém. 3: 167 pp, 7 pls.
1909. Échinodermes provenant des campagnes du yacht Princesse-Alice (Astéries, Ophiures, Échinides, et Crinoides). Rés. Camp. Sci. Monaco, *34:* 317 pp, 32 pls.
1914. Échinides du musée Indien à Calcutta. 1. Spatangidés. Echinoderma of the Indian Museum, Part 8. Echinoidea (1): 258 pp, 20 pls.

KOLOSVÁRY, G. VÓN
1937. Die Echinodermen des Adriatischen Meeres. Eine Auferbeitung der Echinodermen Sammlung der ungarischen "Najade" Expedition im Jahre 1913-14. Festschrift f. Embrik Strand, *2:* 433-474, pls. 29-37.

KONGIEL, R.
1962. Considerations of the variability of Echinoidea. U. S. Dept. Commerce, Office Technical Services Publ. OTS 60-21506, 42 pp. English translation of: Rocznik Polskiego Towarzystwa Geologicznego, *8:* 194-250 (1937).

KRUMBEIN, W. C. AND F. J. PETTIJOHN
1938. Manual of sedimentary petrology. Appleton-Century Crafts Inc., New York. 549 pp.

LAMBERT, M. J.
1911. Notes sur quelques Échinides Eocéniques des Corbières Septentrionales. Ann. de l'Univ. de Lyon, N.S., *1* (fasc. 30): 199 pp.
1915. Échinides néogènes des Antilles anglaises. Mem. Soc. Acad. de l'Aube, *79:* 17-33.

LAMBERT, M. J. AND P. THIÉRY
1924. Essai de nomenclature raisonnée des Échinides, Fasc. 6 and 7. Chaumont, Ferriere. 607 pp.

LOVÉN, S.
1874. Études sur les Échinoidées. K. Sv. Vetenskaps-Akad. Handl., N. S. *11* (7): 91 pp, 53 pls.
1883. On Pourtalesia a genus of Echinoidea. K. Sv. Vetenskaps-Akad. Handl., *19* (2): 95 pp, 21 pls.

LUBISCHEW, A. A.
1962. On the use of discriminant functions in taxonomy. Biometrics, *18* (4): 455-477.

MADSEN, J. JENSENIUS
1957. On a new species of *Meoma* and on a few other echinoids from tropical West Africa. Bull. d'Inst. Français d'Afrique Noire, sér. A. *19* (2): 474-481.

MAYR, ERNEST
1964. Systematics and the origin of species from the viewpoint of a zoologist. 2nd Ed. Dover Publications, New York. 334 pp.
1965. Numerical phenetics and taxonomic theory. Syst. Zool., *14*: 73-97.

MAYR, ERNST, E. G. LINSLEY AND R. L. USINGER
1953. Methods and principles of systematic zoology. McGraw-Hill, New York. 336 pp.

MAZE, J.
1966. A conceptual framework for taxonomy, and numerical taxonomy — a brief comment. Syst. Zool., *15:* 249-250.

MEISSNER, M.
1904. Echinodermen (Stachelhäuter). G. Systematik. *In* Bronn's Klassen und Ordnungen des Thier-reichs, *2* (3): 1321-1413.

METCALF, W. G., A. D. VOORHIST, AND M. G. STALEUP
1962. The Atlantic Equatorial Undercurrent. Journ. Geophys. Res., *67* (6): 2499-2508.

MORISHITA, A.
1953. Fossil species of the Palaeopneustidae from Japan. Trans. Proc. Palaeont. Soc. Japan, N.S. *9:* 27-29, pl. 3.

MORTENSEN, T.
1907. Echinoidea (2). The Danish Ingolf-Expedition, *4* (2): 200 pp, 19 pls.
1910. The Echinoidea of the Swedish South Polar expedition. Wissenschaftl. Ergebnisse der Schwed. Sudpolar-Exped. 1901-1903, *6* (4): 114 pp, 19 pls.
1927a. Handbook of the echinoderms of the British Isles. Oxford Univ. Press, 471 pp.
1927b. Sur les échinides recuellis par l'expédition du "Travailleur" et du "Talisman." Arch. Mus. Paris, Sér. 6, *2:* 21-34.
1913. Die Echiniden des Mittelmeeres. Eine revidierte Übersicht der im Mittelmeere lebenden Echiniden, mit Bermerkungen über neue oder weniger bekannte Formen. Mitteil. Zool. Stat. Neapel, *21:* 1-40, pls. 1-5.
1950. A monograph of the Echinoidea, 5 (1). Spatangoida, *1.* Reitzel, Copenhagen. 432 pp, 25 pls.
1951a. Report on the Echinoidea collected by the "Atlantide" expedition. Atlantide Report, *2:* 293-303, 2 pls.
1951b. A monograph of the Echinoidea, *5* (2). Spatangoida 2. Reitzel, Copenhagen, 593 pp, 64 pls.

NICHOLS, D.
1959. Changes in the Chalk heart-urchin *Micraster* interpreted in relation to living forms. Phil. Trans. B, *242* (693): 347-437.
1962. Differential selection in population of a heart-urchin. Syst. Ass. Publ. 4: 105-118.

POMEL, A.
1883. Classification méthodique et genera des échinides vivants et fossiles. Algiers. 131 pp, 1 pl.

PROSSER, C. L. AND F. A. BROWN, JR.
1965. Comparative animal physiology. 2nd ed. W. B. Saunders, Philadelphia. 688 pp.

RATHBUN, R.
1885. Report upon the Echini collected by the United States Fish Commission Steamer "Albatross", in the Caribbean Sea and Gulf of Mexico, January to May, 1884. Proc. U. S. Nat. Mus., *8:* 83-89.
1886. Catalogue of the collection of recent Echini in the United States National Museum. Proc. U. S. Nat. Mus., *9:* 255-293.

RINKEL, M. O., P. SUND, AND G. NEUMAN
1966. The location of the termination area of the Equatorial Undercurrent in the Gulf of Guinea based on observations during Equalant III. Jour. Geophys. Res., *71* (16): 3893-3901, figs. 1-9.

167

ROIG, S.
1949. Los Equinodermos fosiles de Cuba. Paleontologia Cubana, *1:* 1-302.

ROWE, A. W.
1899. An analysis of the genus *Micraster*, as determined by rigid zonal collecting from the zone of *Rhynchonella cuvieri* to that of *Micraster coranquinum*. Quart. J. Geol. Soc. Lond., *55:* 494-547.

SOKAL, R. R., J. H. CAMIN, F. J. ROHLF, AND P. H. A. SNEATH
1965. Numerical taxonomy: some points of view. Syst. Zool., *14* (3): 237-243.

THROCKMORTON, L. H.
1965. Similarity *versus* relationship in *Drosophila*. Syst. Zool., *14* (3): 221-236.

TORNQUIST, A.
1911. Die biologische Deutung der Umgestaltung der Echiniden im Paläozoikum und Mesozoikum. Zeitsch. indukt. Abstamm. u. Vererbungslehre, Bd. *6:* 29-60.

UEXKÜLL, J. VON
1907. Studien uber den Tonus. IV. Die Herzigel. Zeitsch. Biol., Bd. *49:* 307-332.

WAGNER, J.
1903. Anatomie des Palaeopneustes niasicus. Wissenschaftliche Ergebnisse der deutschen Tiefsee Expedition auf dem Dampfer "Valdivia" 1898-1899, *5:* 1-60, figs 1-8, pls. 1-8.

WRIGHT, T.
1855. On fossil echinoderms from the Island of Malta. Ann. Mag. Nat. Hist., (2) *15* (86-88): 101-126, 175-186, 262-276, pls. 4-7.

ZITTEL, K. A. VON
1879. Echinodermata. *In* Handbuch der Palaeontologie. I. Palaeozoologie. Bd. 1, Stamm 3:308-560, figs. 212-404. München.

Plates

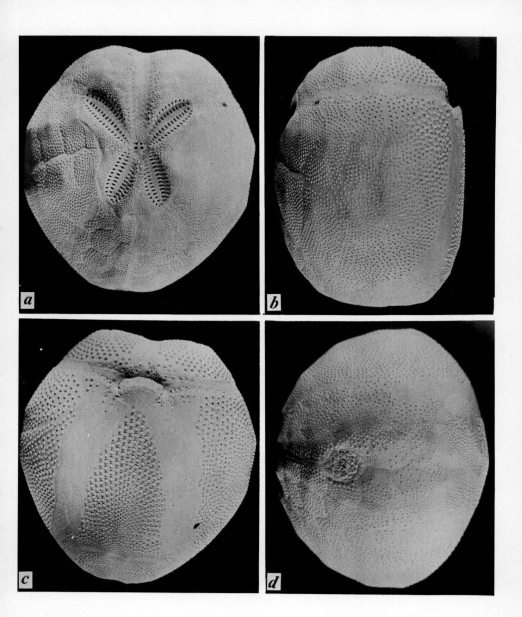

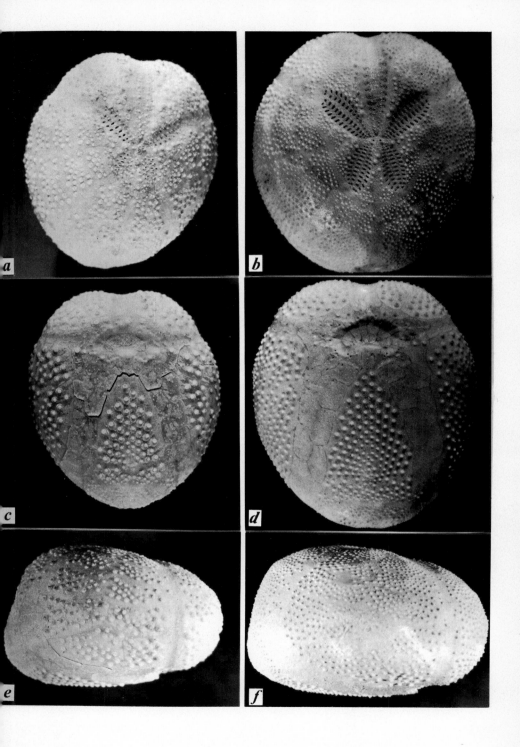

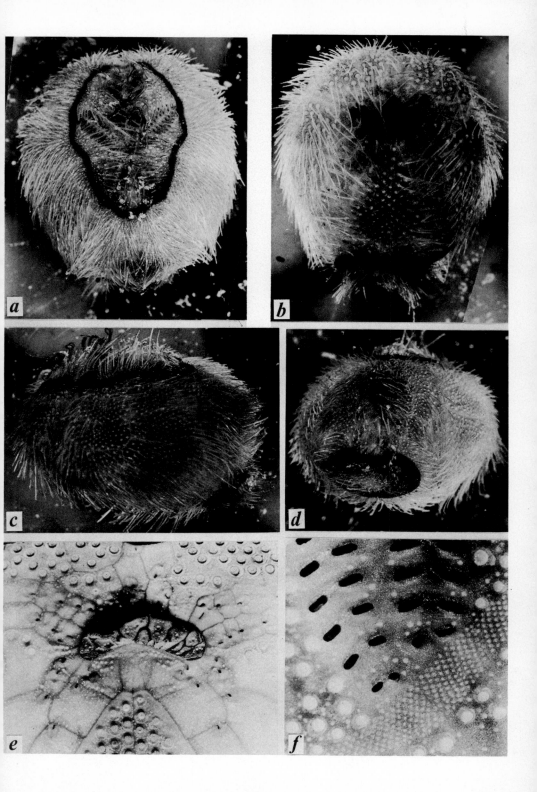

PLATE 4

Brissopsis alta Mortensen

a. Subanal drainage system seen through bottom of a glass-bottomed aquarium. Only one of the two drainage tubes is visible; note accessory branches excavated by subanal tube-feet.

b. The subanal drainage system: both drainage tubes are visible; the urchin is at the top of the photograph. View as in *a* (above).

c. The insertion of the ambulacral plates (V\b) into the subanal fasciole. (Specimen 54 mm T.L.)

d. Pores and interporiferous zone of ambulacrum III (distance between the pores 1.9 mm).

e. Globiferous pedicellariae, valves and stalk (valve length 0.7 mm).

f. Subanal tube-foot and portion of subanal fasciole (disc diameter of the tube-foot 0.4 mm).

g. Feeding tube-feet (disc diameter 1.1 mm).

h. Respiratory tube-feet of anterior paired petal (width of petal 2.5 mm).

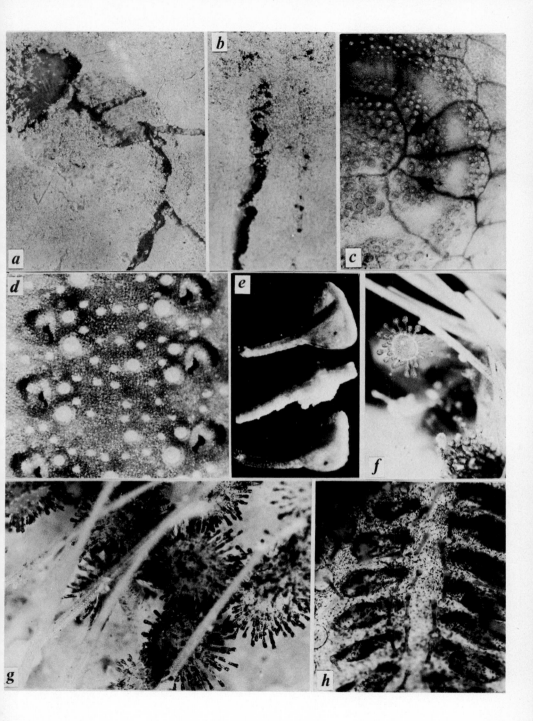

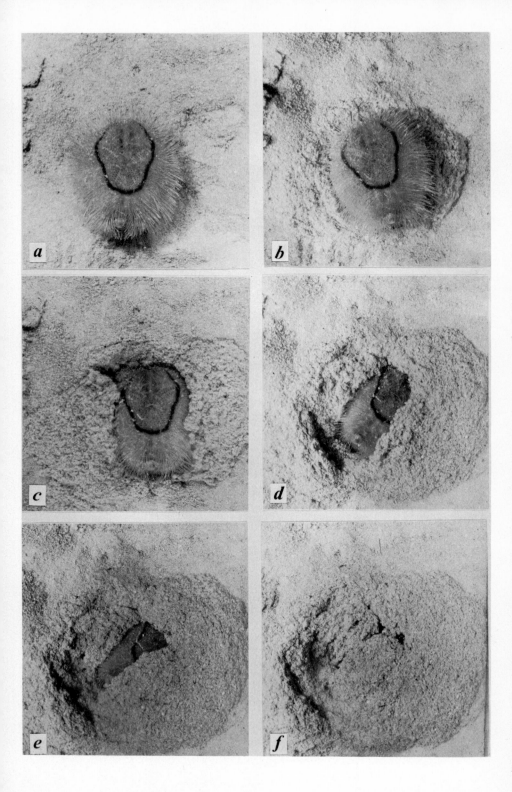

Brissopsis atlantica Mortensen
Test length 65 mm.
Dry Tortugas, Florida.

a. Dorsal view.
b. Ventral view.
c. Lateral view.
d. Posterior view.
e. Insertion of ambulacral plates (I) into the subanal fasciole.
f. Peripodia of the petaloid portion of ambulacrum III from a 28-mm test length specimen.

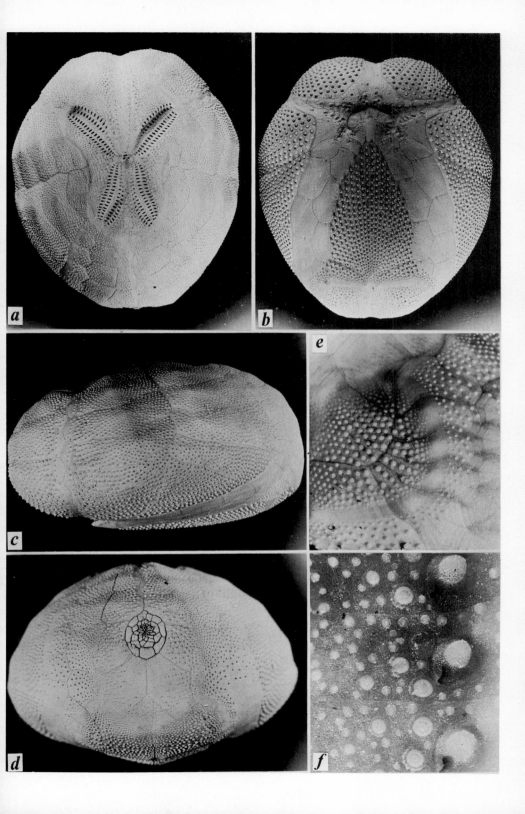

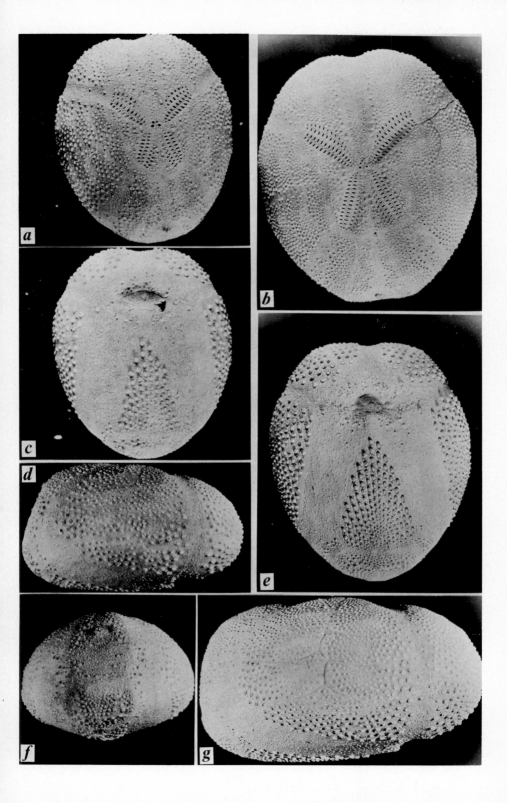

PLATE 8

Brissopsis atlantica Mortensen

Colombian specimen, 100.5 mm in test length.

a. Dorsal view.
b. Ventral view.
c. Lateral view, showing the extremely long and low test.
d. Posterior view.
e. Distal portion of the respiratory petal (IV) showing the respiratory pore-pairs.
f. Ambulacrum III from the same specimen showing the peripodia and tuberculation.

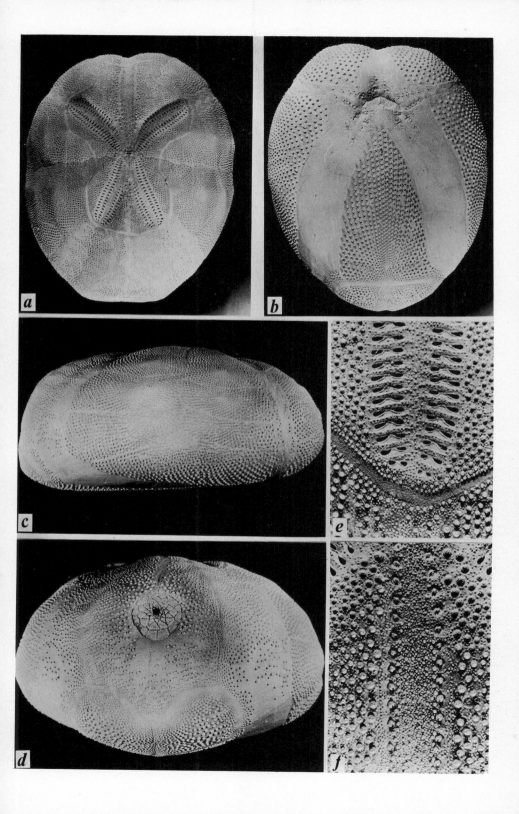

PLATE 9

Brissopsis atlantica Mortensen

Colombian specimen, 93 mm in test length.

Abnormal specimen, extremely narrow and high. Possibly a partial hybrid (F_2) with *B. elongata*.

a. Dorsal view.
b. Ventral view.
c. Lateral view.
d. Posterior view.
e. Valve of globiferous pedicellaria from a typical *B. atlantica* (valve length 1.9 mm).
f. Valve of short form of globiferous pedicellaria from the same specimen as the long form (*e*). (Length of valve 0.9 mm.)

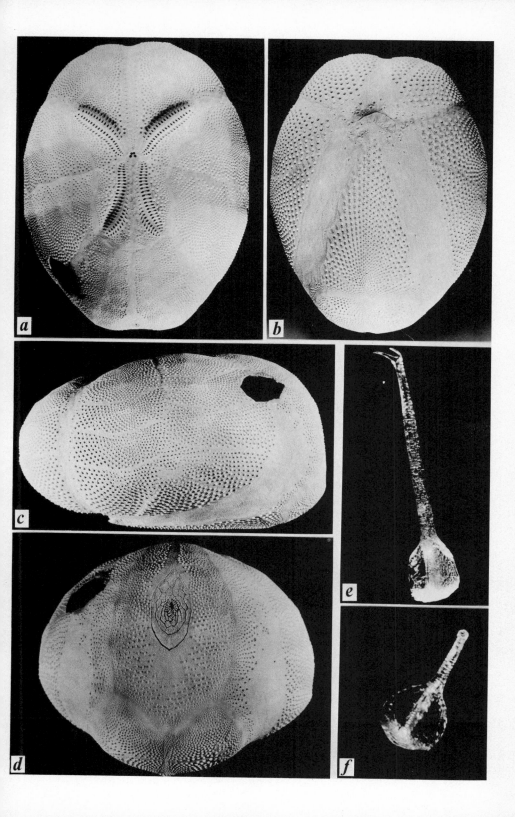

Brissopsis atlantica Mortensen

Growth changes in Colombian specimens.

a. Dorsal view, 29 mm in test length.
b. Dorsal view, 70.6 mm in test length.
c. Peristome from specimen 100.5 mm in test length.
d. Lateral view, 29 mm in test length.
e. Stalk of globiferous pedicellaria, with valve in g below.
f. Valve of rostrate pedicellaria (2.1 mm length).
g. Short form of the globiferous pedicellaria. The terminal ending resembles the rostrate pedicellaria (1.0 mm valve length).
h. Valve of rostrate pedicellaria (1.3 mm valve length).

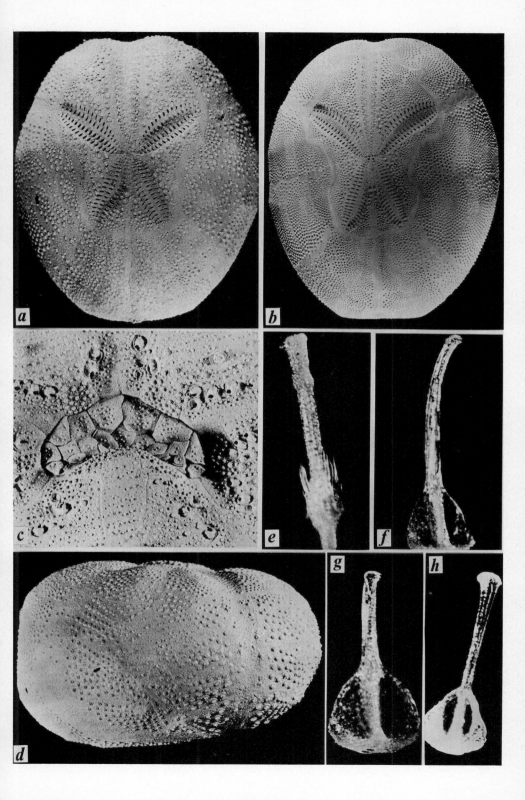

PLATE 11

Brissopsis atlantica Mortensen

a. Progression of entrances into the burrow as the urchin moves along. Diameter of respiratory tunnel is 1.4 mm.

b. Sensory tube-feet adjoining the plastron.

c. Tunneling tube-foot, treated with sodium chloride solution to show the calcite spicules. Disc diameter (expanded) is 1.2 mm.

d. Feeding tube-feet, illustrating the convex position just before the disc is pushed into the mud and just following withdrawal from the mouth.

e. Feeding tube-foot, treated with sodium chloride to show the supporting spicules of the papillae.

f. Subanal tube-foot. Overall disc diameter 1.0 mm.

g. Tunneling tube-foot of *B. alta* (compare with *c* above).

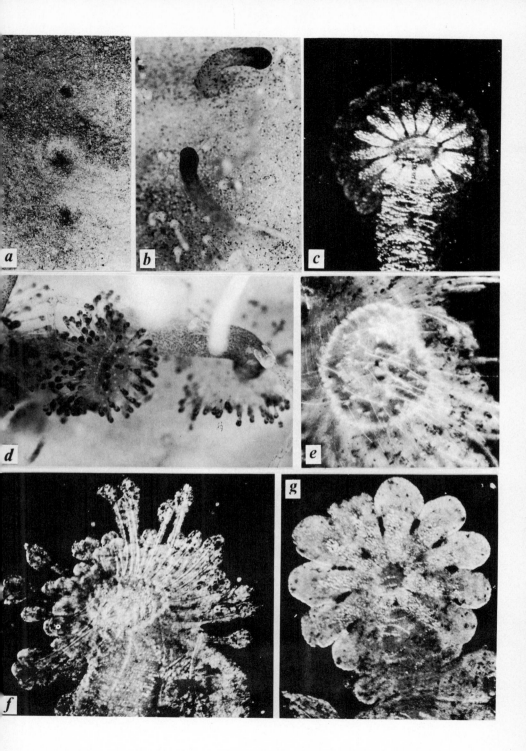

PLATE 12

Brissopsis atlantica Mortensen

Florida specimens.

a. Dorsal view of living specimen 28 mm in test length.
b. Posterior view of the same specimen. Note the dilated anus. The anus is able to expand to almost the full width of the periproct. The specimen shown was anesthetized in magnesium chloride solution.
c. Ventral view of the same specimen.
d. Respiratory tube-feet of the same specimen.
e. Lateral view of the same specimen.
f. Peristome of a 64-mm specimen.
g. Valve of elongate pedicellaria (length of valve, 2.0 mm).
h. Distal end of the petal of ambulacrum IV, showing the respiratory pore-pair and structure of peripetalous fasciole.

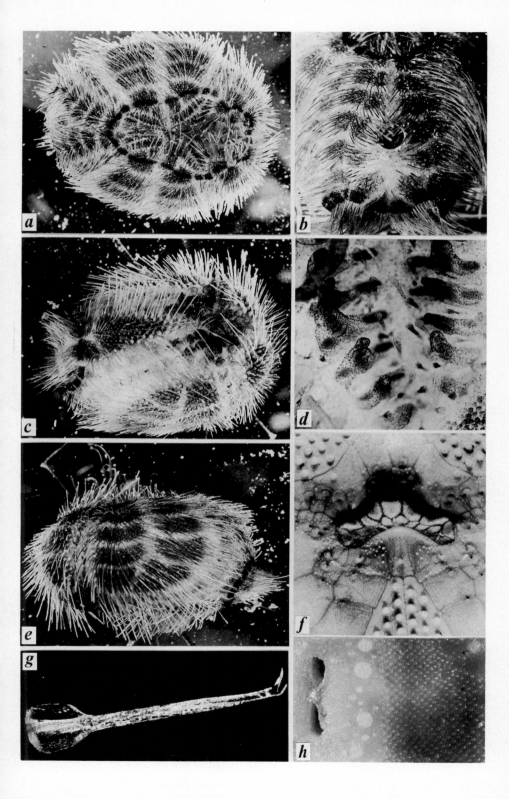

PLATE 13

Brissopsis

a. *Brissopsis atlantica* × *elongata,* test length 36.5 mm, dorsal view.

b. Normal *B. elongata* from same station, test length 31 mm. (Compare with Plate 10*a:* *B. atlantica,* 29 mm, from same station.)

c. Ventral view of hybrid specimen shown in *a.* Labrum to second adjoining ambulacral plates but lip better developed. First ambulacral plate in subanal fasciole is 6.

d. Ventral view of normal *B. elongata.* Labrum to second adjoining plates, normal development of lip. First plate entering the subanal fasciole is number 7.

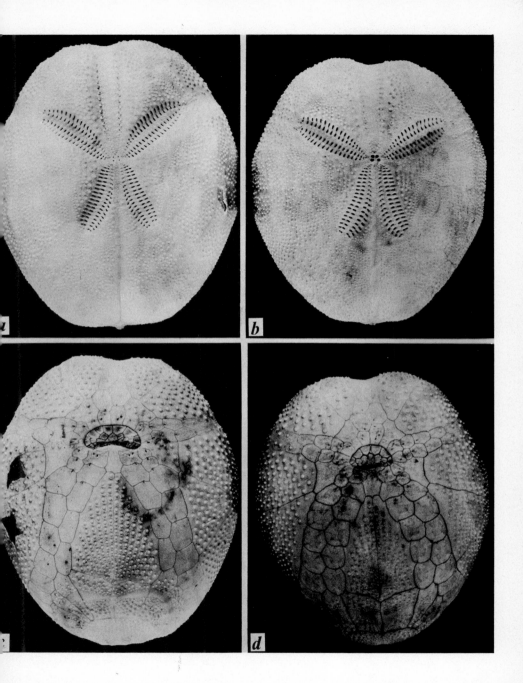

PLATE 14

Brissopsis atlantica Mortensen

Burrowing sequence; specimen 32 mm in test length.
Sequence: *a* to *f*; duration: 4.3 minutes.

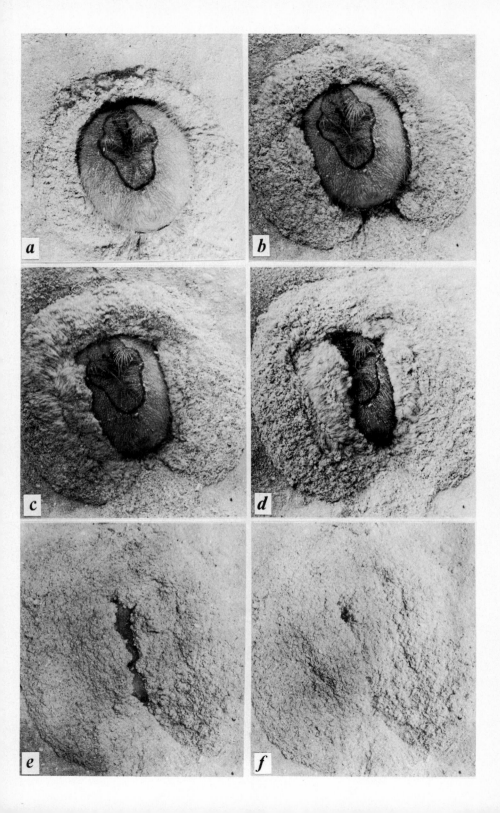

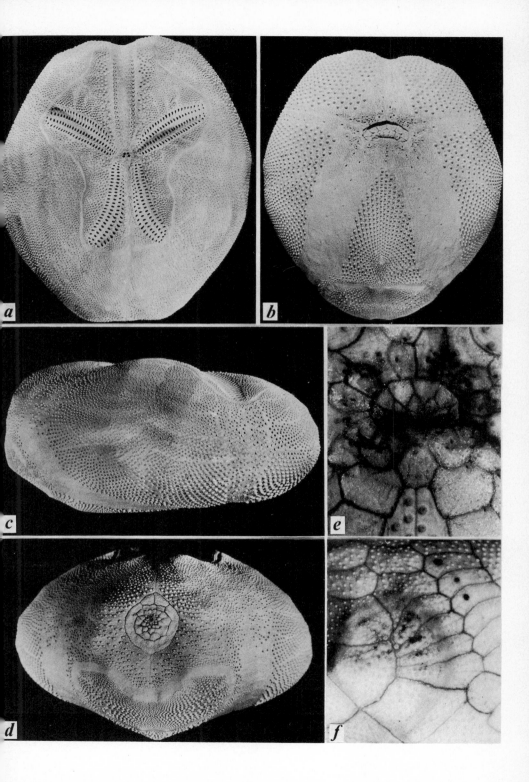

PLATE 16

Brissopsis elongata Mortensen

a. Dorsal view of a specimen 11.6 mm in test length.
b. Same, ventral view.
c. Same, lateral view.
d. Dorsal view of a specimen 42 mm in test length.
e. Same, ventral view.
f. Subanal tube-foot peripodium from the same specimen.
g. Lateral view of a specimen 42 mm in test length.

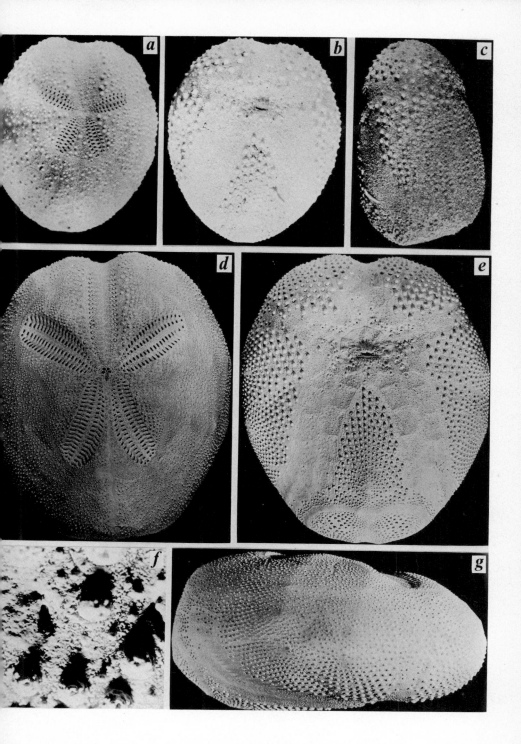

Brissopsis elongata jarlii Mortensen

a. Dorsal view of a specimen 106.3 mm in test length.
b. Same, ventral view.
c. Same, lateral view.
d. Same, apical system.
e. Valves of tridentate pedicellaria 1.3 mm in length.
f. Same.
g. Valves of globiferous pedicellaria with no spines on the side or backs. Valves 2.0 mm in length.
h. Same, note the different shape of the auricles.
i. Same, with thorns on the back.

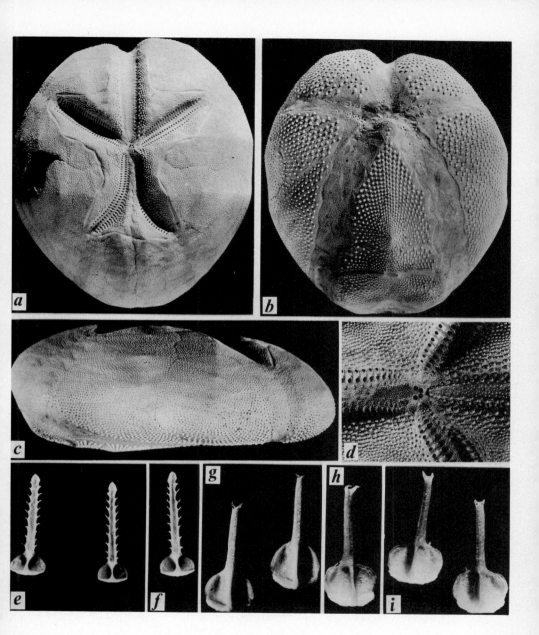

PLATE 18

Brissopsis elongata Mortensen

a. Ventral view of a specimen 43.5 mm in test length showing the structure of the plates.

b. Same, lateral view.

c. Abnormal specimen with depressed apex, 42 mm in test length.

d. Apical system of a specimen 69 mm in test length.

e. The peripodia of ambulacrum III of the same specimen.

f. Valve of a globiferous pedicellaria showing the spine on the midline of the back. Valve is 2.0 mm in length.

g. Valve of a tridentate pedicellaria. Length 1.3 mm.

h. Valve of a tridentate pedicellaria. Length 1.0 mm.

i. Valves of globiferous pedicellariae, 1.9 mm in length.

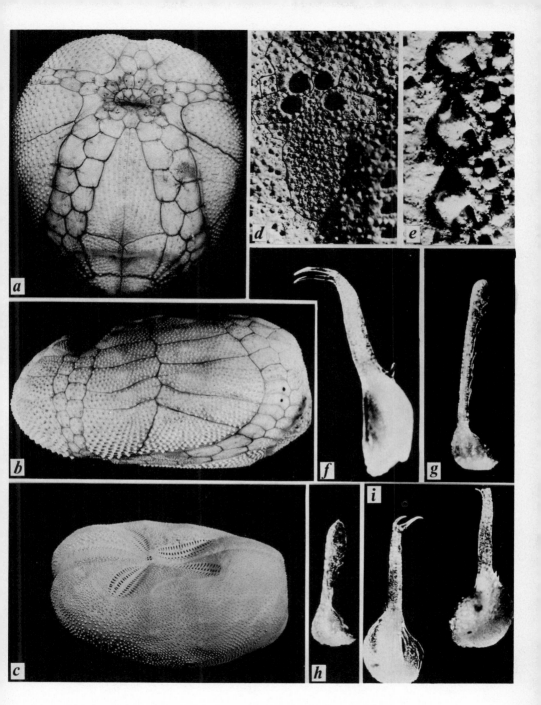

PLATE 19

Brissopsis mediterranea Mortensen

a. Dorsal view of a specimen 79 mm in test length.
b. Ventral view of a specimen 78.3 mm in test length.
c. Lateral view of a sepcimen 79 mm in test length.
d. Same, peristome.
e. Same, posterior view.
f. Same, details of ambulacrum IV.

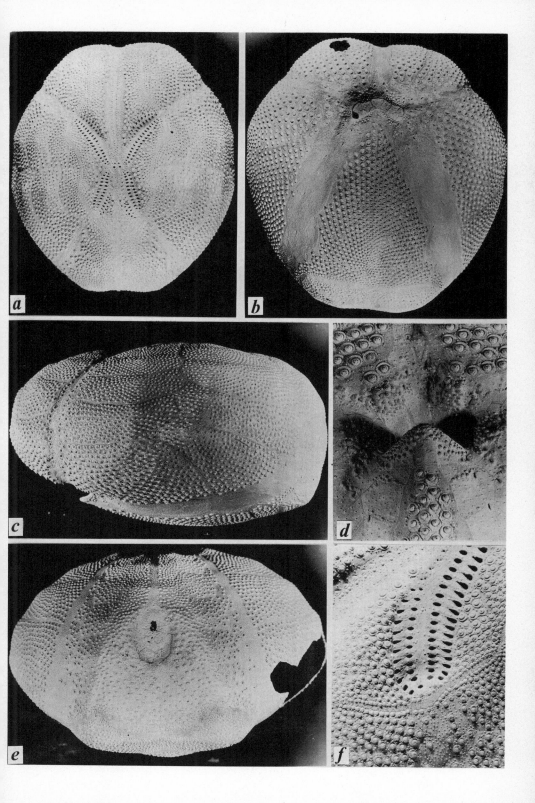

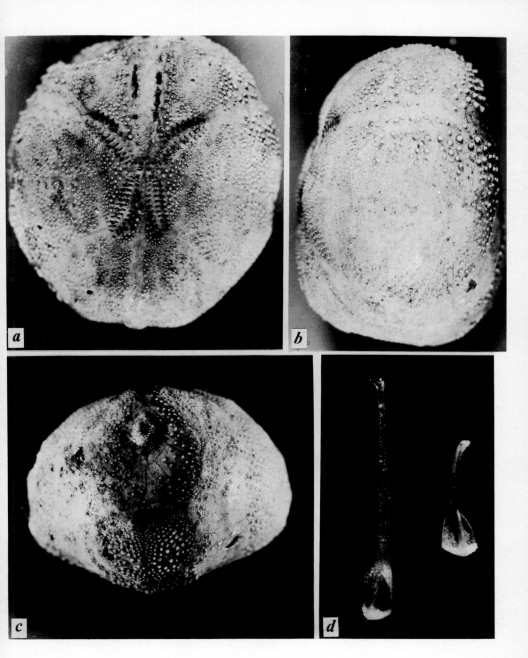

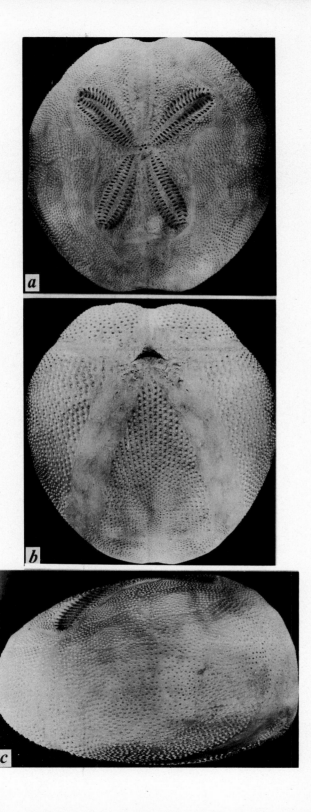

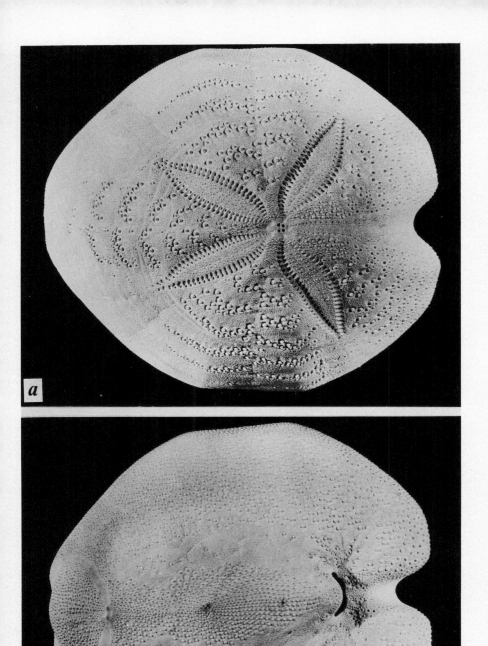

PLATE 23

Plethotaenia spatangoides (A. Agassiz)

a. Lateral view of a specimen 112 mm in test length.
b. Dorsal view of a specimen 95 mm in test length.
c. Posterior view of a specimen 112 mm in test length.
d. Ventral view of a specimen 95 mm in test length.
e. Anterior view of a specimen 112 mm in test length.
f. The frontal notch with the spines intact.
g. Details of the petal and fasciole of a specimen 112 mm in test length.

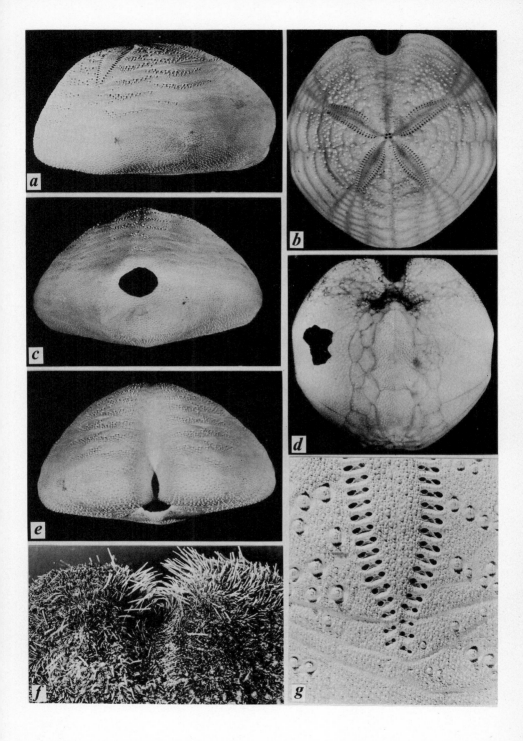

PLATE 24

Plethotaenia angularis, new species
Test length 116.2 mm.
a. Dorsal view.
b. Ventral view.

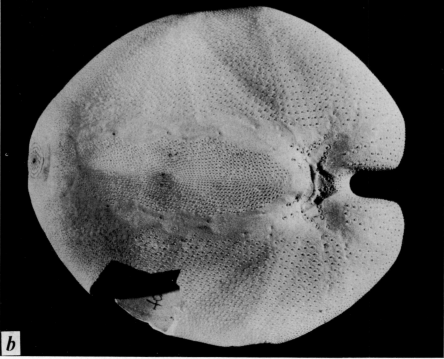

PLATE 25

Plethotaenia angularis, new species

a. Lateral view of a specimen 116.2 mm in test length.
b. Dorsal view of a specimen 112 mm in test length.
c. Anterior view of a specimen 116.2 mm in test length.
d. Ventral view of a specimen 112 mm in test length.
e. Posterior view of a specimen 116.2 mm in test length.
f. Anterior notch with the spines intact.
g. Peristome of 116.2-mm specimen.

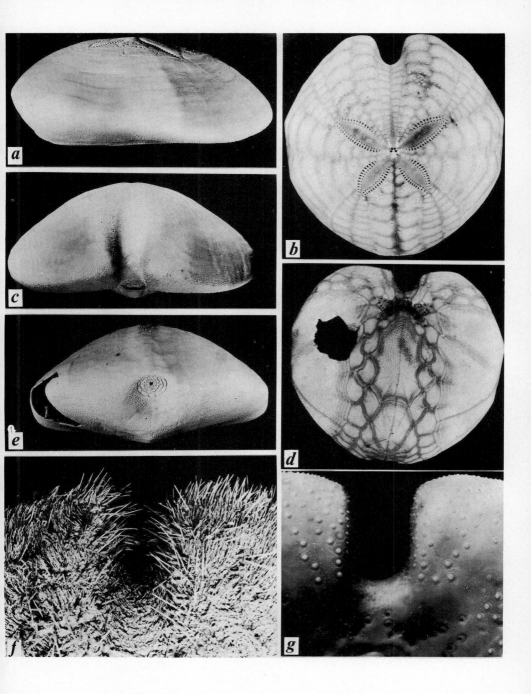

a. *P. angularis,* large tridentate valves, length 0.8 mm.
b. *P. spatangoides,* large tridentate valve (1.5 mm) and small tridentate valve (0.5 mm).
c. *P. angularis,* large tridentate valves, length 1.0 mm.
d. *P. angularis,* elongate tridentate valve, length 2.0 mm.
e. *P. spatangoides,* elongate tridentate valve, length 2.0 mm.
f. *P. angularis,* tridentate valves, lengths 0.5 and 0.7 mm.
g. *P. angularis,* spine from frontal notch, section 3.4 mm long.
h. *P. spatangoides,* tridentate valve, length 1 mm, two spines from frontal notch, sections 1.2 mm long.

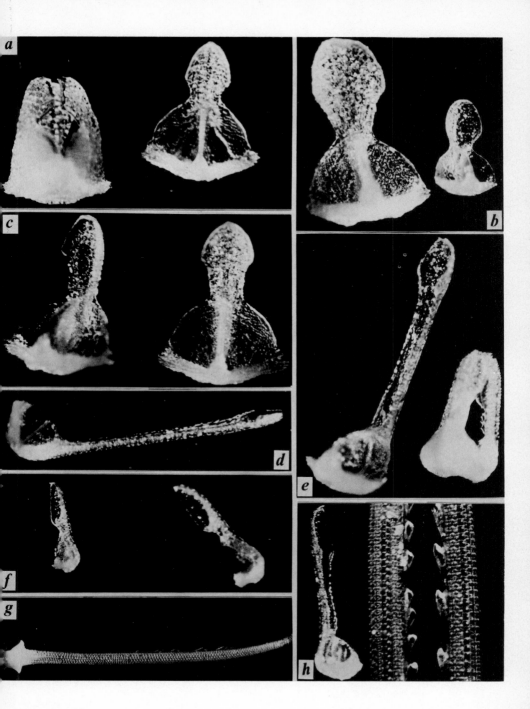

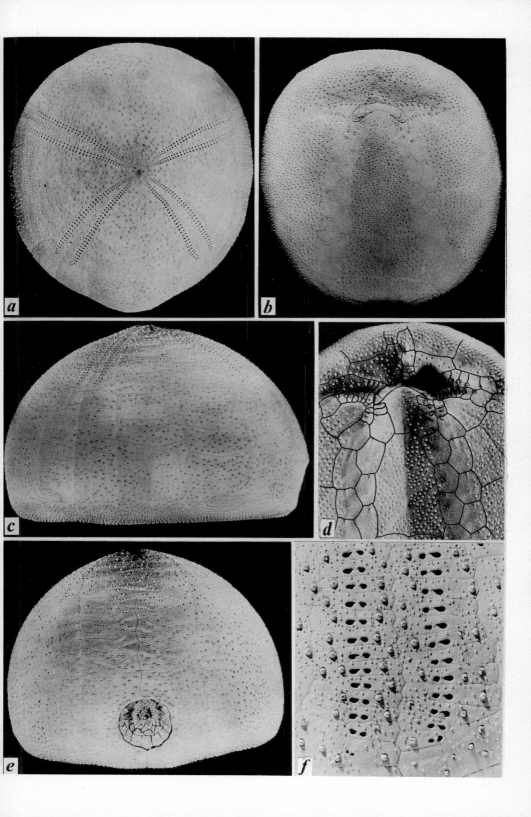

a. *P. cristatus,* ventral view of a specimen 16.7 mm in test length.
b. Same, dorsal view.
c. *P. cristatus,* ventral view of a specimen 33.8 mm in test length.
d. Same, dorsal view.
e. *P. tholoformis,* ventral view of a specimen 50 mm in test length.
f. Same, dorsal view.

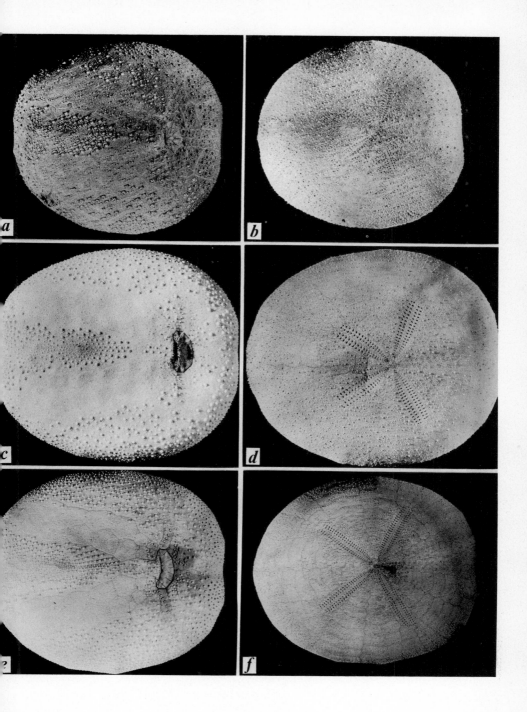

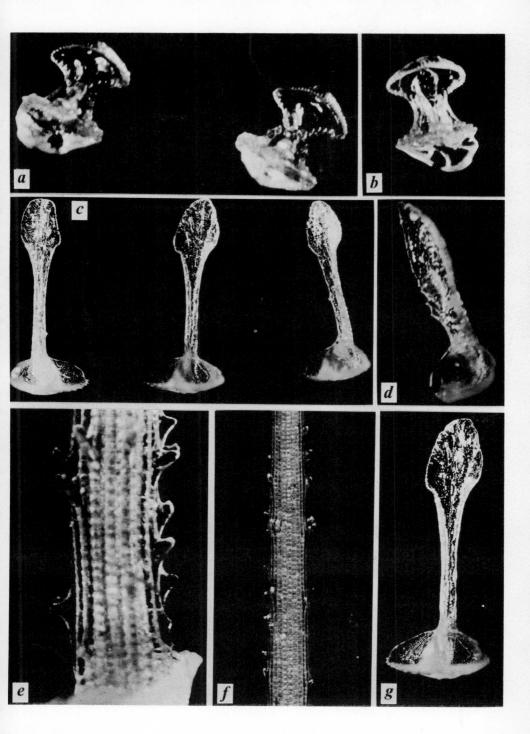

Plate 30

Paleopneustes cristatus A. Agassiz
Test length 119 mm.

a. Dorsal view.
b. Ventral view.
c. Lateral view.
d. Details of distal end of petal (IV).
e. Posterior view.
f. Details of phyllode.

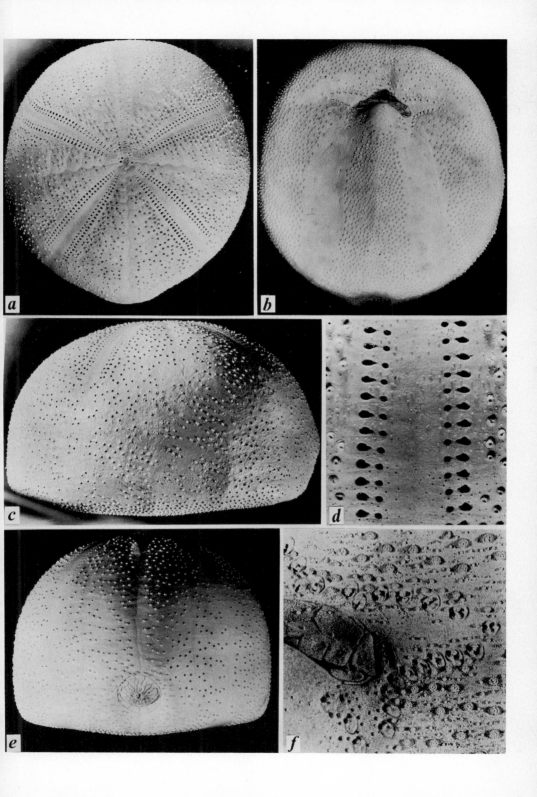

a

b

c

d

e

f

PLATE 32

Paleopneustes

Small specimens and pedicellariae.

a. *P. cristatus,* 16.7 mm in test length, posterior view.
b. *P. cristatus,* 33.8 mm in test length, lateral view.
c. *P. cristatus,* 16.7 mm in test length, lateral view.
d. *P. cristatus,* 33.8 in test length, posterior view.
e. *P. tholoformis,* valves of tridentate pedicellariae, length 1.5 mm.
f. Same.
g. *P. cristatus,* 16.7 mm in test length; details of the distal end of the petal.

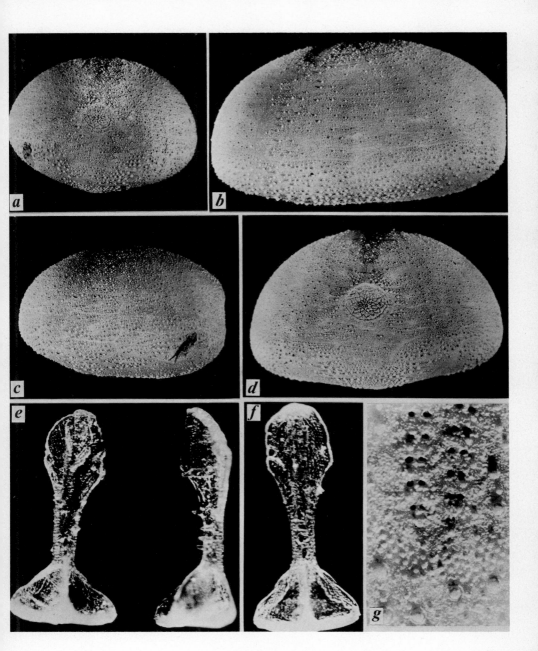

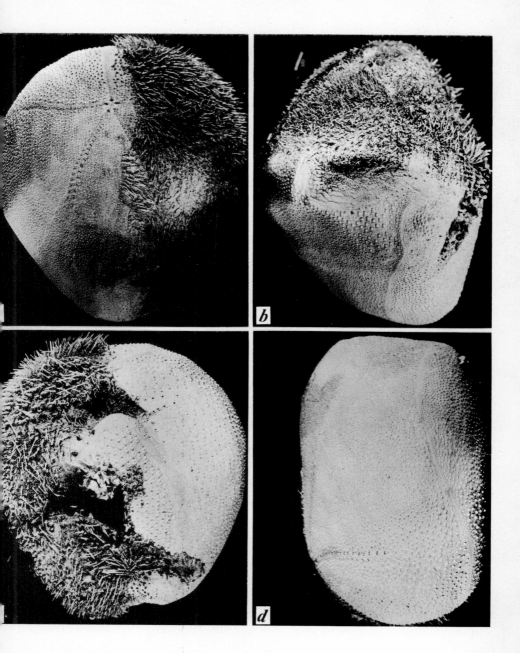

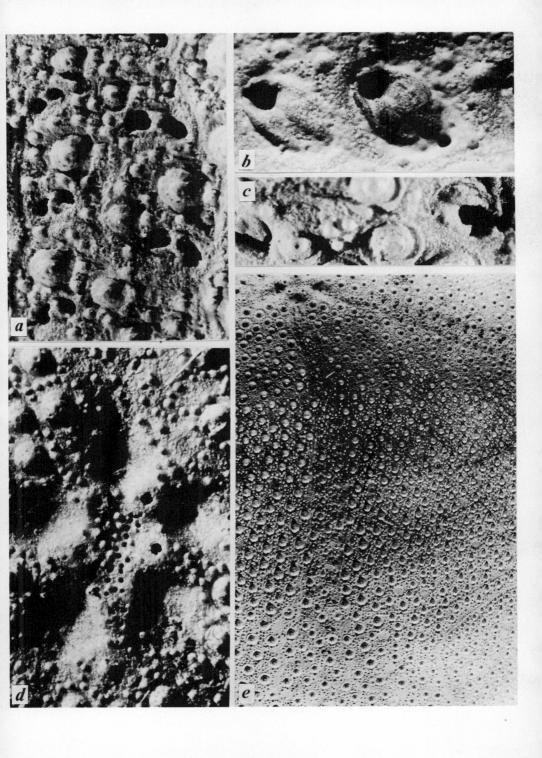

PLATE 35

Saviniaster enodatus, new species
Pedicellariae

a. Tridentate valves, length 1.3 mm.
b. Rostrate valves, length 0.9 mm.
c. Valve of globiferous pedicellaria, length 0.9 mm.
d. Details of the terminal ending of *c.*
e. Valve of globiferous pedicellaria, length 1.0 mm.
f. Tridentate valve, length 1.8 mm.
g. Sphaeridium, length 0.12 mm.
h. Peripodium of ambulacrum III.
i. Details of anal system.

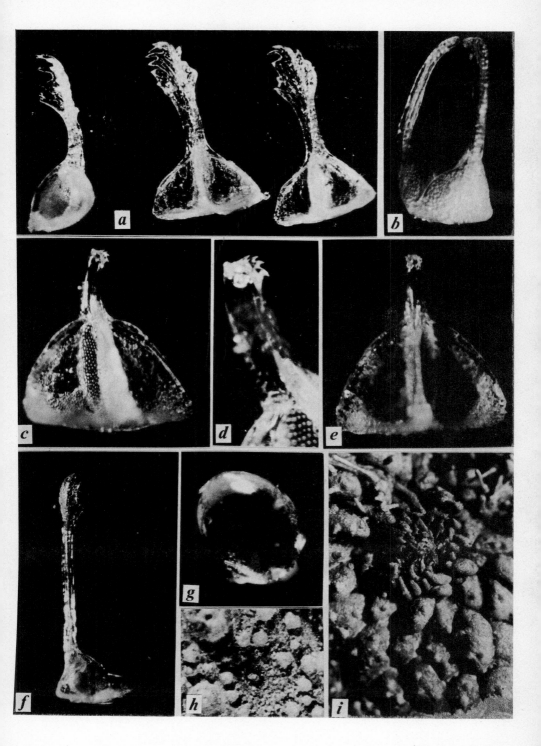